ADVANCED LEVEL

BIOLOGY

For AQA
Specification B

**CHRIS LEA • PAULINE LOWRIE
SIOBHAN MCGUIGAN**

Heinemann

Heinemann Educational Publishers
Halley Court, Jordan Hill, Oxford, OX2 8EJ
a division of Reed Educational & Professional Publishing Ltd
Heinemann is a registered trademark of Reed Educational & Professional Publishing Ltd

OXFORD MELBOURNE AUCKLAND
JOHANNESBURG BLANTYRE GABORONE
IBADAN PORTSMOUTH NH (USA) CHICAGO

First published 2001

ISBN 0 435 58081 7

04 03 02 01
10 9 8 7 6 5 4 3 2 1

Development editor Paddy Gannon

Edited by Teresa MacLeod

Designed and typeset by Ian Foulis and Associates, Plymouth, Devon

Illustrated by Ian Foulis and Associates, Plymouth, Devon and Yvonne Burchell.

Printed and bound in Spain by Edelvives

Acknowledgements
The authors and publishers would like to thank AQA for permission to use the NEAB question
on page 269. The authors and publishers would like to thank the following for permission to use
photographs:

(L = left; R = right; T = top; B = bottom; M = middle)

Cover photo by Science Photo Library.
p7 people Sally & Richard Greenhill, **dogs** Animals Unlimited, **roses** Harry Smith Collection;
p15–8 Biophoto Associates; **p20 T** Sally & Richard Greenhill, **BL** Heather Angel **BR** Bruce
Coleman; **p30** SPL/L.Willat, East Anglian Regional Genetics; **p31** SPL; **p40** Animals Unlimited;
p41 Sally & Richard Greenhill; **p46** R Harding; **p47** and **p48 T** Holt Studios, **B** Bruce Coleman;
p49 both T Holt Studios, **both B** OSF; **p52** Bruce Coleman; **p56 TL** Bruce Coleman, **BL** and **R**
OSF; **p57 L** Holt Studios, **TR** OSF, **BR** Bruce Coleman; **p58** Sally & Richard Greenhill; **p62 M**
and **BL** OSF, **BR** Bruce Coleman; **p63** and **p64 all** SPL; **p65 TL** and **B** Holt Studios, **TR** SPL;
p66 TL and **BL** OSF, **R** Holt Studios; **p67 TL** and **inset** Harry Smith Collection, **ML** and **BL**
Holt Studios, **TR** Bruce Coleman, **MR** OSF, **BR** Holt Studios; **p68 TL** OSF, **BL** and **TR** Bruce
Coleman, **BR** OSF; **p69 TL** Bruce Coleman, **ML** OSF, **BL** Heather Angel; **TR** OSF, **MR** Bruce
Coleman, **BR** Holt Studios; **p80 L** Frank Lane Picture Agency; **R** OSF; **p87** SPL; **p90 T** SPL, **B**
Bayer; **p114** SPL / Quest; **p116 both** SPL; **p117** Ecoscene; **p121** Wellcome Institute; **p122** and
p125 SPL; **p128** Rex Features; **p135 both** Natural History Museum; **p140, p145 all, p148** and
p152 SPL; **p193 L** Holt Studios, **R** OSF; **p194** and **p211 B** Holt Studios; **p219 both** Harry Smith
Collection; **p220 T** Lichenland, **B** Holt Studios ; **p221 T** OSF, **BL** Bruce Coleman, **ML** and **BR**
OSF, **MR** SPL; **p228 all L** and **TR** Ecoscene, **MR** OSF, **BR** Holt Studios; **p229, p230** and **p231**
OSF; **p232** Heather Angel; **p236 T** SPL, **B** Roger Scruton; **p237 all** Roger Scruton; **p244 L**
Environmental Images, **R** Panos Pictures; **p245 both, p247** and **p248** Holt Studios; **p251 T** OSF,
B Holt Studios; **p252** and **p254 both** Holt Studios; **p260** OSF; **p261** and **p264** Holt Studios.

Picture research by Thelma Gilbert

Contents

Module 5 Environment

Introduction

To the student

This book has been written for the new A2 Biology specification. Much of the content of this specification is regarded as more traditional; however, wherever possible recent developments have been included to help you to recognise the role of scientific progress in everyday life.

The book is split into two main modules, which link to the two main themes of A2 Biology. Each module is split into units which cover a main topic area. At the beginning of each module there are concept maps. Three of these are of the main subsections of the module Energy, Control and Continuity. The fourth is of the module Environment. Each concept map shows the links between the main topics within each subsection as well as links to AS and GCSE. The links to AS are particularly important to synoptic assessment as they indicate areas where knowledge from AS supports understanding of A2 Biology. In addition, there is a section about synoptic assessment which gives advice about synoptic assessment and examples of the types of questions you may be asked.

At the start of each unit there is a summary of the content covered together with Memory Joggers which list related knowledge from AS and GCSE. On each page there are diagrams linked to the written text, which help to explain the ideas. At some points in the text you will find words in **bold type**. These are important words that you will meet in articles in scientific publications or on the Internet. You can find out what these words mean in the Glossary at the end of the book. At the end of each unit there are Key Ideas which you can use as a checklist. On some of the pages there are questions for you to answer about the information on those pages. You should do these as you work through each topic, as they will help you find out if you have understood what is being explained. The answers to these questions are at the end of the book.

There are also questions at the end of each unit. These are 'examination style' questions about the content of the unit. The answers to these are at the end of the book. At the end of each module there are more 'examination style' questions which expect you to link information from different units. The answers to these questions are in the Resource Pack which goes with this textbook. There are extra questions and additional activities in the Resource Pack.

To the teacher

This book is written for Advanced (A2) Biology and matches AQA Specification B (6416). The book is written so that each section covers one particular section of the specification. Concept maps at the beginning of each module show links between the different topics and to AS.

A further section addresses synoptic assessment with examples of question styles that may be used. A Resource Pack to complement this textbook gives additional activities and indicates which of them might contribute to key skills.

Module 4

Energy, Control and Continuity

There are three main areas in this module, which build upon AS Biology. The content of these areas, as they are organised in this book, is summarised below.

Continuity comprising: Inheritance, Variation, Selection and evolution, Classification

There are three main threads, with considerable overlap, which build upon AS study of DNA and cell division. Units 1 and 2 are concerned with the transmission of genetic information from one generation to the next. The interaction between genes and environment is also considered. The role of natural selection and evolution in the development of new species is explored in these units. The third section in Unit 2 is concerned with the classification of living organisms based on shared features resulting from evolution.

Control comprising: Survival and co-ordination, Homeostasis, Nervous co-ordination, Analysis and integration, Muscles

Overall this section is concerned with the ability of organisms to survive by maintaining a constant internal environment and responding to changes in the external environment. The work in AS on the control of breathing and the heart is extended. The second section in Unit 3 looks at examples of homeostatic control of the internal environment. These include blood temperature, blood glucose, blood water and excretory materials. The remaining sections concentrate on the nature of nervous communication, from receptors, formation and transmission of nerve impulses, and integration in the brain, to response of effectors by the contraction of muscle.

Energy comprising: Energy supply, Photosynthesis, Respiration

The nature of energy is briefly considered in relation to its availability to living organisms. The roles of photosynthesis and respiration in making energy available to metabolism as ATP are considered in general terms. The role of ATP in providing energy to metabolic processes is also considered, together with a summary of the reactions that are involved in the synthesis of ATP. The first section of Unit 4 ends with energy flow in living organisms, which also relates to Module 5. The second section is concerned with the biochemical events in respiration which lead to the synthesis of ATP. The third section is concerned with the biochemical events in photosynthesis, concerned with the trapping of light energy and the synthesis of new organic molecules.

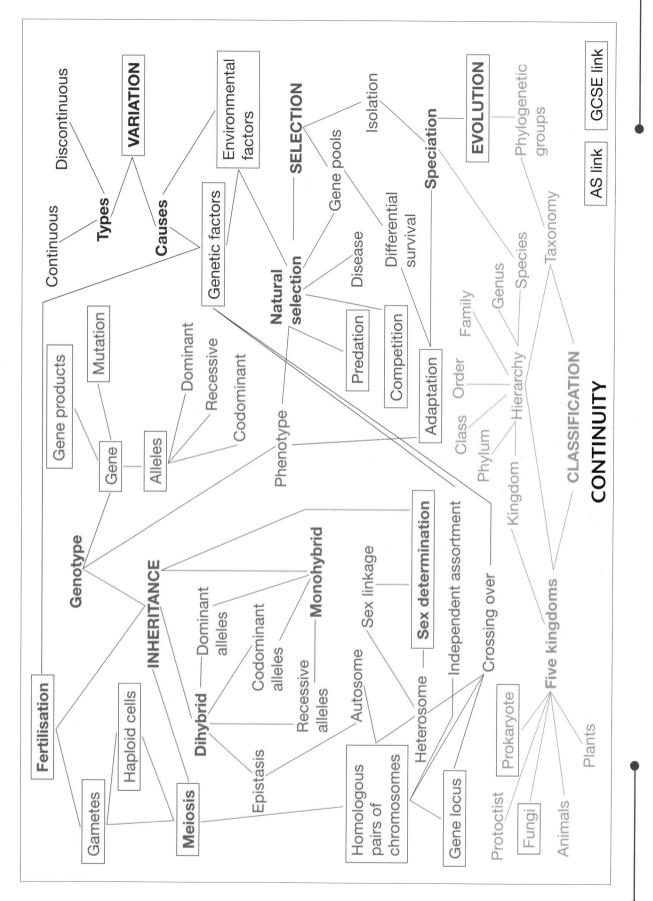

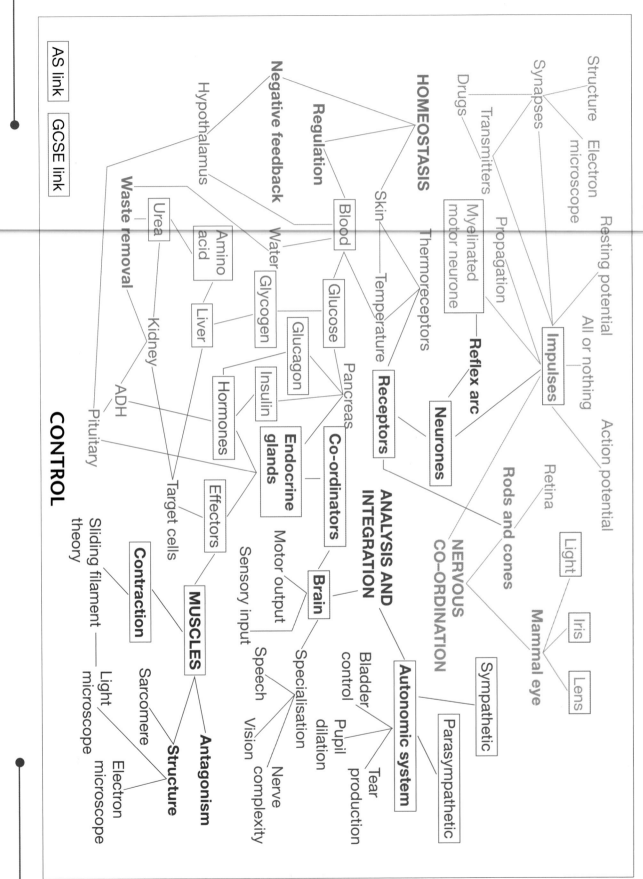

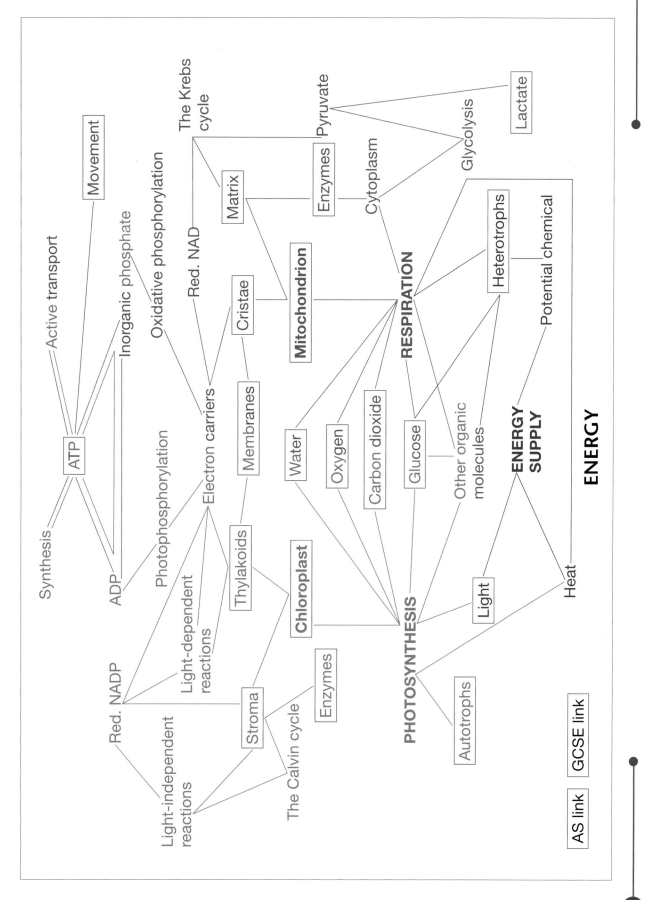

ENERGY

Inheritance

Inheritance is the study of how parents pass information to their offspring. Parents form specialised reproductive cells called **gametes** which contain DNA from each parent. When these cells fuse at fertilisation a **zygote** is formed, which develops into a new individual. Each new individual thus contains genetic information, in the form of DNA, from both parents. The way in which the individual develops is determined by this DNA and is also influenced by environmental factors. An individual therefore develops a unique set of features which is dependent upon the coded information in DNA and environmental influences.

Memory joggers

- DNA is made up of four bases which form a code for the synthesis of a **gene product**, usually a polypeptide.
- A specific sequence of DNA that codes for a particular gene product is a gene.
- Different versions of a gene, which originate by mutation, are called **alleles**.
- A gene is carried at a specific point on a chromosome called a **locus**.
- An individual inherits one set of chromosomes, carrying one allele of every gene, from each parent.
- The sets of chromosomes from each parent form **homologous pairs** so body cells have two alleles of every gene.
- During meiosis, the homologous pairs separate, reducing the chromosome number of the cells from diploid to haploid.
- The cells formed by meiosis develop into gametes.
- Fertilisation restores the diploid number.

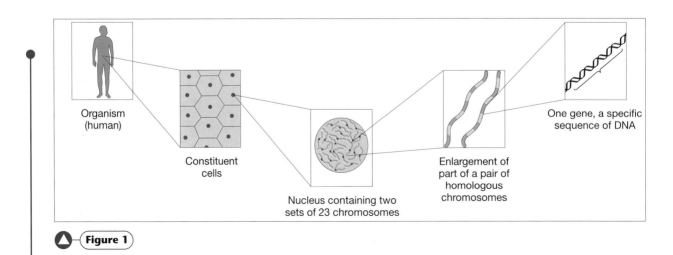

Organism (human) — Constituent cells — Nucleus containing two sets of 23 chromosomes — Enlargement of part of a pair of homologous chromosomes — One gene, a specific sequence of DNA

Figure 1

Genes and environment

The **genotype** of an individual is the alleles of a gene (genetic constitution) that they inherit. The alleles inherited depend on the genotype of the parents, and which gametes fused at fertilisation. An individual always inherits one allele of a gene from each parent, so their cells contain two alleles of every gene.

The expression of a gene may be modified by environmental factors resulting in the **phenotype** of an individual. Differences in phenotype can be measured or described. Examples of phenotypes in different groups of living organisms are shown in figure 2.

Figure 2 Examples of the range of phenotypes in different organisms.

Genes

An individual who inherits the same type of allele from each parent is **homozygous** (homo = same, zygous = zygote) for that gene.

An individual who inherits a different type of allele from each parent is **heterozygous** (hetero = different, zygous = zygote) for that gene.

An individual is usually homozygous for some genes and heterozygous for others. Figure 3 shows a homologous pair of chromosomes, with some of the gene loci shown.

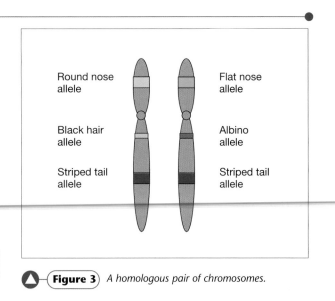

Q 1 Which gene loci are heterozygous?

▲ (**Figure 3**) *A homologous pair of chromosomes.*

Gene expression – how genes work

Gene expression is the synthesis of a gene product by means of transcription and translation of the DNA in the alleles present.

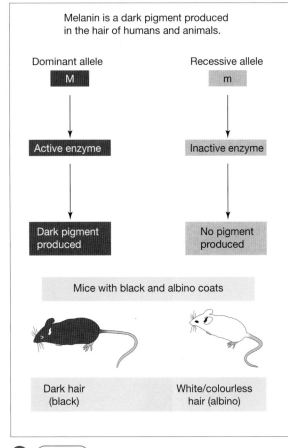

Melanin is a dark pigment produced in the hair of humans and animals.

Dominant allele — M — Active enzyme — Dark pigment produced

Recessive allele — m — Inactive enzyme — No pigment produced

Mice with black and albino coats

Dark hair (black)   White/colourless hair (albino)

Alleles can be **dominant** or **recessive**. The effects of a dominant allele always show in the phenotype, even in a heterozygous individual. A dominant allele codes for the production of a gene product that always has an effect which is detectable in the phenotype. For example, enzymes are gene products that catalyse reactions in cells. The end product of an enzyme-controlled reaction may be easily detected in the phenotype, for example a pigment. Other gene products may be present in the cell surface membranes, which can be detected by biochemical tests. A recessive allele codes for the production of a gene product that only shows its effect when there are no dominant alleles present. A recessive phenotype is always homozygous. For example, a recessive allele may code for a non-functional enzyme, so a pigment is not produced, as shown in figure 4.

▲ (**Figure 4**) *Pigment synthesis in mice.*

Labels for genes

For convenience, letters represent alleles of genes, as shown in figure 5.

The convention is to use the upper case for a dominant allele, for example **B** could be used. The recessive allele of the same gene would be represented by the lower case of the same letter, in this case **b**. There is no rule about which letter to use, although convention often uses the first letter of the dominant allele. A genotype of an individual always has two letters, one for each allele inherited.

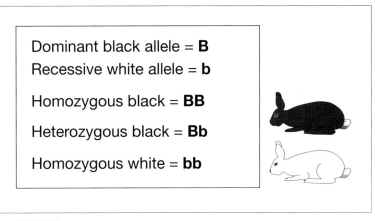

Dominant black allele = **B**

Recessive white allele = **b**

Homozygous black = **BB**

Heterozygous black = **Bb**

Homozygous white = **bb**

Figure 5 *Genotypes and phenotypes for coat colour in rabbits.*

Another convention uses capital letters to represent the chromosomes and superscript letters to show the alleles of the genes carried on the chromosome. For example I^B or I^b. I represents the chromosome and B and b are the alleles of a gene. Look at figure 6 which shows an example of genotypes using this convention.

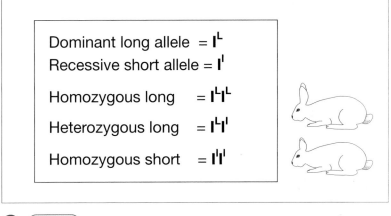

Dominant long allele $= I^L$

Recessive short allele $= I^l$

Homozygous long $= I^L I^L$

Heterozygous long $= I^L I^l$

Homozygous short $= I^l I^l$

Figure 6 *Genotypes and phenotypes for ear length in rabbits.*

Q **2 Use figures 5 and 6 to answer the following question.**
What would be the possible genotypes of a rabbit with:

a) white hair and long ears

b) black hair and short ears?

Conventions should not be mixed. Write out the genotypes using both methods. Remember that each gene must have two letters.

Doing it differently

Different alleles contribute to an individual's phenotype and this is dependent on the type of gene product. The following examples illustrate some of the ways in which genes contribute to an individual's phenotype.

Enzymes

One way to express a gene that controls the production of an enzyme is shown in figure 7.

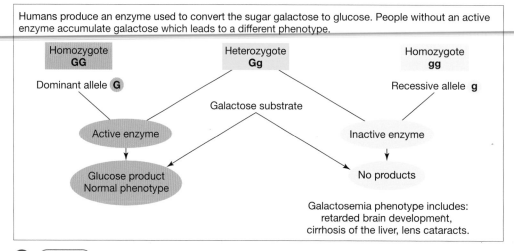

Humans produce an enzyme used to convert the sugar galactose to glucose. People without an active enzyme accumulate galactose which leads to a different phenotype.

Figure 7 *The possible genotypes and phenotypes of the galactosemia gene.*

Membrane proteins

Figure 8 shows the possible genotypes and phenotypes of the cystic fibrosis (CFTR) gene.

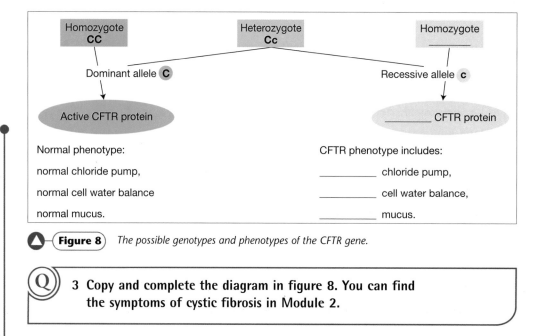

Figure 8 *The possible genotypes and phenotypes of the CFTR gene.*

Q 3 **Copy and complete the diagram in figure 8. You can find the symptoms of cystic fibrosis in Module 2.**

Antigens

Some genes have **codominant** alleles. This increases the number of possible phenotypes because both alleles are expressed and contribute to the phenotype in a heterozygous individual. An example is shown in figure 9. Notice that a different letter is used to represent the two alleles to indicate that they are both dominant.

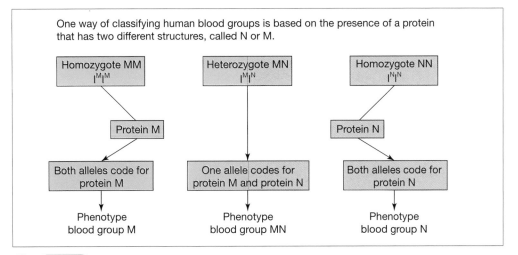

Figure 9 *Possible phenotypes of a blood protein gene.*

An even bigger range of phenotypes occurs when a gene has **multiple alleles** (more than two alleles). For example, another human blood protein gene has three alleles, I^A I^B and I^O. Alleles I^A and I^B are codominant, and code for active proteins. Allele I^O is recessive and codes for an inactive protein. An individual can only have two of these alleles.

Q 4 Copy and complete table 1.

Genotype	Proteins produced	Phenotype
$I^A I^A$	Protein A only	Group A
$I^A I^O$	Protein A and Protein O	
$I^B I^B$		
	Protein B and Protein O	Group B
		Group AB
$I^O I^O$		Group O

Table 1 *Blood types.*

Q 5 a) What would be the phenotype of a person with the genotype $I^A I^O MM$?

b) Write the genotype(s) of a person with blood group AMN.

Genes and metabolic pathways

In cells, enzymes control reactions. Processes such as respiration and photosynthesis are multi-stage pathways, with each step catalysed by a different enzyme. This means that each enzyme is dependent on the previous enzyme for its substrate. If any one of these enzymes is non-functional, the pathway comes to a halt.

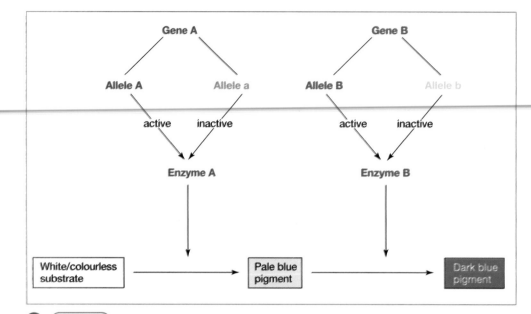

Figure 10 *A metabolic pathway with two enzymes.*

Figure 10 shows a metabolic pathway involving two enzymes. Notice that a different gene codes for each enzyme. The effect of enzyme B depends upon the action of enzyme A. Homozygous recessive individuals for gene A produce an inactive enzyme A, therefore they are unable to catalyse the reaction to form a pale blue pigment. Even if active enzyme B is produced, the individual will be colourless. This is called **epistasis**, meaning that the expression of one gene hides the expression of another. It occurs in metabolic processes controlled by enzymes coded by different genes. Epistasis reduces the number of possible phenotypes.

The genotypes are shown, as before, using letters to represent the alleles of the gene. As there are two genes, two sets of letters are used. For the example shown in figure 11 there are nine possible genotypes and three possible phenotypes. This is because there are three possible combinations of the alleles of each gene.

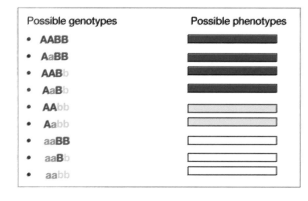

Figure 11 *Possible genotypes and phenotypes for the metabolic pathway shown in figure 10.*

6 Explain the phenotypes of the genotypes AaBb, AAbb and aaBB in figure 11.

Key ideas 6–13

- Genes have two or more alleles that code for different products, usually proteins, which have different effects in an individual.

- The genotype of an individual is the alleles of the genes inherited.

- The phenotype of an individual is the result of the expression of the genotype and any modification due to environmental factors. Differences in phenotype can be measured or described.

- Homozygous individuals inherit the same alleles of a gene from each parent.

- Heterozygous individuals inherit different alleles of a gene from each parent.

- The effects of a dominant allele always show in the phenotype, even in a heterozygous individual. Dominant alleles are represented by upper case letters.

- The effects of a recessive allele only show when there are no dominant alleles present. Recessive alleles are represented by lower case letters.

- A recessive phenotype is always homozygous.

Passing on genes

Genes are passed on by sexual reproduction, which you met in Module 2. Gametes are formed using a special form of cell division called **meiosis**. During meiosis homologous pairs of chromosomes are separated, so a gamete only contains one member of each pair. Because genes are carried on chromosomes, each gamete has one allele of each gene. As a result of meiosis, the gametes formed are different from one another and contain a random selection of one allele of each gene. At fertilisation a gamete from each parent fuses, so each offspring receives a random mixture of the alleles of each parent.

Memory joggers

- Body cells are diploid and produced by mitosis.
- Gametes are haploid.
- Males and females produce gametes for sexual reproduction. Unused gametes die.
- Any of the gametes produced by a female have an equal chance of being fertilised by any of the gametes produced by a male, so fertilisation is random.
- Before cell division DNA replicates.
- Chromosomes containing DNA become visible during cell division due to shortening and thickening.
- At the start of cell division chromosomes exist as two chromatids held together by a centromere.
- Chromatids contain identical DNA.
- The cytoplasm of a cell forms a spindle which is used to separate chromosomes.

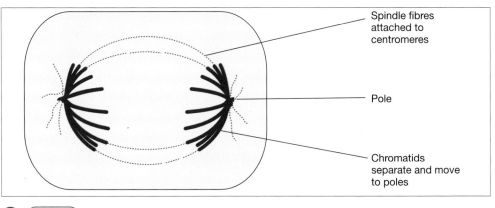

Spindle fibres attached to centromeres

Pole

Chromatids separate and move to poles

Figure 1 *A cell during mitosis.*

Separating alleles by meiosis

Meiosis is a double division of the same cell. It has many features in common with **mitosis**. The replication of DNA, spindle formation and division of the cytoplasm all occur in the same way. The main difference is in the behaviour of the chromosomes. Figure 2 summarises the double division that occurs. Notice that the homologous pairs separate in the first division and the chromatids separate in the second division.

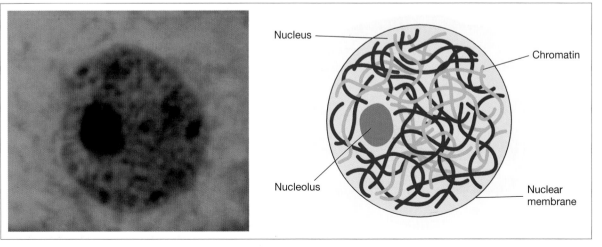

Figure 2   *Summary of meiosis.*

Interphase – preparation

Figure 3 shows a cell during interphase. Cells in the reproductive organs, which give rise to gametes, grow and synthesise organelles. DNA is replicated.

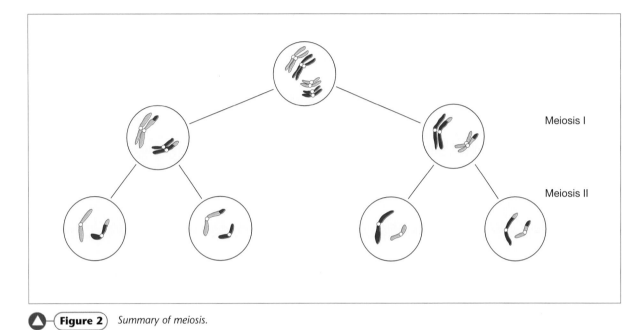

Figure 3   *Interphase of meiosis.*

Prophase I – condensing and pairing

The chromosomes appear as long tangled threads which become shorter and thicker. At the same time the chromosomes are moved around in the nucleus until they find their homologous pair. The pairs match up so the alleles of the same gene are next to each other. Eventually the two chromatids become visible. This association of a homologous pair, each with two chromatids, is a **bivalent**. You can see bivalents in figure 4.

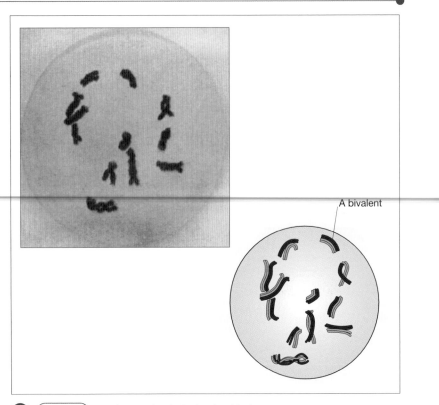

A bivalent

Figure 4 Prophase I of meiosis showing bivalents.

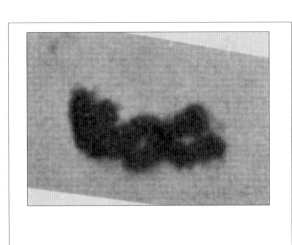

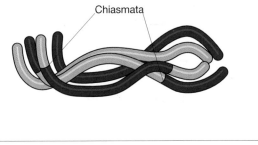

Chiasmata

The chromatids of a bivalent become twisted around each other. At some points of contact, breaks occur and sections of chromatid are exchanged between the homologous pair. Exchange between the chromatids of a homologous pair is random, so every gamete will have a different mixture of the alleles of the genes. As a result, the alleles an individual inherits from its parents are mixed up. This exchange is called **crossing over** and the point at which it happens is a **chiasma** (plural **chiasmata**). Figure 5 shows crossing over.

Figure 5 Crossing over between a homologous pair.

Metaphase I – organising homologous pairs

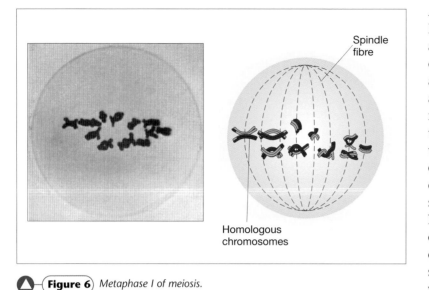

Figure 6 *Metaphase I of meiosis.*

At the end of prophase the homologous pairs start to pull apart. As they do so, the chiasmata become very obvious, as the chromatids tend to stick at these points. The nuclear membrane disintegrates and the bivalents, still partially twisted together, attach to the equator of the spindle formed during prophase. Figure 6 shows metaphase I of meiosis. Notice that the homologous chromosomes are attached opposite to each other on the spindle. There is no rule about which member of the homologous pairs is on which side of the spindle, i.e. it is random.

Anaphase I – separating homologous pairs

The spindle fibres contract and pull the homologous pairs apart. The chromatids of each chromosome *do not* separate. Each homologous pair attaches to the spindle at random in relation to all other homologous pairs. When the pairs are pulled apart, either member of a pair can end up at a pole along with either of the members of the other homologous pairs. This is called **independent assortment of non-homologous pairs**. As a result there is further mixing of the alleles. In humans there are 23 pairs of chromosomes, so there are 2^{23} (or 8 388 608) different possible chromosome combinations. Figure 7 shows a cell with two homologous pairs and illustrates one of the possible ways the chromosomes could separate.

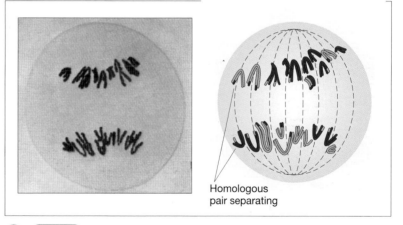

Figure 7 *A cell during anaphase I of meiosis.*

Q
1 **How many different ways could these chromosomes be separated?**
2 **Draw diagrams of a cell with two homologous pairs of chromosomes during anaphase, showing all the different ways the pairs could separate.**

Telophase I – restoring the cell

Figure 8 shows a cell during telophase I. A nuclear membrane forms around each set of chromosomes. Remember that the chromatids, no longer identical because of crossing over, have not separated yet. The chromosome number is now haploid, as there is only one member of each homologous pair present. The cytoplasm starts to separate. In some organisms the cytoplasm is totally separated and meiosis completed later, sometimes years afterwards. In other cells, telophase I and prophase II run into each other.

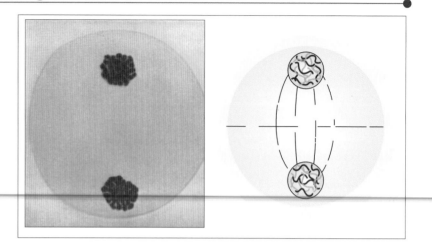

▲ **Figure 8** *A cell during telophase I of meiosis.*

Second meiosis division

Figure 9 shows meiosis II. Notice that it resembles mitosis, except that the cells are haploid. A spindle appears in each of the cells formed at the end of meiosis I and the chromatids are separated during anaphase II. Eventually four cells form which then become gametes.

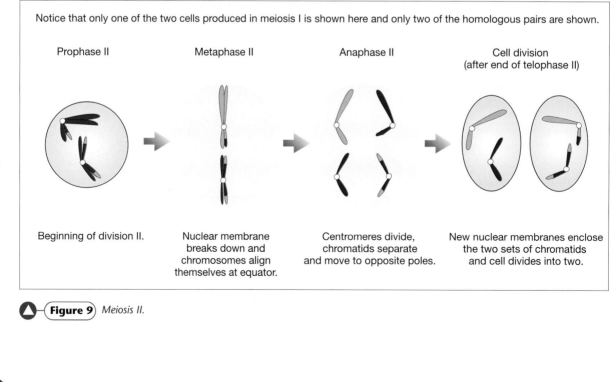

Notice that only one of the two cells produced in meiosis I is shown here and only two of the homologous pairs are shown.

Prophase II	Metaphase II	Anaphase II	Cell division (after end of telophase II)
Beginning of division II.	Nuclear membrane breaks down and chromosomes align themselves at equator.	Centromeres divide, chromatids separate and move to opposite poles.	New nuclear membranes enclose the two sets of chromatids and cell divides into two.

▲ **Figure 9** *Meiosis II.*

At the end of meiosis, each cell has:

- one member of each homologous pair – the haploid number of chromosomes
- one allele of each gene of the parent genes
- a random mixture of non-homologous chromosomes
- a random mixture of the alleles of the different genes resulting from recombination.

Q 3 List all the ways in which meiosis leads to the production of gametes that contain a mixture of alleles of different genes.

Fertilisation – putting homologous pairs back together

At fertilisation, shown in figure 10, any of the gametes produced by one parent has an equal chance of combining with any of the gametes produced by the other parent. This leads to more mixing of alleles.

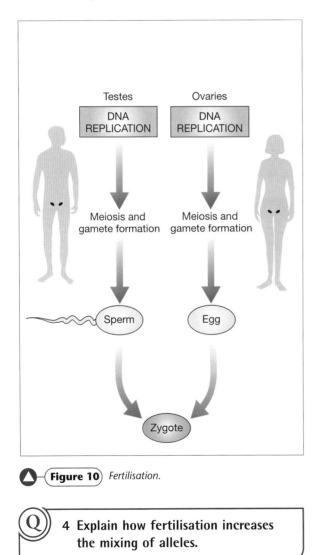

Figure 10 Fertilisation.

Q 4 Explain how fertilisation increases the mixing of alleles.

Key ideas 14–19

- Meiosis is a double division resulting in the reduction of the chromosome number of a cell from diploid to haploid.
- In most living organisms meiosis is associated with the production of gametes for sexual reproduction.
- During meiosis I homologous pairs separate, reducing the chromosome number. During meiosis II sister chromatids separate.
- During prophase I of meiosis homologous pairs associate together as bivalents and crossing over occurs.
- Crossing over between chromatids of homologous pairs results in mixing of genes between chromosomes of maternal and paternal origin.
- Chiasmata are crossover points between homologous pairs, only visible during meiosis I.
- During metaphase I homologous pairs attach independently to the spindle, so in anaphase I independent assortment occurs leading to mixing of chromosomes of maternal and paternal origin.
- In anaphase II independent assortment of sister chromatids leads to further mixing.
- Gametes formed after meiosis have a random mixture of genes.

3 Following inheritance

To study inheritance, genetic crosses are carried out and **pedigrees** are studied. Pedigrees are a record of the inheritance of particular phenotypes through many generations. Breeders of animals and plants keep breeding records of the parents used to produce a particular animal or plant. Patterns in the inheritance of a particular phenotype are due to the different alleles of the genes involved, the behaviour of chromosomes during meiosis and the process of fertilisation.

Memory joggers

- Alleles of a gene occupy the same locus on homologous chromosomes.
- During meiosis the alleles of a gene are separated.
- The alleles of genes on different homologous pairs will separate independently due to independent assortment of non-homologous pairs.
- Alleles of different genes on the same chromosome will be inherited together unless they are exchanged during crossing over.
- Genotypes show the alleles of the genes inherited.
- Phenotypes show the expression of the genes in an individual and any effect of environmental factors.

Figure 1 *Similarities and differences in family groups.*

Doing genetic crosses

To study inheritance it is easier to consider only one or two characteristics at a time, as it becomes difficult to follow all the possible combinations. On page 9, for example, the gene controlling coat colour in rabbits has four possible phenotypes and ten possible genotypes. There are conventions, used in this book, to show the possible ways in which alleles of genes are inherited. You are expected to use these when answering any question on genetic inheritance.

One at a time – monohybrid inheritance

Monohybrid (mono = single, hybrid = cross) inheritance is the inheritance of a phenotype determined by one gene.

Dominant and recessive pairs

The classic examples are the work of Mendel in the 19th century, using the garden pea. Figure 2 illustrates these studies, using a genetic diagram to show inheritance. Pure breeding pea plants with yellow pods when crossed with pure breeding pea plants with green pods always produce pea plants with yellow pods.

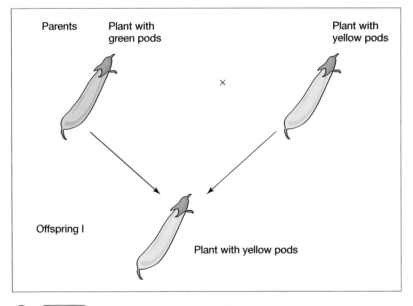

Figure 2 *Crossing of pea plants with different coloured pods.*

From these results the following can be deduced:

* there is a single gene for pod colour which has two alleles
* pure breeding plants are homozygous
* the allele for yellow colour is dominant to the allele for green colour.

Mendel also carried out crosses with pure breeding pea plants with yellow seeds and pure breeding pea plants with green seeds. The results showed the same pattern as for pod colour.

Explaining how

Mendel's results can be explained by the behaviour of chromosomes during meiosis, as shown in figure 3.

Key   Yellow allele **Y**   Green allele **y**

Parental phenotype   Yellow seeds × Green seeds

Parental genotype   YY   yy

Gametes   Y   Y   y   y

Notice carefully how the diagram is labelled. When you show crosses you have carried out, you *must* include all the labels.
You must include a key, the gametes, the offspring genotypes and phenotypes.

The parental phenotypes describe the features of the parents and the genotypes show the alleles present.

Male gametes   y   y

Offspring (1) genotypes

Female gametes

	y	y
Y	Yy	Yy
Y	Yy	Yy

The gametes represent all the types of gamete each parent can produce. In this case there is only one type, although it is convention to show allele separation.

The offspring (1) genotypes show all the possible combinations of the gametes.

Offspring (1) phenotypes   Yellow seeds

The offspring (1) phenotypes describe the features of the offspring.

▲ (**Figure 3**) *Plants with yellow seeds crossed with plants with green seeds.*

In meiosis the pair of alleles separated so that each gamete had one of the alleles. In offspring (1), because both alleles were the same in each parent, the gametes produced were identical. Each parent had only one type of allele (homozygous) so all the offspring had the same genotype and phenotype.

Offspring (1) were allowed to breed with each other (interbreed). In offspring (2) 25% had green seeds, as shown in figure 4.

Key   Yellow allele **Y**   Green allele **y**

Parental phenotype   Yellow   ×   Yellow

Parental genotype   Yy   Yy

Gametes   Y   y   Y   y

Male gametes   Y   y

Offspring (2) genotypes

Female gametes

	Y	y
Y	YY	Yy
y	Yy	yy

Offspring (2) phenotypes   Yellow seeds   Green seeds

Phenotype ratio   3   :   1
                   (75%)   (25%)

◀ (**Figure 4**) *Interbreeding of yellow offspring.*

Offspring (1) were heterozygous so they produced two types of gamete. At fertilisation, there were four ways the gametes from each parent could combine to produce offspring (2). These gave the genotypes YY, Yy, Yy and yy. Notice that two of these genotypes are homozygous and two are heterozygous. As the yellow allele is dominant, the heterozygous offspring show the yellow phenotype, giving a phenotype ratio of:

3 yellow (dominant phenotype) : 1 green (recessive phenotype)

Test cross

A **test cross** is carried out between an individual of unknown genotype showing the dominant phenotype and an individual showing a recessive phenotype. Peas from offspring (1) crossed with peas with green pods produce a different phenotype ratio:

1 yellow (dominant phenotype) : 1 green (recessive phenotype)

This cross is shown in figure 5.

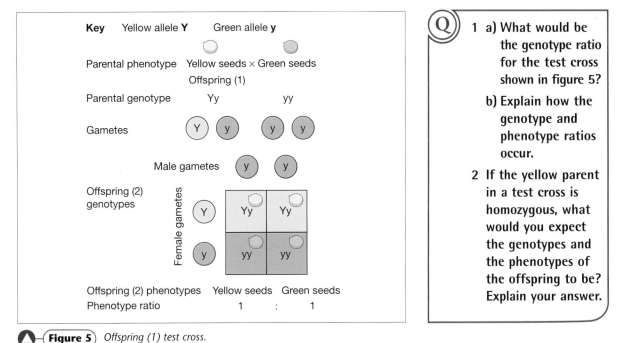

 **Figure 5** *Offspring (1) test cross.*

Q 1 a) What would be the genotype ratio for the test cross shown in figure 5?

   b) Explain how the genotype and phenotype ratios occur.

2 If the yellow parent in a test cross is homozygous, what would you expect the genotypes and the phenotypes of the offspring to be? Explain your answer.

Golden rules

For a phenotype controlled by a single gene with two alleles, one allele dominant to the other:

- a cross between a homozygous dominant parent and a homozygous recessive parent always gives heterozygous offspring showing the dominant phenotype
- a cross between two heterozygous parents always gives two homozygous and two heterozygous genotypes
- a cross between two heterozygous individuals always gives the 3:1 phenotype ratio
- a cross between a heterozygous parent and a homozygous recessive parent always gives the 1:1 phenotype ratio.

Codominant genes

Codominance occurs when the alleles of a gene have equal dominance. Because both alleles are expressed, an individual with a heterozygous genotype will have a phenotype that is different from either of the homozygous individuals. Check back to the example of human blood groups on page 11 to remind yourself if necessary. Crosses involving heterozygous individuals give different phenotype ratios. Figure 6 is a pedigree showing the inheritance of coat colour in horses: cream, chestnut and palomino.

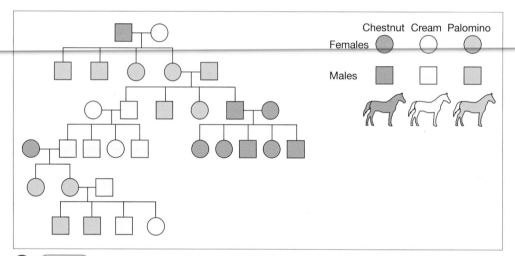

Figure 6 *A pedigree showing the inheritance of coat colour in horses.*

> **Q**
>
> 3 a) Draw a series of genetic diagrams to show crosses between: i) a chestnut horse and a cream horse; ii) two palomino horses; iii) a chestnut horse and a palomino horse; iv) a cream horse and a palomino horse.
>
> b) What are the genotype and phenotype ratios of a cross between: i) two heterozygous individuals; ii) a heterozygous individual and a homozygous individual?

Golden rules

For a phenotype controlled by a single gene with two alleles which are codominant:

- a cross between two different homozygous dominant parents always gives heterozygous offspring showing a different phenotype from either parent
- a cross between two heterozygous parents always gives two homozygous and two heterozygous genotypes
- a cross between two heterozygous individuals always gives the 1:2:1 phenotype ratio
- a cross between a heterozygous parent and a homozygous parent always gives the 1:1 phenotype ratio.

Multiple alleles

You can find an example of multiple alleles at a single locus on page 11. A gene that codes for a human blood protein has three alleles: I^A, I^B and I^O. A gene with multiple alleles also controls coat colour in rabbits. Figure 7 shows the variety of phenotypes and genotypes resulting from the four alleles of this gene.

> **Q** 4 Write out the order of dominance of these alleles, starting with the most dominant.

Alleles	Possible genotypes	Phenotype	
C	CC, CH, CCh, Ca	Agouti	
H	HH, HCh, Ha	Himalayan	
Ch	ChCh, Cha	Chinchilla	
a	aa	Albino	

 Figure 7 *Phenotypes and genotypes for coat colour in rabbits.*

Figure 8 shows the results of a number of crosses between rabbits with different coat colour.

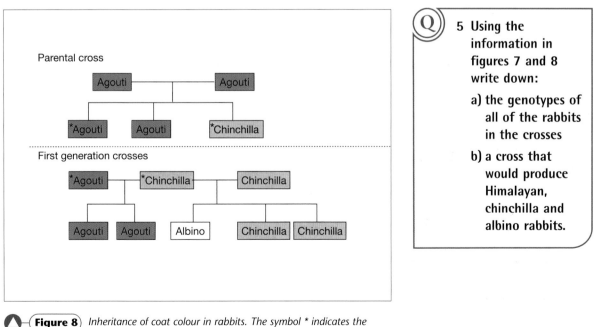

> **Q** 5 Using the information in figures 7 and 8 write down:
> a) the genotypes of all of the rabbits in the crosses
> b) a cross that would produce Himalayan, chinchilla and albino rabbits.

Parental cross

Agouti —— Agouti

*Agouti   Agouti   *Chinchilla

First generation crosses

*Agouti —— *Chinchilla —— Chinchilla

Agouti   Agouti   Albino   Chinchilla   Chinchilla

Figure 8 *Inheritance of coat colour in rabbits. The symbol * indicates the rabbits crossed from the first generation.*

Two at a time – dihybrid crosses

Dihybrid (di = two, hybrid = cross) inheritance is the inheritance of a phenotype that is determined by two different genes. The general principles applied to a monohybrid cross do not change. The alleles of each gene still separate during meiosis, and for each gene the same possible combinations occur. However, the number of possible phenotypes increases because the number of ways in which the alleles of two different genes can combine is greater.

Dominant and recessive pairs

Mendel's classic experiments also included examples of dihydrid crosses. Homozygous pea plants producing yellow seeds with a wrinkled surface crossed with pea plants producing green seeds with a smooth surface always give offspring with yellow, wrinkled seeds. When the offspring with yellow, wrinkled seeds are interbred, offspring (2) show all combinations of colour and surface type. Figure 9 shows the way in which this happens. Notice that each parent in the first cross has only one type of gamete, but in the offspring (1) cross each parent can produce four different types of gamete. This is because during meiosis either allele of the colour gene can end up in a gamete with either allele of the surface gene. At fertilisation these gametes give sixteen possible combinations in offspring (2). Look carefully at the genotypes. You can see the expected phenotype ratio for each individual gene of:

**3 yellow : 1 green and
3 wrinkled : 1 smooth**

The extra combination, due to independent assortment of non-homologous pairs of chromosomes, gives a phenotype ratio for the two genes of:

9 yellow and wrinkled : 3 yellow and smooth : 3 green and wrinkled : 1 green and smooth

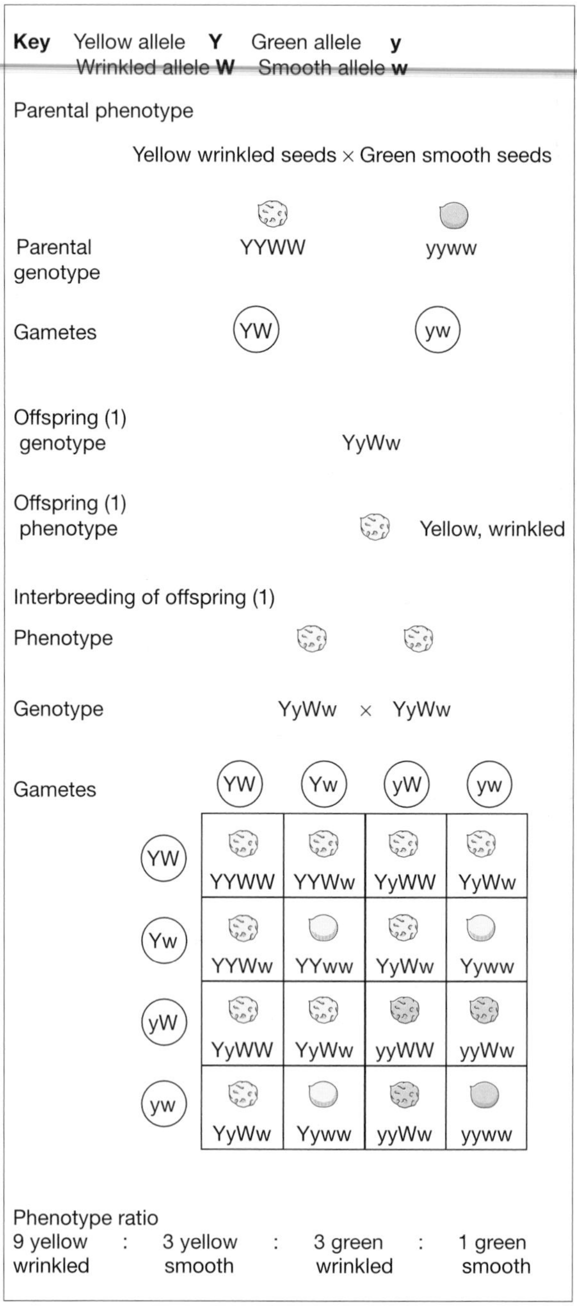

Figure 9 contents:

Key: Yellow allele **Y** Green allele **y**
Wrinkled allele **W** Smooth allele **w**

Parental phenotype

Yellow wrinkled seeds × Green smooth seeds

Parental genotype: YYWW   yyww

Gametes: YW   yw

Offspring (1) genotype: YyWw

Offspring (1) phenotype: Yellow, wrinkled

Interbreeding of offspring (1)

Phenotype

Genotype: YyWw × YyWw

Gametes: YW, Yw, yW, yw

	YW	Yw	yW	yw
YW	YYWW	YYWw	YyWW	YyWw
Yw	YYWw	YYww	YyWw	Yyww
yW	YyWW	YyWw	yyWW	yyWw
yw	YyWw	Yyww	yyWw	yyww

Phenotype ratio
9 yellow : 3 yellow : 3 green : 1 green
wrinkled   smooth   wrinkled   smooth

Figure 9 Dihybrid inheritance in peas.

Test cross

A **test cross** is carried out between a pea plant of unknown genotype showing the dominant phenotype for each gene with a pea plant showing the recessive phenotypes.

> (Q) **6 Copy and complete table 1 showing the genotype of the parents, their gametes and the genotypes and phenotypes of the offspring.**

Parent phenotype	Yellow wrinkled seeds	Green smooth seeds
Parent genotype	YyWw	_____
Parent gametes	(YW)(Yw)(yW) _____	(yw)
Offspring genotypes	YyWw Yyww	_____ _____
Offspring phenotypes	yellow _____ wrinkled _____	green _____ wrinkled _____
Phenotype ratio	_____	

▲ Table 1

> (Q) **7 What would be the results of the test cross if the unknown plant was:**
> **a) homozygous for both features**
> **b) heterozygous for colour and homozygous for the surface gene**
> **c) homozygous for colour and heterozygous for the surface gene**
> **d) heterozygous for both features?**

Golden rules

For phenotypes controlled by two different genes, each of which has two alleles with one allele dominant to the other:

- a cross between a parent homozygous dominant for both genes and a parent homozygous recessive for both genes always gives offspring heterozygous for both genes showing the dominant phenotype of each gene
- a cross between parents heterozygous for both genes always results in a 9:3:3:1 phenotype ratio
- a test cross between a parent heterozygous for both genes and a parent homozygous recessive always results in a 1:1:1:1 phenotype ratio.

Epistatic genes

As discussed on page 12, the effects of these genes are most noticeable in metabolic pathways. Figure 10 shows an example of a pathway involved in the production of petal colour in sweet pea flowers.

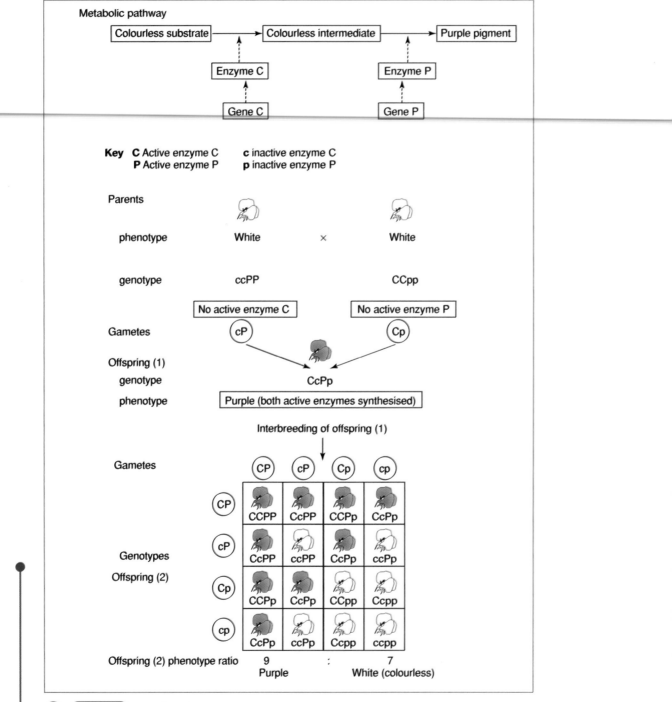

Figure 10 *The effect of epistasis.*

Notice that colour only develops where there is at least one dominant allele of each gene present.

Q 8 What is the effect of epistasis on the phenotype ratio?

9 Draw a diagram of a cross between plants with genotypes Ccpp and ccPp.

Key ideas 20–28

- Monohybrid inheritance is the inheritance of a phenotype determined by one gene.

- Dihybrid inheritance is the inheritance of a phenotype determined by two different genes.

- A test cross is carried out between an individual of unknown genotype showing the dominant phenotype with an individual showing a recessive phenotype to determine the genotype of the unknown individual.

- For a phenotype controlled by a single gene with a dominant and recessive allele, a cross between two heterozygous individuals always gives a 3:1 phenotype ratio.

- For a phenotype controlled by a single gene with a dominant and recessive allele, a cross between a heterozygous parent and a homozygous recessive parent always gives a 1:1 phenotype ratio.

- For a phenotype controlled by a single gene with a pair of codominant alleles, a cross between two different homozygous dominant parents always gives heterozygous offspring showing a different phenotype from either parent.

- For a phenotype controlled by a single gene with a pair of codominant alleles, a cross between two heterozygous individuals always gives a 1:2:1 phenotype ratio.

- For a phenotype controlled by two genes, each with a dominant and recessive allele, a cross between parents heterozygous for both genes always gives a 9:3:3:1 phenotype ratio.

- For a phenotype controlled by two genes, each with a dominant and recessive allele, a test cross between a parent heterozygous for both genes and a parent homozygous recessive always gives a 1:1:1:1 phenotype ratio.

- Genes with multiple alleles and interaction between genes at different loci give different phenotypic ratios.

- Epistasis reduces the number of phenotypes.

Sex inheritance

Unlike other aspects of phenotype, gender (the sex of an individual) is determined by a particular combination of certain chromosomes. In addition to genes that control the development of sex organs and other body features related to sex, these chromosomes also carry genes that control other body features. The way in which sex chromosomes are inherited varies in different types of organism. In this section you will be looking mainly at the chromosomes of humans, which you may have studied in GCSE. Human males produce two types of gamete determining gender so they are known as the **heterogametic** (hetero = different, gametic = gamete) sex. The gametes of human females are all of the same type so they are called the **homogametic** (homo = same, gametic = gamete) sex.

Memory joggers

- Humans have two types of sex chromosome.
- X chromosomes are longer than Y chromosomes.
- Males inherit one X chromosome and one Y chromosome.
- Females inherit two X chromosomes.
- Humans have 23 pairs of chromosomes; one pair are the sex chromosomes and the other 22 pairs are autosomes..

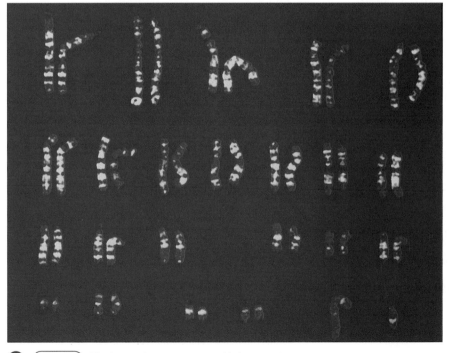

Figure 1 *The human karyotype.*

Chromosomes for sex

The sex chromosomes are sometimes called **heterosomes** (hetero = different, some = body) because they are different in appearance. The other chromosomes in a cell are called **autosomes**.

Figure 2 is a diagram of the human sex chromosomes and a photograph of the sex chromosomes as they appear under the microscope. Notice that the X chromosome is very much longer than the Y chromosome.

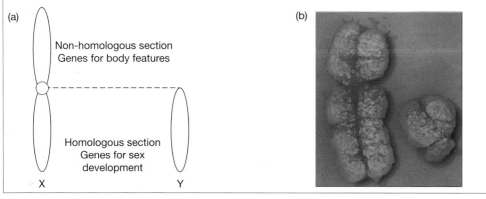

(a)

Non-homologous section
Genes for body features

Homologous section
Genes for sex
development

X   Y

(b)

 Figure 2 *The human sex chromosomes. (a) Diagram of the X and Y chromosomes. (b) Electron micrograph of X and Y chromosomes of a human male.*

The extra length means that an X chromosome can carry more genes than a Y chromosome. In humans, almost all of the alleles on the Y chromosome are involved in male sexual development. The X chromosome has corresponding alleles, involved in female sexual development, on the homologous part of the chromosome. The extra, non-homologous part has other genes.

> **Q** **1 Explain why recessive alleles on the non–homologous part of an X chromosome are always shown in the phenotype of a male.**

Figure 3 shows inheritance of sex in humans.

Sons always inherit a Y chromosome from their father and an X chromosome from their mother. Daughters inherit an X chromosome from each parent. Notice that the ratio of males to females is always

1 male : 1 female.

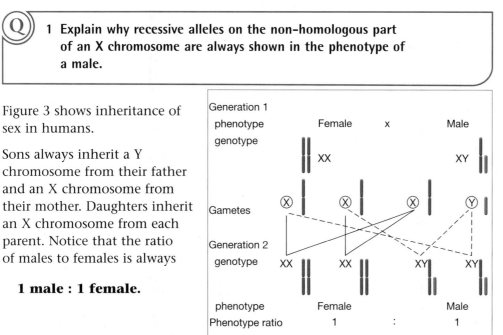

Generation 1
phenotype   Female   x   Male
genotype   XX   XY

Gametes   Ⓧ   Ⓧ   Ⓧ   Ⓨ

Generation 2
genotype   XX   XX   XY   XY

phenotype   Female   Male
Phenotype ratio   1   :   1

Figure 3 *Sex inheritance in humans.*

Sex-linked phenotypes

These are phenotypes that either are found only in one sex or occur more frequently in one sex than the other. The majority of sex-linked phenotypes are due to alleles carried on the non-homologous part of the X chromosome. The gene that controls the synthesis of the blood-clotting protein, **factor VIII**, is an example of **sex linkage**. Another example is the gene that controls the synthesis of a pigment found in the retina of the eye, which is used in colour vision.

Red-green colour blindness occurs as a result of a mutant allele so that one of the types of pigment found in the eye is not synthesised. If you look at the section on colour vision on page 127 it shows that normal colour vision depends on three types of pigment in the cone cells of the retina. If there is no red-absorbing pigment, red light is not detected so some colours cannot be distinguished.

Figure 4 shows the inheritance of red-green colour blindness in humans. Notice that the way of showing sex-linked alleles is X^N or X^n, which is a modification of the convention shown on page 9. You can see that there are two types of X chromosome. Females with the genotype $X^N X^n$ are called carriers. They have inherited one X chromosome from each parent. A male inherits an X chromosome from his mother and a Y chromosome from his father. If a male inherits the X^n chromosome he will be colour blind.

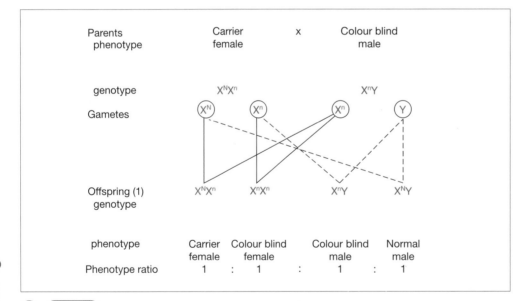

Figure 4 *Inheritance of red-green colour blindness in humans.*

Q **2 Draw a diagram to show how a man with colour blindness, whose wife has normal colour vision, can pass colour blindness on to his grandson, but not his daughter.**

Sex-linked codominant alleles

Some coat colours in cats are sex-linked. The colour ginger is controlled by a yellow allele of a coat colour gene, which is codominant with the black allele of this gene. Figure 5 shows a cross between a ginger male and a black female.

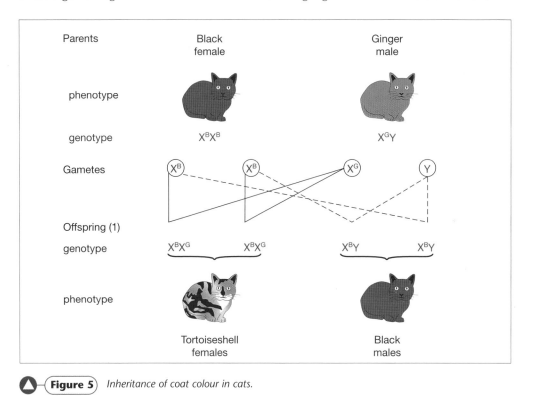

Figure 5 *Inheritance of coat colour in cats.*

Q 3 Explain why it is not possible to have a tortoiseshell male.

Sex in other organisms

Sex inheritance in birds is different from that in humans: in birds the male is the homogametic sex and females are heterogametic. The same letters, X and Y, are used to represent the chromosomes.

Q 4 Draw a diagram to show how sex is inherited in birds.

Insects show the greatest variation in sex inheritance. The inheritance of sex in fruit flies is controlled in the same way as in humans. Honeybees, however, have an unusual system in which males develop from eggs that are unfertilised and females develop from fertilised eggs. Figure 6 shows sex inheritance in honeybees.

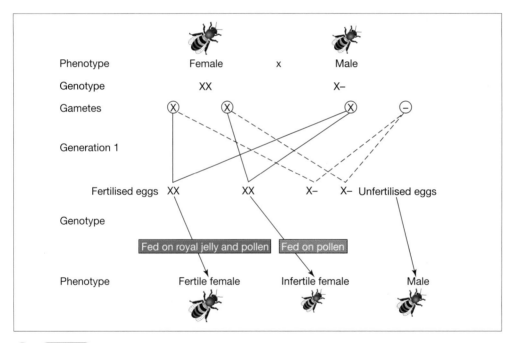

Figure 6 *Sex inheritance in honeybees.*

Notice that an additional difference occurs in female development: environmental factors cause some females to develop into fertile egg-laying queens while others develop into sterile workers.

Key ideas 30–34

- Human males produce two types of gamete determining gender: they are the heterogametic sex.

- The gametes determining gender of human females are all of the same type: they are the homogametic sex.

- In humans, most of the alleles on the Y chromosome are involved in male sexual development. The homologous part of the X chromosome has alleles involved in female sexual development.

- Sex-linked phenotypes are due to alleles carried on the non-homologous part of the X chromosome.

- The ratio of sex inheritance in humans is always 1 male : 1 female.

Unit 1 – Questions

1   Figure 1 shows the inheritance of a rare condition called polydactyly in which a person has extra fingers or toes.

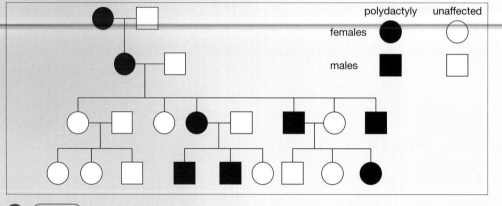

▲ Figure 1

a) What evidence in the pedigree suggests that the polydactyly allele is:
   i)   dominant
   ii) carried on an autosome?   (2 marks)
b) i)   What proportion of children without polydactyly would
        be expected if both parents were heterozygous for
        polydactyly?   (1 mark)
   ii) Explain your answer.   (3 marks)
                                                          (Total 6 marks)

2   Breeding between two short haired rabbits resulted in eight offspring.
   Six of these had short hair and two had long hair.

a) What conclusions can be drawn about the inheritance of coat
    length in rabbits from the results of this cross?   (2 marks)
b) Using suitable symbols to represent the alleles of the gene for coat
    length, complete table 1 which shows the possible genotypes of the
    parents and offspring of this cross.   (4 marks)

Rabbit phenotype	Genotype
Short haired parent	
Long haired offspring	
Short haired offspring	

▲ Table 1

                                                          (Total 6 marks)

3 a) What is meant by:
    i)   homozygous
    ii) heterozygous?   (2 marks)

b) Explain how the breeder could find out if an animal showing a dominant phenotype was homozygous or heterozygous.   (2 marks)

c) Crosses between roan coloured horses gave offspring that had roan, grey or chestnut coloured coats. Use a genetic diagram to show how these coat colours are inherited.   (4 marks)
    (Total 8 marks)

4 a) What is meant by sex linkage?   (2 marks)

b) The X chromosome carries one of the genes that controls coat colour in cats. In some cats this gene has two alleles, **O** and **B**. Table 2 shows the possible genotypes and phenotypes of female cats.

Genotype	Phenotype
$X^O X^O$	Orange
$X^O X^B$	Tortoiseshell
$X^B X^B$	Black

 Table 2

    i)   Give the possible genotypes and phenotypes of male cats.   (4 marks)

    ii) A tortoiseshell female was bred with a black male. Use a genetic diagram to show the chances of black male kittens resulting from this cross.   (4 marks)
    (Total 10 marks)

5 Figure 2 shows a biochemical pathway for the production of pigment in a variety of flower.

Step 1	Step 2
Colourless substrate ⟶ Purple intermediate	⟶ Blue pigment

▲ **Figure 2**

Step 1 is controlled by an enzyme determined by gene P, which has two alleles, **P** and **p**. Step 2 is controlled by an enzyme determined by gene B, which has two alleles, **B** and **b**. The recessive alleles of both genes code for inactive enzymes.
Blue-flowered plants were allowed to breed amongst themselves. The offspring included plants with blue, purple and white flowers.

a) What were the genotypes of the parent plants?   (2 marks)

b) Use a genetic diagram to show the expected proportions of purple, blue and white offspring of a cross between the blue-flowered parents.   (4 marks)
    (Total 6 marks)

Variation

Variation refers to the small differences that exist between members of the same species. There are two components that contribute to total variation – genetics and the environment – and these interact to give the final characteristics of an individual.

Memory joggers

- Living organisms resemble their parents because genetic information is passed on from the parents to the gametes from which new organisms develop.
- Genes carry information.
- Different genes control the development of different characteristics.
- New forms of genes (alleles) arise from mutations in existing genes.
- Differences between organisms of the same species are due to the genes they inherit (genetics) and the conditions in which they develop (the environment).
- Gamete formation involves meiosis, in which the number of chromosomes is reduced from the diploid number to the haploid number.

Figure 1

Genetic causes of variation

Mutation

This causes changes in genes giving rise to new alleles which code for different gene products. Changes in gene products cause changes in the phenotype. Examples of these are given in the section 'Following inheritance' (pages 20–29).

Meiosis

Meiosis leads to variation in two ways:

1 crossing over
2 independent assortment of chromosomes.

Crossing over occurs during prophase I of meiosis. This mixes the alleles of genes on homologous pairs. As a result the maternal and paternal genes of an individual are redistributed onto different chromosomes. Figure 2 represents part of a homologous pair of chromosomes and some of the gene loci.

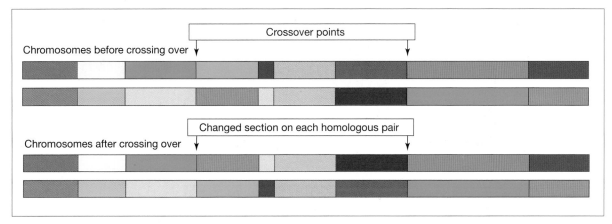

 Figure 2 *Effect of crossing over.*

Independent assortment occurs in anaphase I of meiosis as the homologous pairs separate. It also occurs in anaphase II as the chromatids separate. As a result, all the gametes are different.

Examples of crossing over and independent assortment were considered in the section 'Passing on genes' (pages 14–19).

Fertilisation

Random fertilisation increases variation as each offspring receives a gamete from each parent. As a result of meiosis, all the gametes of an individual are different. Because any gamete of one parent can fuse with any gamete of the other parent, fertilisation is random and no two zygotes can have the same genotype, except identical twins.

Q **1 Explain why identical twins have the same genotype.**

Environmental causes of variation

The environmental causes of variation can be either internal or external factors which regulate the expression of genes in the phenotype. These environmental influences cannot be inherited and are unique to an individual.

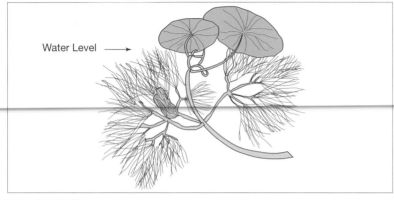

Water Level →

▲ Figure 3 Water lily leaves.

Figure 3 shows an example of an environmental influence on a plant. The leaves of a water lily above water are flat and float on the surface of the water. The leaves below the water are almost hair-like to reduce resistance to water flow. As the leaves are on the same plant the genotype must be the same, so differences in phenotype are due to the environment.

The characteristic coloration of Siamese cats, which you can see in figure 4, is due to differences in internal environment. The allele that controls pigment production in the body hair is sensitive to temperature. At the extremities of the body, blood circulation is less efficient so blood temperature is lower. The allele controlling the synthesis of dark pigment can function, so the hair is darker. The rest of the body is pale cream. Breeders of Siamese cats have bred cats with mutations of these alleles, giving a wide range of different colours.

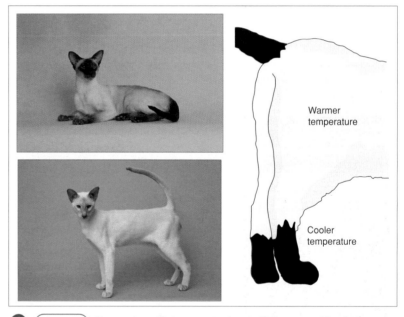

Warmer temperature

Cooler temperature

▲ Figure 4 Temperature effects on coat colour in Siamese cats. The photographs show two varieties of Siamese cat, both with characteristic darker coloration of extremities, where the blood temperature is lower.

As genes and environment interact, it is difficult to measure the relative contribution of each. One way is to use clones, but even in the most carefully controlled environments there are always minor differences that can influence individuals.

(Q) **2 Why are clones used to study the influence of the environment?**

Human inheritance

Human phenotype is also influenced by interaction between genes and environment. The study of humans is an even greater problem as there are relatively few clones. Many studies are carried out on twins. The results of one study into the inheritance of height and mass are shown in table 1.

Twin groups studied	Mean difference in height/cm	Mean difference in mass/kg
Identical twins, reared together	1.7	2.0
Identical twins, reared apart	1.8	4.8
Non-identical, same sex twins reared together	4.4	4.9

 Table 1 *Inheritance of height and mass.*

These results suggest that height is largely controlled by genes as there is very little difference between the two types of identical twin groups, even though the twins reared apart may have been in very different environments.

Q 3 **What do the results suggest about the control of body mass?**

Environmental influences in humans are also studied using data collected from different groups of people.

In pattern baldness, shown in figure 5, the hair is very thin on top of the head. It is controlled by a single gene carried on an autosome, but its expression is modified by hormones produced as a result of sexual development.

Table 2 shows the genotypes and phenotypes for pattern baldness.

Genotype	Phenotype	
	Male	Female
BB	Bald	Bald
Bb	Bald	Not bald
bb	Not bald	Not bald

 Table 2 *Genotypes and phenotypes for pattern baldness.*

Q 4 **Describe the pattern of the expression of pattern baldness. Suggest an explanation for this pattern.**

Figure 5 *Pattern baldness in humans*

Different types of variation

Variation is studied by observing a phenotype of interest, such as blood group or body mass, and recording the different types that exist in a population. The individuals are then placed into categories according to which variation of the phenotype they express. By collecting data from a large number of individuals, the frequency of the different types of phenotypes can be calculated. As a result of this type of study, two types of variation are recognised.

In **discontinuous variation** the phenotypes:

- have distinct categories into which individuals can be placed
- tend to be qualitative with no overlap between the categories
- are controlled by a small number of genes with little environmental influence.

An example in humans is blood group; the inheritance of blood group is described on page 11. If the ABO system is used there are four distinct categories: group A, group B, group AB and group O. If the MN system is used, there are three distinct categories: group M, group MN and group N. The results of surveys are usually presented as ratios or as bar charts as shown in figure 6.

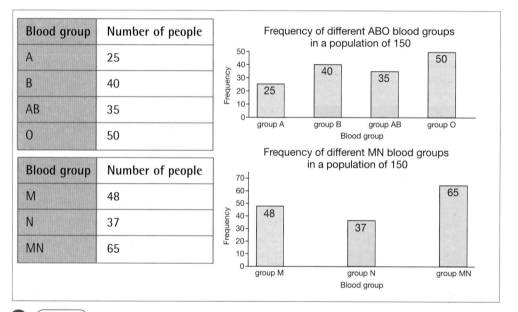

Blood group	Number of people
A	25
B	40
AB	35
O	50

Blood group	Number of people
M	48
N	37
MN	65

Figure 6 *Results of a survey of blood groups of 150 people.*

Q 5 The results of a survey into coat colour in horses are shown in table 3.

   a) Plot these data as a frequency bar chart.

   b) Suggest how coat colour in horses may be genetically controlled.

Coat colour	Grey	Black	Dun	Roan	Bay	Chestnut
Number of horses	32	18	28	56	28	38

Table 3

In **continuous variation** the phenotypes:

- have no distinct categories into which individuals can be placed
- tend to be quantitative, with overlaps between the categories
- are controlled by a large number of genes with a large environmental influence.

Examples include height, mass and shade of colour. The results of a survey are usually tabulated using artificial categories.

Table 4 is a tally of the length of 500 leaves from one plant.

Leaf length/cm	1.0	1.1	1.2	1.3	1.4	1.5	1.6	1.7	1.8	1.9
Number of leaves	30	38	49	75	95	68	50	45	32	18

▲ (**Table 4**)

These data can be plotted in a number of ways. The most common method is as a frequency histogram. Merging some categories can reduce the number of categories in the range. Figure 7 shows a histogram of the raw data, plotted by merging the size categories into 0.2 cm categories.

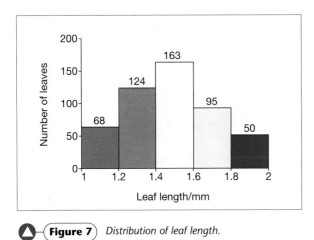

▲ (**Figure 7**) *Distribution of leaf length.*

Q **6 Plot the same data using 0.3 cm categories.**

Environmental influence on different types of variation

As a general rule:

- quantitative phenotypes are more likely to be influenced by environmental factors
- the more genes that contribute to a phenotype, the more likely there is to be environmental influence.

However, the expression of some qualitative phenotypes may be affected by an environmental factor, as in the example of Siamese cat coat colour on page 40. In flowering plants, the green pigment in chlorophyll does not develop unless the plant is exposed to light, thus the leaves of a plant germinated in the dark are yellow, but turn green when exposed to light.

Interaction between genes and the environment

Figure 8 shows the effect of genes and environment on the mass of seeds.

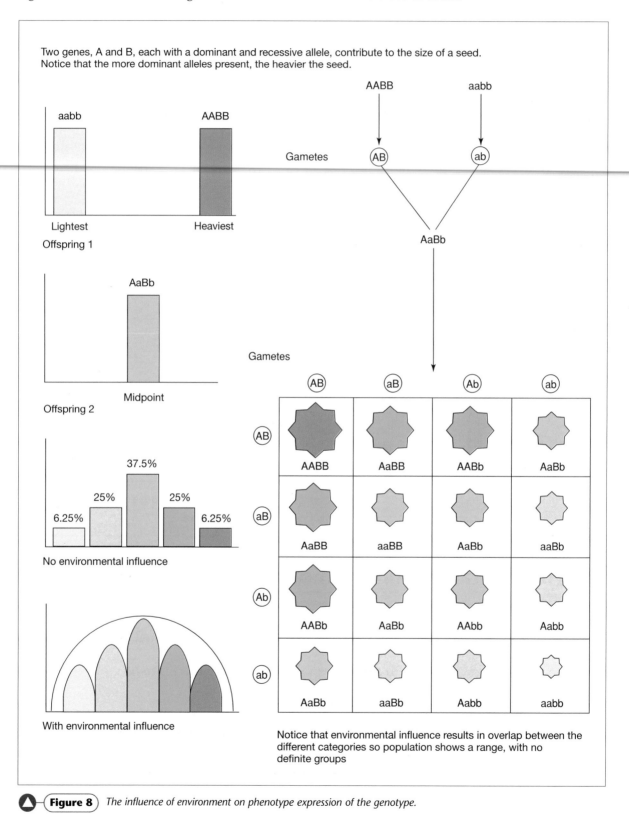

Figure 8 *The influence of environment on phenotype expression of the genotype.*

Heritability

Heritability is a means of estimating the proportion of total variation due to genetic effects. This is of interest to breeders of plants and animals because if a particular phenotype is greatly influenced by environment, then selective breeding is unlikely to make much difference to the phenotype expression. A formula is used to calculate heritability that has a theoretical range between 0 and 1. A value of 0 indicates no genetic contribution and a value of 1 indicates no environmental influence. In practice most values lie somewhere in between. Table 5 shows the heritability values for some organisms.

Organism	Phenotype	Heritability value
Poultry	Egg production Egg mass Body mass	0.01 0.50 0.20
Cattle	Body mass Milk yield	0.65 0.40
Pigs	Mass gain Litter size	0.40 0.05
Maize	Height Seed number Ear number	0.76 0.40 0.20
Humans	Height Mass IQ	0.76 0.78 0.4–0.8

 **Table 5** *Heritability values.*

From a breeder's point of view, egg production in poultry is unlikely to be changed by selective breeding, but egg mass could be changed.

> **Key ideas 38–45**
>
> - **Variation refers to the small differences in phenotype between individuals in the same species.**
> - **Variation occurs as a result of differences in genotype and environmental influence.**
> - **Genetic factors influencing variation are mutation, meiosis and fertilisation.**
> - **Two types of variation are recognised: discontinuous and continuous.**
> - **Variation in populations is estimated by observing or measuring differences in phenotype.**
> - **The proportion of the genetic contribution to total variation is important in selective breeding.**

Natural selection

Natural selection is a process that acts on phenotypes so that those organisms with the best features survive to breed. Any phenotype that gives an advantage, however small, increases the survival chances. Any phenotype that is a disadvantage decreases the chances of survival. As phenotype is usually the result of genotype and environmental influences, selection is also acting on the genotype. Organisms that survive to reach adulthood are more likely to breed and pass on their genes, so over time some genotypes become more frequent in the population than others.

Memory joggers

- To survive, an organism needs to obtain sufficient energy and organic materials (food) to grow.
- An organism must be able to resist damage due to environmental factors.
- Plants use solar energy, carbon dioxide, water and mineral salts to synthesise organic molecules which are used by all other living organisms.
- Parents pass alleles of genes to their offspring by means of sexual reproduction, so offspring resemble their parents.
- Sexual reproduction results in a mixing of the alleles of genes caused by meiosis and fertilisation.
- Variation exists within species as a result of differences in genotype and its expression.
- Mutation causes permanent changes in gene expression.

Figure 1

Survival against the odds

The ability of living organisms to reproduce is very great, so over time there is a tendency for the size of a population to increase. Since environmental resources are limited, individuals in a population must **compete** with one another to obtain sufficient resources. The individuals that obtain sufficient resources survive, and the others die. Figure 2 shows a turtle hatching; it has only a small chance of reaching adulthood. Organisms that are unable to resist damage from environmental factors, such as low pH or extremes of temperature, also die. This is called **differential** (= differences in) **survival** (= living) or differential **mortality** (= death).

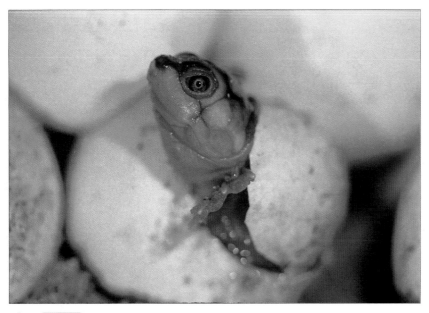

 Figure 2 *A turtle hatching.*

Sea turtles lay about 100 eggs in nests in sand above the tide-line. The eggs may be eaten if land predators, such as dogs or foxes, find the nest. When the eggs hatch the young turtles make their way to the sea, normally at night in order to avoid day predators. As the young turtles cross the beach, predators such as birds and crabs prey on the newly hatched turtles. This is shown in figure 3. As the turtles enter the sea, fish eat even more of them. Estimated mortality is 90% for newly hatched turtles.

Figure 3 *Shore birds prey on a newly hatched turtle.*

Selective forces

Variation between individuals means that some individuals are better **adapted** for their environment, that is some are better at surviving than others. These organisms are the ones more likely to breed and pass on the alleles of their genes. Better adapted does not necessarily mean physically better, but also genetically and reproductively better. Some organisms may be better adapted physically than others but may not breed as successfully, so their alleles will not be passed on. There are many selective forces that act on organisms, some of which are discussed in this section. Figure 4 shows the effect of height above sea level on the growth of clones from seven different plants.

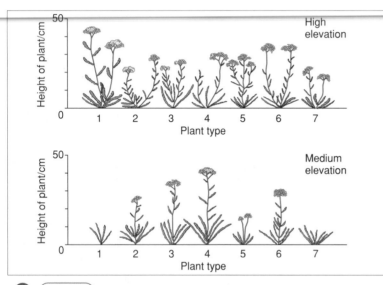

 Figure 4 *The effect of height above sea level (elevation) on cloned plants: cuttings from seven different plants were grown at high and medium elevations. Notice that plant 4 grows much taller at medium than at high elevation. Plant 5, however, is taller when grown at high elevation.*

Competition

There are limited resources in the environment so individuals must compete with each other. As the type of environment varies from place to place, the adaptations needed to survive also vary. Over long periods of time, environments change, so a species that has a lot of variation is more likely to be able to adapt. Competition can be so intense that even minor differences are important. Plants compete for light, so plants that grow faster or have bigger leaves will out-compete slower growing plants. Fast growing plants have a high nutrient requirement, so they do not grow as fast in nutrient-poor soils. Slower growing plants may then be able to compete. An example is shown in figure 5. One grassland has added fertiliser which favours faster growing grasses. The other is unfertilised.

(a)

(b)

Figure 5 *The grassland in (a) has fertiliser added, and the grassland in (b) has not.*

Q 1 **Explain why the unfertilised grassland has a greater variety of plants.**

Predation

Some animals feed on other animals for food. The food animal is the **prey** and the animal eating it is the **predator**. The best adapted organisms are not eaten.

(**Figure 6**) *Coloration of (a) a wasp and (b) a sawfly.*

Adaptations among prey animals are very variable. Some, such as zebra and chameleons, use camouflage; others, such as horses and deer, depend on speed. Many insects, like wasps, have coloration that warns predators they are toxic or distasteful. Other prey often mimic this warning coloration. Figure 6 shows a wasp and sawfly with similar coloration.

Predators also show a wide variety of adaptations to obtain their food. Some, like cheetahs, depend on speed, while others have excellent vision, for example owls. Some predators hunt alone by stealth, such as snakes, while others, like spiders, trap their prey. Lions and jackals hunt in packs to increase their chances of catching large prey animals. Like their prey, a predator that is poorly adapted will not survive to breed. Figure 7 shows two different predators and their prey.

(**Figure 7**) *Predator–prey relationships. (a) A spider has trapped an insect in its web. (b) An eagle has just caught a fish.*

Disease

Disease affects both plants and animals and may kill an organism directly or result in disability, making the organism less able to compete. In the case of animals it may make them more susceptible to predation. Disease is more likely to infect very young or very old organisms which are less able to resist the effects of the disease. Certain genotypes may also make some organisms in a population more susceptible to infection. Disease spreads more rapidly in overcrowded populations and can result in very high mortality. The organisms that survive an outbreak of disease are the best adapted to resist the effects of the disease, so when they breed the alleles giving disease resistance will be passed on.

Selection in action

Selective forces act on the phenotype of organisms in a population. The various genotypes in the population give a range of phenotypic variations, some of which are more suited to an environment than others. Mutation gives rise to new genotypes, which may result in different phenotypes. Selection favours those organisms best adapted to a particular environment.

Stabilising selection

If a new phenotype appears in a population but is not an advantage, then it does not become established within the existing population. This is **stabilising selection** to retain the existing phenotype. Figure 8 shows a hypothetical example.

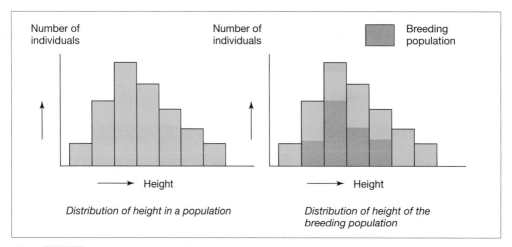

 Figure 8 *Stabilising selection for height in a population.*

The whole population has a greater range of phenotypes. The most frequent phenotype is best suited to the environment. These individuals breed more frequently than other individuals. The very short and very tall individuals do not contribute to the next generation.

An example of this type of selection is seen in human birth mass. Figure 9 shows that children born with a birth mass on either side of the optimum, 3.4 kg, have a higher mortality. Notice that this is particularly true at the lower end of the range.

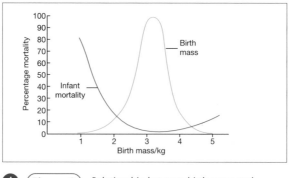

Figure 9 *Relationship between birth mass and mortality in humans.*

Q **2 Suggest why babies with a very low birth mass have a high mortality.**

Directional selection

Stabilising selection will continue unless there is a change in the environment. For example in figure 10 the existing best adapted height is no longer suited to the changed environment. In this situation a different type of selection called **directional selection** will occur. A change in the population height occurs until the most suitable height is established.

Figure 10 shows what happens if it becomes an advantage to be taller. Notice that the breeding population changes, so that taller phenotypes breed. It takes several generations before the new optimum height is established in the population.

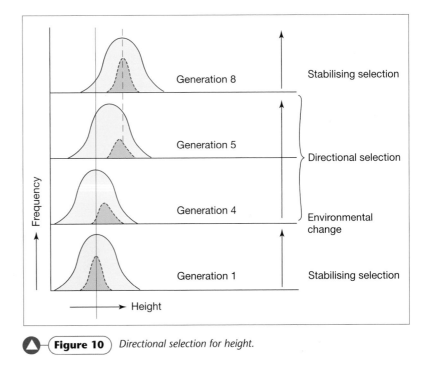

Figure 10 Directional selection for height.

An example of directional selection was observed in ground finches on the Galapagos Islands during the 1970s.

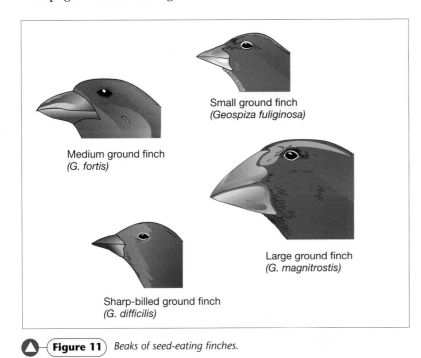

Medium ground finch
(G. fortis)

Small ground finch
(Geospiza fuliginosa)

Large ground finch
(G. magnitrostis)

Sharp-billed ground finch
(G. difficilis)

Figure 11 Beaks of seed-eating finches.

Figure 11 shows the beaks of seed-eating ground finches of the Galapagos. The beak size of the ground finch showed a wide variation in depth, from 7 to 12 mm. In 1977 a drought killed most of the small-beaked individuals within a species because they were unable to eat as wide a range of seeds as the large-beaked individuals. The survivors bred and their offspring inherited alleles giving large beaks. Over a period of two years the mean beak size increased by 0.5 mm.

Disruptive selection

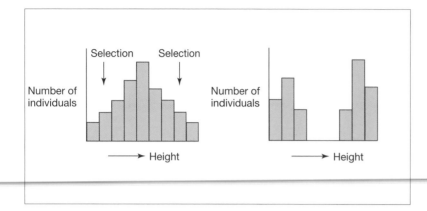

Figure 12 shows **disruptive selection**. The two extremes of the phenotype range are selected, so that over time the middle of the range disappears. This occurs when a population is exposed to two different environments.

◀ (**Figure 12**) *Disruptive selection.*

The examples of selection considered so far have involved quantitative phenotypes that are normally controlled by a number of different genes. Selection also acts on qualitative phenotypes in the same way.

One of the earliest recorded examples of this was in the peppered moth (*Biston betularia*). This moth is very common in Britain and rests on the branches of trees. It has camouflage coloration to avoid predation by birds.

The usual form, the wild type moth, has cream wings with black speckles and blends in with tree bark. In 1848 a different form, the melanic type, was first recorded in Manchester. After that time its numbers increased rapidly. Figure 13 shows these two forms of moth. A survey in the 1950s showed that the melanic form was most common in polluted areas where tree bark had been blackened by soot. The wild type was more common in unpolluted areas.

▲ (**Figure 13**) *The wild and melanic forms of the peppered moth at rest on tree bark.*

(Q) **3 Look at figure 13 and explain how selective predation could explain the difference in the moth populations in industrial and unpolluted areas.**

Other examples include antibiotic resistance in bacteria, toxic metal tolerance in plants, and rat poison (warfarin) resistance in rats.

(Q) **4 Explain how resistance to antibiotics might have developed in bacteria.**

Genes and selection

Differences in phenotype are usually related to differences in genotype. Mutations constantly lead to new alleles, which may result in new phenotypes in the population. If a new phenotype gives an advantage, individuals with this phenotype are more likely to breed and pass on their alleles. Over time more individuals with the new phenotype appear in the population and the original phenotype eventually disappears. If the new phenotype results in a disadvantage it will not be selected and will disappear from the population. This is known as **differential selection**.

An example of differential selection in humans involves the haemoglobin molecule. There is a codominant mutation of one of the genes that codes for a polypeptide in human haemoglobin. The mutation results in a different form of haemoglobin, called sickle haemoglobin. This molecule has a slightly different tertiary structure, so in low oxygen concentrations it becomes less soluble. As a result, red blood cells containing this haemoglobin become sickle shaped and can block blood capillaries. The cells are brittle and they burst. This reduces the blood cell count, resulting in anaemia.

There are three possible phenotypes for this mutation, each corresponding to a different genotype. These are shown in figure 14. In parts of the world where malaria is common, the heterozygous genotype is an advantage as it gives some resistance to malaria.

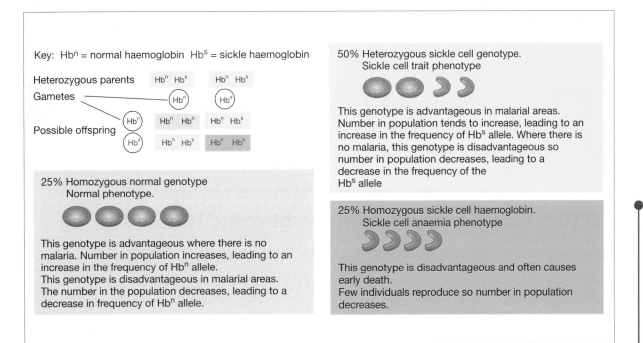

Figure 14 *The effects of differential selection.*

Making changes – speciation

All the alleles of all the genes in a population of a species, which result in variation, are the **gene pool**. A **species** is a group of organisms that share a common gene pool, so they are able to interbreed and produce fertile offspring. The gene pools of different species have too many differences for successful reproduction to take place. Although there are examples of **hybridisation**, the offspring are rarely fertile. New species arise as a result of natural selection occurring over long periods of time.

Forming a new species

Selection acts on the gene pool so that alleles which give favourable phenotypes will occur more frequently in the pool as they are passed on more often. As environments change, selection acts differently on the gene pool.

If part of the population of a species becomes **isolated** (separated into a different environment from the main population) then selection may result in big differences between the two gene pools. These differences may prevent interbreeding.

Figure 15 shows a model of the gene pool of the population of a species and the different ways it can change. Notice that mutation and **immigration** increase the gene pool, while selection and **emigration** cause the gene pool to decrease.

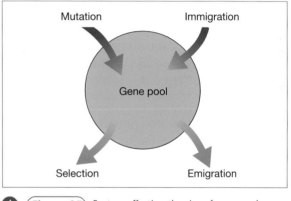

Figure 15 Factors affecting the size of gene pools.

Q 5 Explain why:
   a) mutation and immigration increase the gene pool
   b) emigration and selection decrease the gene pool.
   6 What would be the effect on the gene pool of:
   a) stabilising selection
   b) disruptive selection?

Factors causing populations to become isolated

There are two main causes of **isolation**.

1 Overcrowding causes **migration**, which means that some of the population move to another environment. The genes of the migrating individuals become the basis of the gene pool of a separate population. The pool is often smaller than the original pool as there are fewer individuals.

2 Geological changes, such as volcanic eruptions and earthquakes, may cause areas of land or water to become separated from each other. This can act as a barrier for some organisms but not for others.

Look at figure 16 which shows what may happen when part of a population becomes isolated.

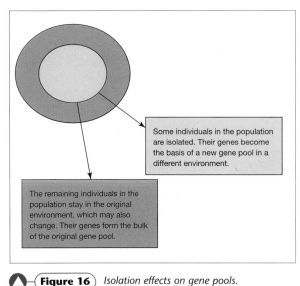

Some individuals in the population are isolated. Their genes become the basis of a new gene pool in a different environment.

The remaining individuals in the population stay in the original environment, which may also change. Their genes form the bulk of the original gene pool.

Over time, as changes occur in the gene pools reproductive isolation takes place. Individuals in the different populations may no longer be attractive to each other. Breeding only occurs within the gene pool of each population.

▲ **Figure 16** *Isolation effects on gene pools.*

Working together

Mutation, isolation and selection are all involved in the development of a new species. Time is also critical. Populations separated for a short time start to show changes, but if they remix, the gene pools merge and the differences disappear.

An example of this is the meadow brown butterfly shown in figure 17. A storm caused the populations to become separated and the two populations started to change. Recolonisation of the soil separating the populations allowed them to mix, so the differences disappeared.

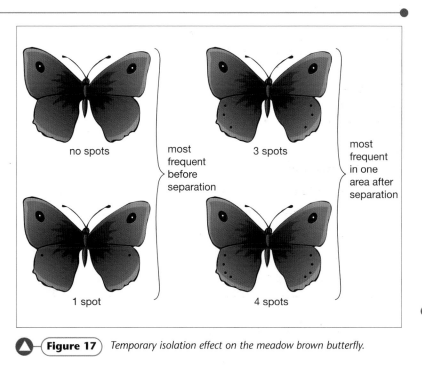

no spots

most frequent before separation

3 spots

most frequent in one area after separation

1 spot

4 spots

▲ **Figure 17** *Temporary isolation effect on the meadow brown butterfly.*

For a new species to develop, a number of factors must work together:

- mutation, to bring about changes in the gene pool
- isolation, so gene pools are exposed to different environments
- selection, to bring about sufficient change in the gene pool so that interbreeding is impossible
- time, to enable selection to act on phenotypes and cause a large number of changes.

The variety of life

The processes described in the previous section have resulted in all the different types of plants and animals living today. During Earth's history of many millions of years, many other forms of life have existed which have become extinct as a result of changes in the environment. Figure 18 shows some examples of species no longer in existence.

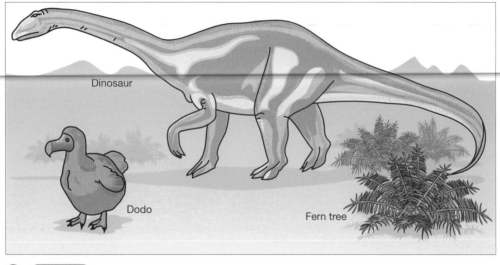

Figure 18 *Extinct species.*

Some forms of life have existed unchanged for millions of years because they are well adapted to their environment, which has changed little over the years. Examples are shown in figure 19.

Figure 19 *Long-term survivors. (a) Shark. (b) Nautilus. (c) Ginkgo.*

Examples of the huge variety of different surviving species are shown in figure 20.

▲ (**Figure 20**) *Some modern-day species. (a) Oak. (b) Salmon. (c) Chimpanzees.*

Q **7 Since humans have spread so rapidly, the rate of extinction of species has increased. Explain why humans have such a dramatic effect on the survival of other species.**

Key ideas 46–57

- Variation is due to differences in genes.
- Mutation gives rise to new alleles.
- Organisms adapt to their environment as a result of natural selection.
- New species develop as a result of mutation, isolation and selection.
- New species do not develop unless the environment changes.
- Long periods of time are needed for a new species to develop.

3 Putting into groups

Systematics is the study of diversity in living organisms and the search for relationships between them. It includes taxonomy, the study of methods of grouping organisms in terms of similarities and differences. Classification involves devising a specific grouping process and assigning different organisms to a group.

Memory joggers

- Similarities exist between living organisms because of common genes that control aspects of the phenotype.
- Genes are passed from parent to offspring by means of sexual reproduction.
- Natural selection brings about changes in gene frequencies.
- Closely related organisms have more genes in common and so share more features.

Figure 1

Taxonomy

Humans use a wide variety of different systems for classifying organisms. For instance, in everyday life plants are classified for eating purposes into herbs, spices, fruit and vegetables. Biological classification of the same plants would produce very different groupings. Within any classification system there is a **hierarchy**, which means a large group is subdivided into subgroups, which in turn are subdivided into even smaller groups with no overlap. Figure 2 shows part of a hierarchy for plants in relation to eating.

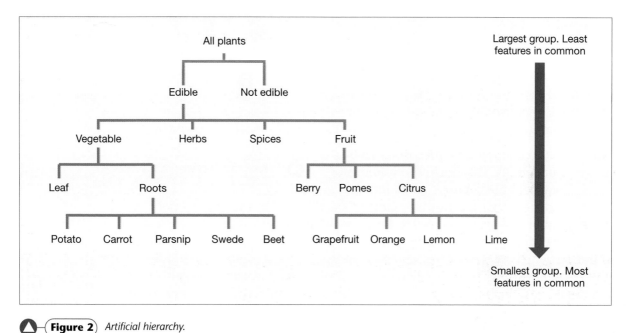

Figure 2 Artificial hierarchy.

The kingdom hierarchy

The most commonly used taxonomic system in biology is based on five large groups called **kingdoms**. Members of these kingdoms all share some features which make them living organisms. This hierarchy comprises phylum, class, order, family, genus and species. Two examples of classification are shown in table 1.

Table 1 The kingdom hierarchy.

Taxonomic rank	Plant example	Animal example	
Kingdom	Plant	Animal	Largest
Phylum	Angiosperm	Chordate	
Class	Dicotyledon	Mammal	
Order	Urticales	Carnivore	
Family	Urticaceae	Felidae	
Genus	*Urtica*	*Panthera*	
Species	*dioica*	*tigris*	
Common name	stinging nettle	tiger	Smallest

Q **1 Find out the classification of humans and an oak tree.**

Biological classification

Biological classification is based on phenotypic similarities between organisms. Classification depends upon the number of common features shared by a group of organisms. As selection occurs, some genes remain in the pool and are shared by all organisms; other genes are not common to all pools. Thus classification reflects the changes in organisms due to selection and **evolution**. Classification based on patterns of evolutionary history places organisms in phylogenetic groups depending on the number of common features. Figure 3 shows the principle of evolutionary links between living organisms.

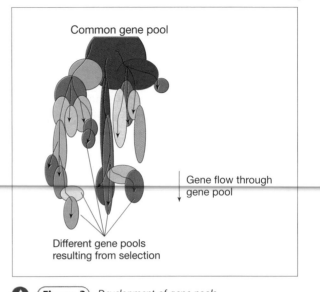

▲ (Figure 3) *Development of gene pools.*

Notice that a common gene pool is shared by all living organisms. This originated millions of years ago. Over time, groups of organisms became isolated, taking with them some of the genes from the original pool. As each group of organisms evolved to form a new species, some genes were lost and others added to the new gene pool. Each new species has diverged from the common gene pool. Over time, more and more species developed, giving rise to a large number of different gene pools. The evolutionary history of organisms is used as a basis for classification. Organisms that diverged a relatively short time ago will have more features in common than those that diverged a relatively long time ago. You can see in figure 4 the common gene pool of mammals.

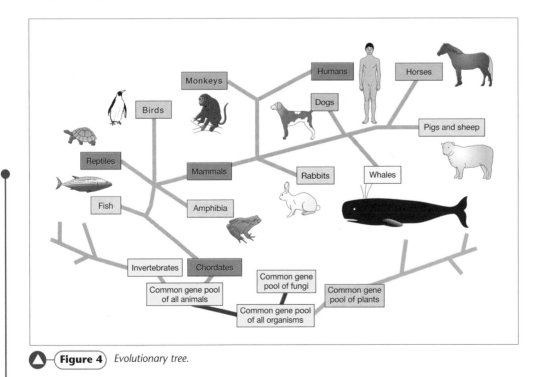

▲ (Figure 4) *Evolutionary tree.*

Classification by common features

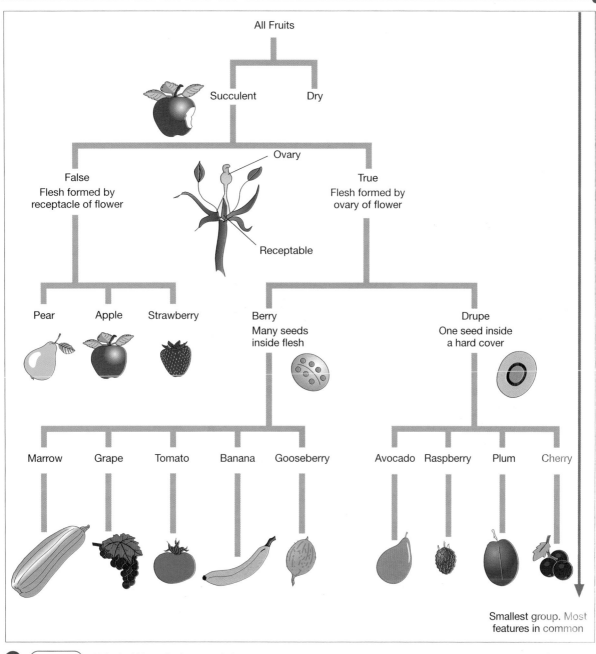

All Fruits

Succulent — Dry

Ovary

False
Flesh formed by
receptacle of flower

True
Flesh formed by
ovary of flower

Receptable

Pear   Apple   Strawberry

Berry
Many seeds
inside flesh

Drupe
One seed inside
a hard cover

Marrow   Grape   Tomato   Banana   Gooseberry

Avocado   Raspberry   Plum   Cherry

Smallest group. Most
features in common

▲ **Figure 5** *Biological hierarchy for some fruits.*

The principle of biological classification is shown in figure 5. All flowering plants
produce fruits which are grouped by common features.

Naming organisms

Organisms are named using an international convention called the **binomial** (bi = two, nomial = naming) **system**. The **genus** name is written first, starting with an upper case letter, followed by the **species** name, starting with a lower case letter. The binomial is written in italics. Closely related organisms have the same genus name and a different species name, for example a lynx is *Felis lynx*, the wild cat is *Felis sylvestris* and the domestic cat is *Felis catus*.

A rose is still a rose by any other name

Scientific names are important for clear communication. In agriculture, precise names are critical for selective breeding and pest control. This is also true in medicine where antibiotics and drugs are developed to kill specific organisms. In different parts of the world the same common name is used for different organisms. Even in the same country, local names for the same species of plant vary greatly.

Wild rose, red rose, dog rose, Lancashire rose, Yorkshire rose and English rose are some of the names used to describe a variety of the **family** Rosacea, with the species name *Rosa canina,* shown in figure 6. The English rose used as a symbol by the Labour party is a cultivated hybrid rose.

 Rosa canina. *Many different common names are given to this species.*

A robin in Britain is quite different from the bird known as a robin in America. Figure 7 shows the British robin (*Erithacus rubecula*) and the American robin (*Turdus migratoria*).

Figure 7 *Same name, different birds. (a) British robin. (b) American robin.*

Spot the kingdom

Each kingdom has specific features which are common to all members of the group. On the next pages, the main features of each kingdom are described and some of the organisms within each are shown.

Prokaryotes

The distinguishing features of members of this kingdom are:

- microscopic prokaryotic cells
- lack of membrane-bound organelles
- presence of small distinctive ribosomes
- presence of a single chromosome consisting only of nucleic acid.

There are two major phyla, examples of which are shown in figure 8.

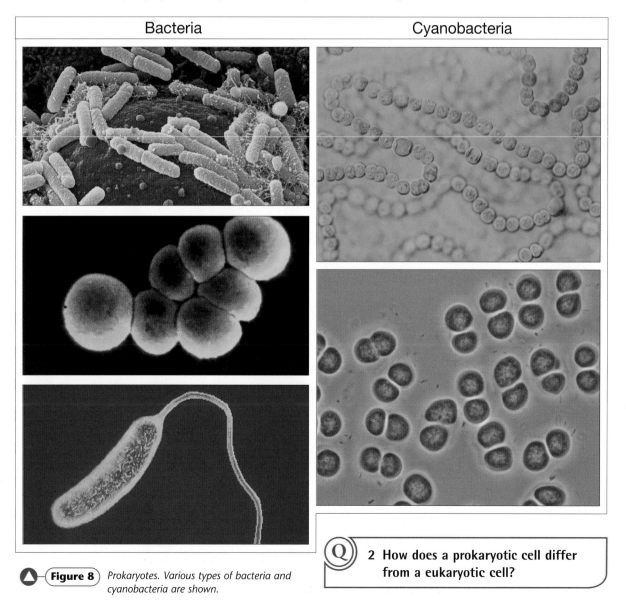

Bacteria	Cyanobacteria

Figure 8 Prokaryotes. Various types of bacteria and cyanobacteria are shown.

> **Q** 2 How does a prokaryotic cell differ from a eukaryotic cell?

Protoctists

This kingdom includes all the organisms that do not fit into any of the other kingdoms. The distinguishing features of members of this kingdom are:

- eukaryotic cell structure
- simple body form, either unicellular, filamentous (chains), colonial (ball) or macroscopic (large and visible).

The common names protozoa and algae are still used for the members of this kingdom by many biologists.

There are ten phyla; examples from some of these are shown in figure 9.

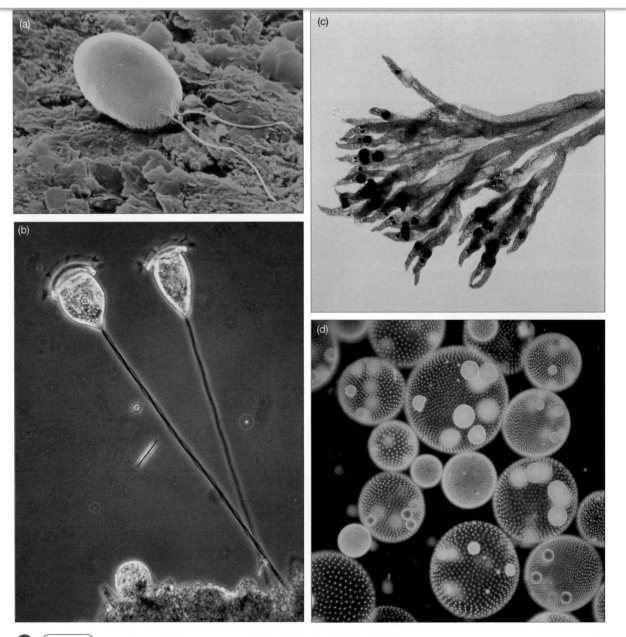

(a)

(b)

(c)

(d)

△ **Figure 9** *Protoctists. (a) Chlamydomonas. (b) Vorticella. (c) Red alga. (d) Volvox.*

Fungi

The distinguishing features of members of this kingdom are:

- heterotrophic nutrition
- body consisting of a network called a **mycelium** made of thread-like **hyphae**
- cell walls containing chitin.

There are three phyla, examples of which are shown in figure 10.

Figure 10 *Fungi. (a)* Polyporous sulphureus *(bracket fungus).* (b) Mucor mucedo *(bread mould).* (c) Penicillium *fungus.*

Plants

The distinguishing features of members of this kingdom are:

- multicellular with eukaryotic cell structure
- cell walls containing cellulose
- complex body form
- photoautotrophic nutrition
- presence of photosynthetic cells with chloroplasts containing chlorophyll and other **pigments**
- two stages in the life cycle: a **diploid** spore-producing stage and a **haploid** gamete-producing stage.

There are two major subkingdoms: non-flowering plants and flowering plants.

Non-flowering plants

These have either spores inside capsules or cones containing seeds, as shown in figure 11.

△ **Figure 11**   *Non-flowering plants. (a)* Bryophyta musci *(moss). (b)* Dicksonia antarctica *(fern).* *(c)* Equisetum telemeia *(horsetail).*

Q   **3 Notice that a moss is an example of a non–flowering plant. Describe the life cycle of a moss (covered in Module 2).**

Flowering plants

All of these produce flowers, and seeds which develop inside fruits. Many are important as food plants. They include soft **herbaceous plants** and woody shrubs and trees. There are two major classes: **monocotyledons** and **dicotyledons**. Examples of these are shown in figure 12.

Figure 12 *Flowering plants. (a) Pinus sylvestris (pine tree) and a pinecone.*
(b) Aesculus hippocastrenum (horsechestnut tree). (c) Viola tricolor (wild pansy).
(d) Bamboo. (e) Lilium species. (f) Urtica dioica (stinging nettle).

Q **4 What is the difference between a monocotyledon and a dicotyledon? (dicotyledonous plants were mentioned in Module 1)**

Animals

The distinguishing features of members of this kingdom are:

- multicellular with eukaryotic cell structure
- cells without cell walls
- heterotrophic nutrition
- highly organised organs and tissues including nervous co-ordination
- the only haploid cells they have form gametes.

There are eight main phyla, seven of which have no internal supporting skeleton.

Animals without internal skeletons

The animals without an internal skeleton are often grouped together as **invertebrates**, although this is not accepted as a taxonomic group. Examples of invertebrates are shown in figure 13.

Figure 13 *Invertebrates. (a)* Actinia equina *(sea anemone). (b)* Octopus cyanea *(octopus). (c)* Helix aspersa *(land snail). (d)* Calliphora *species (bluebottle).*

Animals with internal skeletons

Animals with an internal skeleton are **chordates**. There are five classes, examples of which are shown in figure 14.

Figure 14 *Chordates. (a)* Plectorhinchus lineatus *(sweetlips). (b)* Leptophis ahaetulla *(parrot snake).*
(c) Balaenoptera musculus *(blue whale). (d)* Agalychnis callidryas *(leaf frog).*
(e) Amazilia saucerrotte *(hummingbird). (f)* Sorex araneus *(shrew).*

Q **5 What is the difference between an animal and a plant cell?**

Non-conformists

Although the system of classification seems complex enough for all organisms, some still do not fit into any group.

The virus controversy

Are **viruses** alive? This has been a point of discussion ever since they were discovered. A virus consists of a protein coat surrounding a nucleic acid. It can only reproduce inside other cells. There are two views.

1 A virus is not alive and is an association of molecules normally found in cells.
2 A virus is a highly evolved parasite which originated from prokaryotic cells.

Figure 15 shows a variety of viruses. Although the commonly used five-kingdom model does not include viruses, they are still classified using their physical and chemical properties. This information is critical in the diagnosis and treatment of viral diseases.

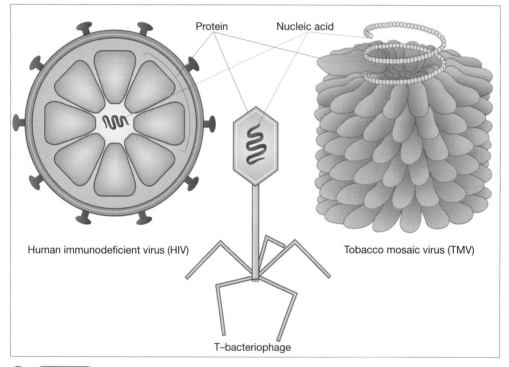

Figure 15 *A variety of viruses.*

What to do with sponges?

Sponges are a very old group in terms of their origin. They have been around for at least 570 million years.

They consist of a number of different types of cell, similar to some unicellular protoctists. Some of the cells are specialised for feeding, some for water circulation and some for reproduction. All the cells are enclosed in a skeleton. This pattern does not fit any of the other classification groups so, like the viruses, sponges have their own special group that is not in the five-kingdom model.

Summary of the five-kingdom model

The accepted five-kingdom model proposed by American biologists Margulis and Schwartz in the 1960s is shown in figure 16.

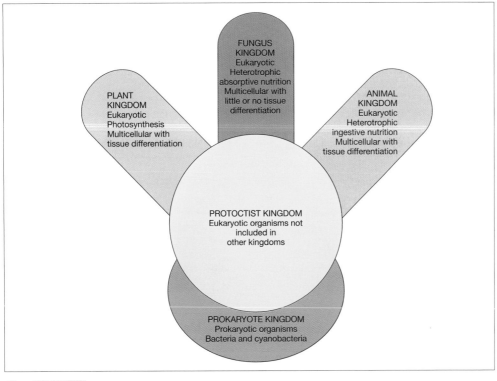

FUNGUS KINGDOM
Eukaryotic
Heterotrophic
absorptive nutrition
Multicellular with
little or no tissue
differentiation

PLANT KINGDOM
Eukaryotic
Photosynthesis
Multicellular with
tissue differentiation

ANIMAL KINGDOM
Eukaryotic
Heterotrophic
ingestive nutrition
Multicellular with
tissue differentiation

PROTOCTIST KINGDOM
Eukaryotic organisms not
included in
other kingdoms

PROKARYOTE KINGDOM
Prokaryotic organisms
Bacteria and cyanobacteria

Figure 16 *The five-kingdom system of Margulis and Schwartz.*

Key ideas 58–71

- There are millions of different living organisms so classification is essential.

- Organisms are classified according to evolutionary relationships.

- Taxonomy is the study of classifying groups into hierarchies.

- The five-kingdom model is workable for most organisms.

- The smallest group in the taxonomic system is a species.

- A species is a group of organisms that share sufficient common features to interbreed and produce viable offspring.

- Species are grouped into genera, genera into families, families into orders, orders into classes, classes into phyla and phyla into kingdoms.

- Within a hierarchy, the largest grouping has the widest variety of different types of organism with a few common features. The smallest grouping has only one type of organism with individuals sharing many common features.

Unit 2 – Questions

(1) Tables 1 and 2 show the results of measurements made on the distribution of height in maize plants and the number of bristles on the legs of fruit flies.

Height/cm	Number of plants
100	20
110	60
120	90
130	130
140	180
150	120
160	70
180	40
190	30

▲ Table 1

Number of bristles	Number of fruit flies
1	20
2	120
3	10
4	0
5	15
6	70
7	12
8	0
9	2
10	0

▲ Table 2

a) What types of variation are shown by these characteristics? Give a reason for your answer. (2 marks)

b) Explain how the causes of genetic variation could explain the difference in the pattern of variation in:
   i)   height of maize plants
   ii) number of bristles in fruit flies. (2 marks)

c) Explain why clones are used to study the influence of environment on variation. (2 marks)

(Total 6 marks)

(2) The leopard, cheetah, tiger, lion and panther are all species of the large cat family, and are believed to have evolved from a common ancestor.

a) Suggest how these different species of cat may have evolved from a common ancestor. (5 marks)

b) The large cat family is part of the animal kingdom. Give three features large cats share with all other members of the animal kingdom. (3 marks)

(Total 8 marks)

3 **a)** Give *three* different sources of variation in a population. (3 marks)

b) Describe the role of i) natural selection and ii) isolation in the evolution of a new species. (6 marks)

(Total 9 marks)

4 Table 3 shows the mean differences in height and mass measurements made on pairs of twins.

Mean difference in	Identical twins		Non-identical twins	
	reared together	reared apart	reared together	reared apart
Mass/kg	1.9	4.5	4.5	6.6
Height/cm	1.7	1.8	4.4	4.6
Hand span/mm	2	2.2	3.6	3.8

 Table 3

a) In which of these features is variation controlled mainly by differences in
   i)   genotype
   ii) the environment?
   Explain your answer. (4 marks)

b) Explain why identical twins are used to study causes of variation in humans. (2 marks)

(Total 6 marks)

5 **a)** Complete the following passage.
   The classification of living organisms is based on a _____, in which groups are contained in larger groups with no overlap. The bulbous buttercup (*Ranunculus bulbosus*) belongs to the genus _____. It is a different _____ from the creeping buttercup (*Ranunculus repens*) as these types of buttercup cannot breed together to produce _____ _____. All different genera are grouped in the Ranunculaceae family. (4 marks)

b) Complete table 4 to show the classification of the wood anemone (*Anemone nemorosa*).

Kingdom	Plant
	Angiosperm
Class	Dicotyledon
	Ranales
Family	Ranunculaceae
Genus	
	nemorosa

◀ **Table 4**

(4 marks)

(Total 8 marks)

Stimulus and response

Organisms increase their chances of survival by responding to changes in their environment. These changes are called **stimuli**. Stimuli may be changes in the external environment, for example movement of another organism or a sound. They may also be changes in the organism's internal environment, for example a change in pH or temperature. Stimuli are detected by receptors and the information is passed to a **co-ordinator**. From the co-ordinator, information is sent to **effectors**, which are usually glands or muscles, to bring about a **response**.

Multicellular organisms have evolved internal communication systems to respond to stimuli. These systems take two forms.

(1) **Nervous system** – used in animals to respond quickly to a changing environment.

(2) **Endocrine system** – used in plants and animals to control some aspects of their responses.

Memory joggers

- The nervous system enables humans to react to their surroundings and co-ordinates their behaviour.
- Cells called receptors detect stimuli. These include receptors in the eye which are sensitive to light.
- Information from receptors passes along nerves to the brain. The brain co-ordinates the response.
- Proteins in membranes can act as receptors and carriers because of their specific shape.
- Chemicals called hormones co-ordinate many processes within the body.
- Hormones are produced by glands and are transported to their target organs in the bloodstream.

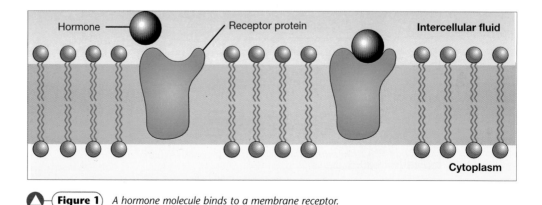

Figure 1   A hormone molecule binds to a membrane receptor.

Nervous system

The nervous system can be divided up, based on its structure, into the **central nervous system** and the **peripheral nervous system** as shown in figure 2.

The central nervous system consists of the brain and spinal cord. The peripheral nervous system is made up of all the nerves and sense organs which send information into the central nervous system, or take information to effectors. The key cells in the nervous system are **neurones**. **Sensory neurones** carry information to the central nervous system, and **motor neurones** carry information to effectors. A nerve impulse involves electrical signals, produced by the movement of ions across cell membranes. Where two neurones meet, there is a tiny gap called a **synapse**. Impulses pass across synapses using chemical transmission.

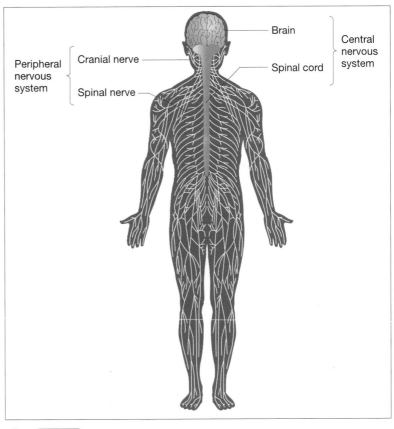

Figure 2 The organisation of the nervous system.

Nervous tissue is composed of many closely packed neurones (nerve cells) forming a bundle, which is held together by connective tissue to form nerves. Figure 3 shows the structure of a nerve.

Nerves run in distinct pathways and can contain both motor and sensory neurones, although one or other may be present in greater numbers.

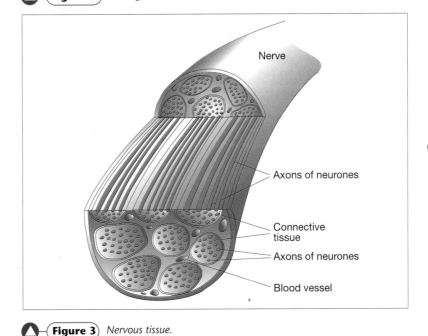

Figure 3 Nervous tissue.

A simple reflex arc

A **reflex** is an automatic response to a sensory stimulus. The pathway of neurones involved in a reflex action is called a **reflex arc**. A good example is the pathway involved in removing your hand from a hot object, such as a hot ring on a cooker. If this has ever happened to you, you may recall that, by the time your brain makes you aware that the ring was hot, your hand has already moved away. The pathway by which this response occurs is shown in figure 4. Three neurones are involved: a sensory neurone, a motor neurone and a connector neurone.

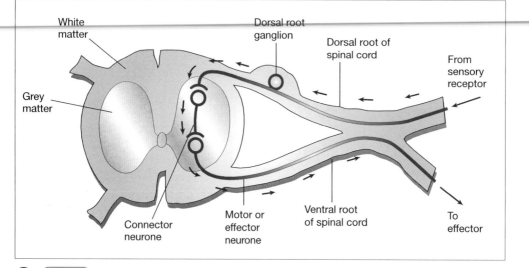

Figure 4 A simple reflex arc.

The sensory neurone carries nerve impulses from the temperature receptor cells in the skin to the spinal cord. Here, the nerve impulse passes to the connector neurone and then to the motor neurone. The nerve impulse then passes along the motor neurone to the effector. In this case, the effectors are the muscles in your arm, which contract, moving your hand away from the hot ring.

A simple reflex arc like the one described above is:

- **immediate** – it is very quick because there are only three neurones involved, and time is not lost in processing information in the brain
- **invariable** – it cannot be varied in the light of experience
- **involuntary** – it happens without any conscious thought
- **innate** – it is present from birth.

Q

1 In the reflex arc shown in figure 4, another neurone carries information up the spinal cord to the brain so that you become aware of the hot ring, but only after your hand has been moved. Suggest why this neurone is important.

Endocrine system

The nervous system is not the only way in which organisms respond to stimuli. Communication may also involve **hormones**, which are chemicals secreted by **endocrine glands** into the bloodstream. Endocrine glands lack ducts and use the bloodstream to transport hormones to distant target sites.

There are two main kinds of hormone:

1 peptide and protein hormones
2 steroid hormones, such as testosterone and oestrogen.

Although hormones travel all around the body in the bloodstream, they do not affect all the body's cells. This is because the target cells have specific membrane proteins on the outside of their cell surface membranes. These proteins are called **receptor proteins**. A hormone binds to a receptor protein that has a complementary shape.

How peptide and protein hormones work

Target cells for peptide and protein hormones have receptor proteins in their membranes which have a complementary shape to these hormones. Figure 5 shows that when the hormone binds to the receptor, it activates an enzyme, called adenylate cyclase, on the inside of the membrane. This enzyme converts ATP to cyclic AMP (usually written as cAMP). This brings about changes in the target cell, for example specific enzymes may be activated. The hormone is sometimes called the first messenger and cyclic AMP is called the second messenger. Note that the hormone does not enter the cell but still changes the activities that go on inside the cell.

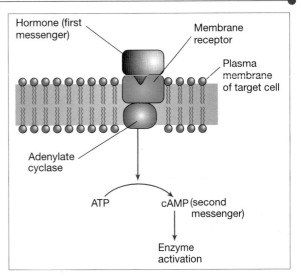

Figure 5 Peptide and protein hormones bind to receptor proteins in the membranes of their target cells.

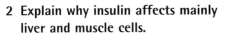
Q 2 Explain why insulin affects mainly liver and muscle cells.

How steroid hormones work

Steroid hormones are lipid-soluble, so they can pass through the phospholipid bilayer of a cell membrane and enter a cell. Once inside a cell, the hormone binds with a specific receptor protein found on the inside of the membrane. The hormone/receptor complex enters the nucleus and binds to the cell's DNA, switching on or off particular genes, which affects protein synthesis.

Q 3 Draw a diagram to show how steroid hormones function.

Differences between hormonal and nervous communication

Table 1 shows the differences between hormonal and nervous communication.

Hormonal communication	Nervous communication
By chemicals called hormones	By nerve impulses. Chemicals are released at synapses
Slow response	Rapid response
Slower transmission	Very rapid transmission
Hormones travel in blood stream to all parts of the body	Impulses travel along nerve fibres which are fixed pathways to specific parts of the body
Strength of a stimulus is determined by a change in hormone concentration	Strength of a stimulus is determined by a change in the frequency of the impulses
Hormones can have a permanent and irreversible effect	Nerve impulses have a temporary and reversible effect

 Table 1

All these differences mean that nervous control is suited for rapid, short-term responses in specific parts of the body. However, hormones are much better at controlling long, slow and widespread responses.

Key ideas 74–78

- Organisms increase their chances of survival by responding to changes in their environment.

- Information is transferred in the nervous system through detection of stimuli by receptors and the initiation of a nerve impulse, leading to an associated response by effectors by means of a co-ordinator.

- A simple form of nervous control is shown by a simple reflex arc involving three neurones.

- Information is transferred by hormones released by endocrine glands and affecting the physiological activities of target cells.

Homeostasis

Homeostasis refers to the way in which the body regulates all its physiological processes so that it keeps its internal environment as stable as possible. The internal environment must be carefully controlled, because physiological processes depend on enzymes and other globular proteins working properly. Enzymes and other globular proteins need optimum conditions, such as exactly the right pH and temperature, to maintain full activity. However, living organisms must constantly take in substances from their environment, such as nutrients and gases, and waste materials need to be removed. This means that living organisms need to have systems to regulate the internal environment while constantly exchanging substances with their external environment.

Memory joggers

- Carbohydrates are digested into simple monosaccharides, such as glucose, which are transported in the blood. The monomer glucose can be converted to the carbohydrate polymer glycogen for storage.

- The entry and exit of substances to and from cells are controlled by cell membranes.

- Diffusion is the passive movement of substances in the direction of a concentration gradient.

- Osmosis is a special case of diffusion across a partially permeable membrane, net movement of water depending on difference in water potentials.

- Active transport is the movement of molecules or ions through a membrane by carrier proteins against a concentration gradient. This process requires the transfer of energy derived from respiration.

- The hormones insulin and glucagon, which are produced by the pancreas, control the blood sugar level.

- Diabetes is a condition in which a person's blood sugar may rise to a fatally high level because the pancreas does not produce enough of the hormone insulin. Diabetes can be treated by careful attention to diet and by injecting insulin.

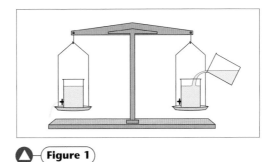

▲ Figure 1

How homeostasis works

The maintenance of a constant internal environment requires control systems that detect stimuli and make the necessary adjustments to return the environment to the normal level. Look at figure 2. When a factor changes from the normal level, the body detects the change. Hormones and/or nerve impulses are used to initiate a corrective mechanism to change the factor back to the normal level. The amount of correction is regulated by a mechanism called **negative feedback**. This ensures that, as conditions return to normal, the corrective mechanism is reduced.

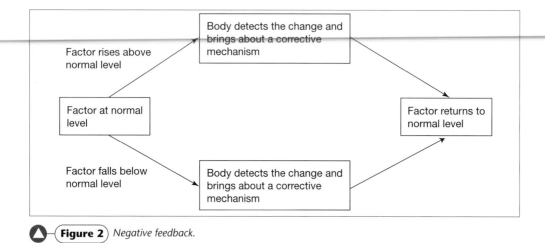

Figure 2 *Negative feedback.*

One important example of homeostasis is the regulation of body temperature. This is known as **thermoregulation**. If there is a change in temperature, the body responds by reversing the change, returning it to a normal body temperature.

(Q) **1 Draw a diagram to show the negative feedback control of temperature.**

Figure 3 *Birds and mammals are able to regulate their body temperatures.*

Animals that are able to regulate their body temperature are called **homeotherms** (may also be spelt **homoiotherms**). These include birds and mammals, as shown in figure 3. Most mammals have body temperatures between 37°C and 39°C, and birds have body temperatures between 40°C and 42°C.

Controlling temperature

Thermoregulation is brought about by balancing heat production in the body with heat loss to the environment.

There are three main ways in which heat is lost and gained:

1 radiation – energy that travels from one place to another as electromagnetic waves
2 conduction – the transport of heat by the collisions of molecules: liquids and solids conduct heat better than air
3 convection – the transfer of heat by currents of air or water.

Evaporation (the conversion of water to water vapour) also plays an important role in heat loss by using heat from the body to evaporate water. Heat is also lost in substances leaving the body, such as exhaled air, urine and faeces. Heat can also be gained through metabolic activities inside body cells, such as respiration, by increasing the metabolic rate. Mammals gain and lose heat through any surface with which they come into contact.

Q 2 **Why do you get colder more quickly if your clothes are wet and a wind is blowing?**

Mammals show adaptations to their environment. Hot climate mammals have a large surface area:volume ratio and little insulation of the skin. They have thin fur and little body fat, allowing them to lose heat more easily. Cold climate mammals have a small surface area:volume ratio and a well insulated skin. They have a lot of body fat, especially under the skin, and thick fur which help to reduce heat loss.

Q 3 **Suggest how: a) the body of an elephant is adapted to increase surface area**

b) the body of a polar bear is adapted to reduce surface area.

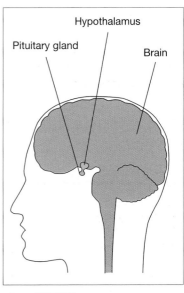

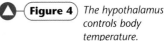
Figure 4 *The hypothalamus controls body temperature.*

In mammals, body temperature is controlled by the hypothalamus, part of the brain just above the pituitary gland. You can see the position of the hypothalamus in figure 4.

The hypothalamus acts like a thermostat. Sensory cells called thermoreceptors detect changes in body temperature. The central thermoreceptors in the hypothalamus measure the temperature of the blood passing through the hypothalamus. This is called the core body temperature. There are also peripheral thermoreceptors in the skin which measure skin temperature. Both types of thermoreceptor send nerve impulses to the hypothalamus. However, the central thermoreceptors are the most important because they measure core temperature. The hypothalamus controls body temperature.

Conserving heat

If the central thermoreceptors detect a decrease in core body temperature, the hypothalamus brings about corrective mechanisms. The sequence of events that takes place in response to a decrease in core body temperature is shown in figure 5.

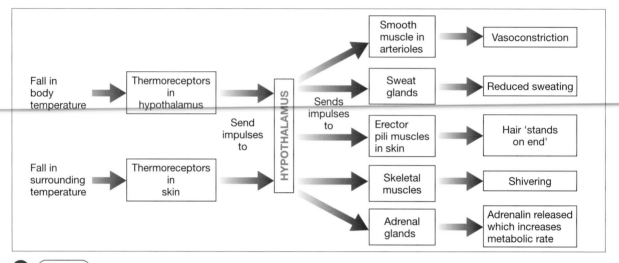

Figure 5 *Heat conservation responses occur when a decrease in core body temperature is detected.*

Q 4 Look at the control system shown in figure 5. Name a) the receptor, b) the co-ordinator, c) the effectors and d) the responses.

Notice that there are two main types of response: heat conservation, which reduces heat loss by physical changes, and heat production, which generates additional heat by metabolic changes.

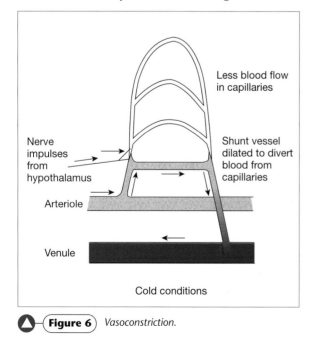

Figure 6 *Vasoconstriction.*

Heat conservation responses

Heat conservation responses include:

1 Vasoconstriction – nerve impulses in sympathetic nerves from the hypothalamus cause smooth muscle in the skin arterioles to contract. Shunt vessels dilate and divert blood away from the capillaries. Blood flow to the surface capillaries is restricted, so less heat is lost from the skin by radiation. This is shown in figure 6. Reduced blood flow decreases the temperature of the body surface and explains why cold people look much paler.

2 **Decreased rate of sweating** – vasoconstriction reduces blood flow to sweat glands, so less sweat is produced. Less heat energy from the body will be used to convert the water in sweat to water vapour.

3 **Piloerection** – hairs on the skin surface 'stand on end', as shown in figure 7a. The erector pili muscles in the skin contract, pulling the hairs upright. In humans, this does not have any effect in conserving heat, but in hairy and furry mammals this makes the fur thicker so that it traps a larger layer of air. Air acts as an insulator because it is a poor conductor of heat.

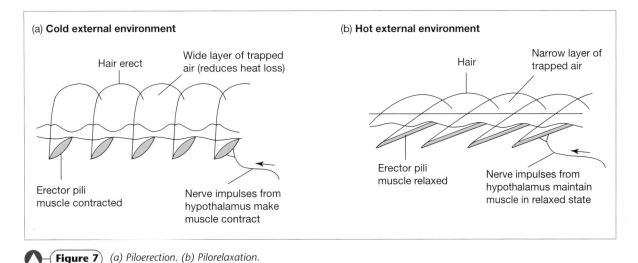

(a) **Cold external environment**

Hair erect

Wide layer of trapped air (reduces heat loss)

Erector pili muscle contracted

Nerve impulses from hypothalamus make muscle contract

(b) **Hot external environment**

Hair

Narrow layer of trapped air

Erector pili muscle relaxed

Nerve impulses from hypothalamus maintain muscle in relaxed state

Figure 7 *(a) Piloerection. (b) Pilorelaxation.*

All three responses occurring in the skin are involuntary and are controlled by the hypothalamus.

Behavioural responses also occur. Reducing surface area by curling up is involuntary, but most are voluntary responses. Nerve impulses from the peripheral and central thermoreceptors travel to the cerebral cortex of the brain (the thinking part of the brain), so that you become aware that you are cold. You may take appropriate action to retain heat. For example, you may turn the central heating on or put on a jumper. Other mammals also show behavioural responses. For example, **huddling** occurs when sheep move closer together to keep warm, or animals may move to a more sheltered position where it is warmer.

Heat production responses

1 **Shivering** – skeletal muscles contract and relax rapidly. As the muscles are active the rate of respiration increases and extra heat is generated.
2 **Increased metabolic rate** – the hormone adrenaline is released causing a rapid increase in the metabolic rate, so more heat is produced. Long-term exposure to low temperature causes the body to produce more of the hormone thyroxine, increasing the metabolic rate.

Metabolic changes are often not needed as the core temperature can be maintained by physical responses. When the environmental temperature falls to a critical value, metabolic rate increases as the physical responses are insufficient. In humans the critical temperature is about 27°C. In cold climate adapted animals the critical temperature is much lower.

Losing heat

If the central thermoreceptors detect an increase in core body temperature, the hypothalamus brings about corrective mechanisms. The sequence of events that takes place in response to an increase in core body temperature is shown in figure 8.

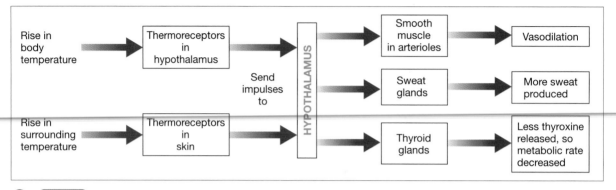

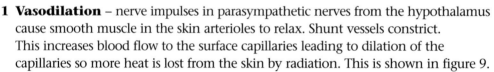
Figure 8 Heat loss responses occur if an increase in core body temperature is detected.

Notice that there are two main types of response: heat loss, which increases heat loss by physical changes, and heat reduction, which decreases heat production by metabolic changes.

Heat loss responses

Heat loss responses include:

1 **Vasodilation** – nerve impulses in parasympathetic nerves from the hypothalamus cause smooth muscle in the skin arterioles to relax. Shunt vessels constrict. This increases blood flow to the surface capillaries leading to dilation of the capillaries so more heat is lost from the skin by radiation. This is shown in figure 9.
2 **Increased rate of sweating** – vasodilation increases blood flow to the sweat glands. More sweat is secreted onto the surface of the skin where the water in sweat evaporates using latent heat from the body.
3 **Panting** – some animals, particularly dogs and birds, have very few or no sweat glands. They lose heat by panting. Panting consists of very quick, shallow breaths of air, which evaporate water from the tongue and mouth, producing a cooling effect.
4 **Pilorelaxation** – hairs on the body surface lie flat. Parasympathetic nerves cause the erector pili muscles to relax so the hairs lie close to the body surface. Less air is trapped next to the skin, reducing insulation. See figure 7b on page 83.

Behavioural responses also occur. Increasing surface area by stretching out is involuntary but most are voluntary responses. Nerve impulses from the peripheral and central thermoreceptors travel to the cerebral cortex of the brain so you become aware that you are hot. You may take appropriate action to lose heat. For example, you may remove a jacket or go for a swim. Other mammals show behavioural changes such as seeking shade and rolling in mud or water.

Q 5 **Explain why the evaporation of water is so effective at cooling the body.**

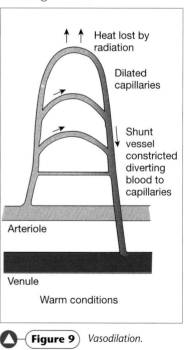
Figure 9 Vasodilation.

Heat reduction responses

1 **Inactivity** is a behavioural change that results in less muscle contraction so respiration rate in muscle decreases and less heat is produced.
2 **Decreased metabolic rate** – long-term exposure to high temperature causes the body to release less thyroxine, reducing the metabolic rate.

Metabolic changes are not usually needed. However, if the external temperature rises above a critical value, the cooling mechanisms fail and the metabolic rate increases. The core body temperature starts to rise rapidly as a result of positive feedback.

> (Q)
> 6 Explain why core temperature rises due to positive feedback when the body's cooling mechanisms fail.
>
> 7 When a rise in blood temperature is detected, shivering stops and the hairs on the surface of the skin lie flat. Explain why these responses lead to heat loss.
>
> 8 When body temperature rises above normal, behavioural responses have an important role to play. List the behavioural responses that may occur and explain how they lead to a fall in temperature.

Too hot or too cold

An increase in temperature above the normal range of values is called **hyperthermia**. One example of hyperthermia is fever. Fever is caused by substances called **pyrogens**, that are released from cells of the immune system. Pyrogens act on the thermoreceptors in the hypothalamus, resulting in an elevation of the set-point temperature and activation of heat conservation responses.

Hypothermia occurs if there is a reduction in body temperature below the normal range of values. Once human body temperature falls below about 35.5 °C, the central thermoreceptors detect that body temperature has fallen and heat conservation responses are initiated by the hypothalamus. These lead to an increase in blood temperature, which is detected by the central thermoreceptors. Heat conservation responses are then reduced. This is an example of negative feedback. Similarly, when the central thermoreceptors detect an increase in blood temperature, the hypothalamus initiates heat loss responses. These lead to a fall in blood temperature, which is detected by the central thermoreceptors. Heat loss responses are then reduced.

Thermoregulation

The flow diagram in figure 10 summarises thermoregulation in mammals.

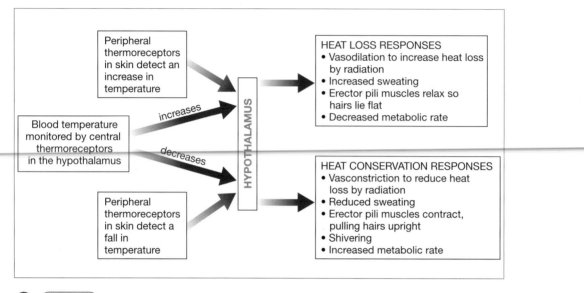

Figure 10 *Thermoregulation in mammals.*

Thermoregulation in babies

Babies are very vulnerable to changes in temperature. However, they are not able to gain or lose heat by behavioural means, as adults and older children are. They can lose some heat by sweating, but babies have fewer sweat glands than adults. It also takes a much greater increase in body temperature to stimulate sweating in babies than it does in adults. The main mechanism by which a baby can lose heat is by vasodilation.

Keeping warm is another difficulty for babies. Newborn babies are not able to gain heat by shivering, although the reason for this is not known. However, babies do have an additional mechanism for gaining heat, which adults do not have. This is called **non-shivering thermogenesis**. Babies have a special kind of adipose (or fat) tissue called brown adipose tissue, which is found in various parts of the body.

This kind of tissue is packed with mitochondria and generates heat by releasing energy as heat instead of using it to make ATP. Non-shivering thermogenesis is stimulated by the nervous system when the baby becomes cold. Once the stores of brown adipose tissue have been used up, they cannot be renewed. They are mainly used during the first six months of life, although some may remain even in teenagers.

Control of blood glucose levels

Blood glucose levels are regulated in a healthy human, usually within the range of 70–100 mg per 100 cm^3 of blood. Blood glucose levels need to stay reasonably constant because glucose is the major respiratory substrate in humans. Glucose levels need to be controlled to keep the blood water potential constant. If the blood glucose level is too high (**hyperglycaemia**), muscle tissue breaks down and weight loss and tiredness occur. If the blood glucose level is too low (**hypoglycaemia**), sweating and double vision occur accompanied by hunger and irritability.

Q 9 a) **What happens to the water potential of the blood when the blood glucose level is too high?**

b) **Why is it important to keep the blood water potential constant?**

Glucose regulation depends on a part of the pancreas called the **islets of Langerhans**. You have already met the pancreas as a source of digestive enzymes. However, the pancreas has another function. The islets of Langerhans are endocrine tissue, which means that they secrete hormones. There are two main types of cell in the islets of Langerhans: the β-**cells** which secrete the hormone **insulin**, and the α-**cells** which secrete the hormone **glucagon**. Figure 11 shows the structure of the pancreas. The islets of Langerhans receive blood from the **hepatic portal vein**.

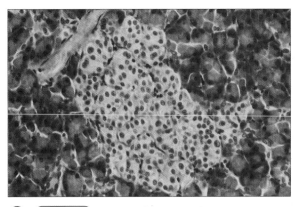

Figure 11 Light micrograph of pancreas. The islets of Langerhans are in the centre (coloured pale pink). Magnification ×65.

Figure 12 shows the changes that occur to blood glucose levels during the morning of a typical day.

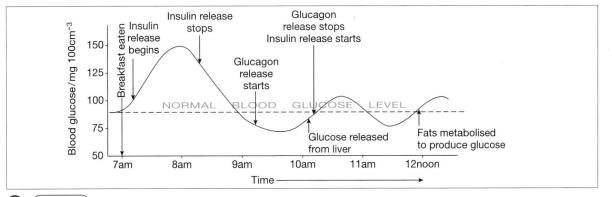

Figure 12 Insulin and glucagon together regulate blood glucose levels.

Q 10 **Copy the diagram in figure 12 and extend the day to 6pm to show the changes that occur if a meal is eaten at 1pm.**

High levels of blood glucose

If the level of glucose in the hepatic portal vein is above the normal level, the β-cells in the islets of Langerhans secrete insulin into the bloodstream.

> **Q**
>
> **11 When does the glucose level in the hepatic portal vein rise above normal?**

On reaching the target cells (liver and muscle), insulin acts by binding to specific receptor proteins on the target cell membrane as shown in figure 13.

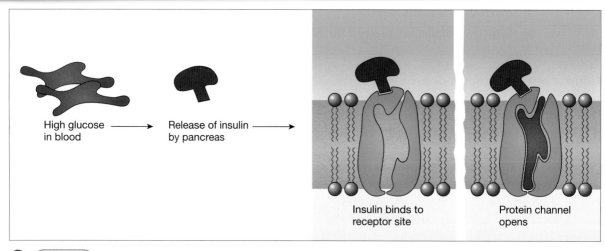

High glucose ⟶ Release of insulin ⟶
in blood   by pancreas

Insulin binds to
receptor site

Protein channel
opens

▲ (**Figure 13**) *Insulin binds to receptor proteins on the target cell membrane.*

This lowers blood glucose levels in several ways.

- Insulin stimulates the uptake of glucose by all respiring cells in the body, but mainly liver and muscle cells. In some cells it does this by increasing the number of opened glucose transport proteins in the cell surface membrane. This allows more glucose to enter these cells.
- Insulin stimulates the increased use of glucose in respiration.
- Insulin activates enzymes inside liver and muscle cells, increasing the rate at which glucose is converted to the storage compound glycogen. Glycogen is then stored in the liver and muscles. This process is called **glycogenesis**.
- Insulin activates other enzymes which convert glucose to fatty acids, and increase fat deposition in adipose (fat storage) tissue.

The β-cells continue to secrete insulin until they detect the blood glucose level returning to normal.

> **Q**
>
> **12 Use your knowledge of how protein hormones work to explain how insulin activates enzymes inside liver and muscle cells.**
>
> **13 Use the control system described above to name a) the receptor, b) the co-ordinator, c) the effectors and d) the responses involved in lowering the blood glucose level.**

Low levels of blood glucose

If the islets of Langerhans detect a fall in blood glucose levels, the α-cells in the islets of Langerhans secrete glucagon. Glucagon binds to receptor proteins on cell surface membranes, activating enzymes which catalyse the conversion of glycogen to glucose. This is called **glycogenolysis**. Glucagon also stimulates the conversion of amino acids and glycerol to glucose. This is called **gluconeogenesis**. As a result, glucose is produced and released into the blood.

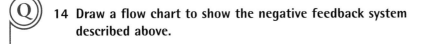

Q 14 Draw a flow chart to show the negative feedback system described above.

Insulin and glucagon

The way in which insulin and glucagon regulate blood glucose levels is summarised in figure 14.

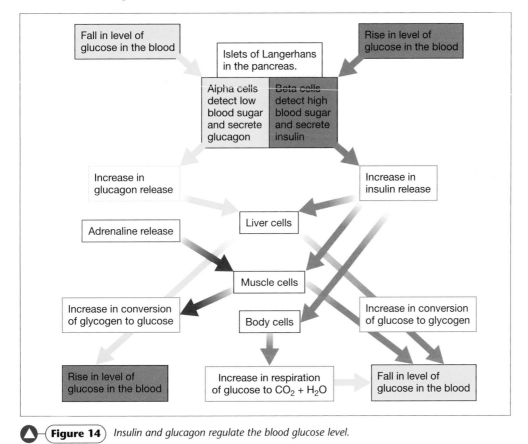

▲ Figure 14 Insulin and glucagon regulate the blood glucose level.

As you can see in figure 14, when blood glucose level rises, insulin is secreted. This reduces the blood glucose level so that insulin secretion is reduced. Similarly, when blood glucose level falls, glucagon is secreted. This raises the blood glucose level so that glucagon secretion is reduced. Both are examples of negative feedback, because a change in the internal environment brings about effects to counteract that change.

Diabetes mellitus

Some people are unable to control the level of their blood glucose because they suffer from the condition **diabetes mellitus**. There are two kinds of diabetes mellitus, type 1 and type 2. Type 1 diabetes appears early in life. Type 1 diabetics do not produce enough insulin, so when they eat a meal, although their blood glucose level is high, very little glucose can enter the cells. Because the blood glucose level is very high, glucose is present in the urine. Untreated type 1 diabetics suffer from excessive thirst, excessive urination and weight loss. This is because the body cells do not receive enough glucose because it is excreted. So diabetics use lipids and proteins from body tissues, such as muscles, instead. If this type of diabetes is untreated it is fatal.

Type 1 diabetes can be treated by regular insulin injections, as seen in figure 15. It is important that the right amount of insulin is injected. By injecting too much insulin, diabetics become **hypoglycaemic** (the blood glucose level is abnormally low) and can fall into a coma and die. For this reason diabetics often carry glucose-containing sweets or biscuits with them, to eat if their glucose level falls too low. If the blood glucose level is too high because too little insulin has been injected or the diabetic has consumed too much sugar, the person is said to be **hyperglycaemic**. This too can lead to coma.

Type 2 diabetes tends to occur in older people, especially those who are overweight. It can result from the islet cells being less efficient at producing insulin, or from a reduced sensitivity of the target cells to insulin. Type 2 diabetes develops over a period of time, and it is usually controlled by a combination of exercise and diet. Blood glucose levels can be tested using a blood testing meter, as shown in figure 16.

Figure 15 Type 1 diabetics have to inject themselves with insulin.

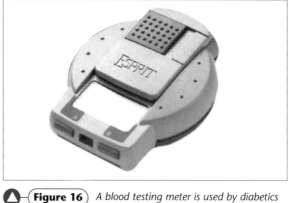

Figure 16 A blood testing meter is used by diabetics to test their blood glucose levels.

> **Q** 15 Suggest how type 2 diabetes could be controlled by exercise and diet.

Key ideas 79–90

- Homeostasis is the ability of mammals to maintain a constant internal environment.

- An important part of homeostasis in mammals is negative feedback. This refers to the process by which a deviation from the normal situation triggers corrective responses, which then bring the environment back to the normal situation.

- Thermoregulation is the control of body temperature. This involves thermoreceptors in the hypothalamus and in the skin which detect a change in body temperature.

- The body temperature is returned to normal by heat loss responses, including increased sweating and vasodilation, or heat conservation responses, including shivering, vasoconstriction, piloerection and increased basal metabolic rate.

- Blood glucose levels are regulated by means of the hormones insulin and glucagon. These hormones interact with specific membrane receptors and activate enzymes to bring about their effects.

- Insulin reduces blood glucose levels by increasing the permeability of cells to glucose and increasing the rate at which glucose is converted to glycogen for storage.

- Glucagon increases blood glucose levels by stimulating the conversion of glycogen to glucose.

The role of the kidney

The waste left over from food that you do not digest leaves your body as faeces. However, there are other waste products produced by the body including carbon dioxide and water made during respiration, and a substance called urea. **Urea** is made in the liver from excess amino acids. Some urea leaves your body in sweat but most of it is lost in **urine**. Urine is a liquid produced in the kidneys and is made up mainly of water and urea. The kidneys help to control the amount of water in the body by regulating the amount of urine that is produced.

Memory joggers

- The entry and exit of substances to and from a cell are controlled by cell membranes.

- Proteins in the membrane may act as receptors and carriers.

- Osmosis is a special form of diffusion across a partially permeable membrane. It is the net movement of water from an area of high water potential to an area of low water potential.

- A hypotonic solution has a lower concentration of dissolved solutes (a higher water potential) than another solution.

- A hypertonic solution has a higher concentration of dissolved solutes (a lower water potential) than another solution.

- An isotonic solution has the same concentration of dissolved solutes (the same water potential) as another solution.

- Diffusion is the passive movement of substances in the direction of a concentration gradient. Surface area and distance affect the rate of diffusion. Carrier and channel proteins are involved in facilitated diffusion.

- Concentration gradients may be maintained by the countercurrent principle.

- Active transport is the movement of molecules across a membrane from an area where they are at a lower concentration to an area where they are at a higher concentration. Specialised transport molecules are used which require energy from respiration.

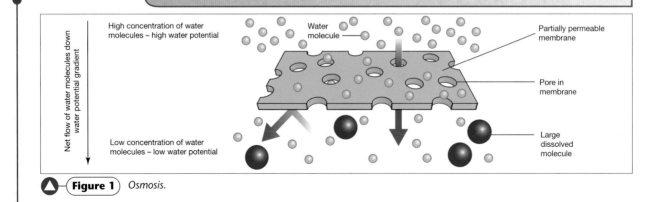

Figure 1 Osmosis.

Waste management

You have already seen that blood glucose levels are regulated so that cells always have a 'pool' of glucose available for respiration. Similarly, a 'pool' of amino acids is maintained. Amino acids from the gut enter the bloodstream, and are removed for use in protein synthesis. Figure 2 shows the amino acid pool in the blood.

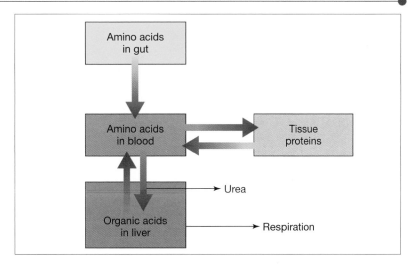

Figure 2 *The amino acid pool in the blood.*

Excess amino acids that are not needed for protein synthesis can be modified for use in respiration. This modification process is called **deamination** and takes place in the liver. This is shown in figure 3. The amino group (–NH₂) and a hydrogen atom are removed from the amino acid and ammonia is formed. This leaves an organic acid, called carboxylic acid, that can be used in respiration. Ammonia, which is highly toxic, is converted to urea in the liver by the **ornithine cycle** as shown in figure 3. Urea is toxic, but it is less toxic than ammonia.

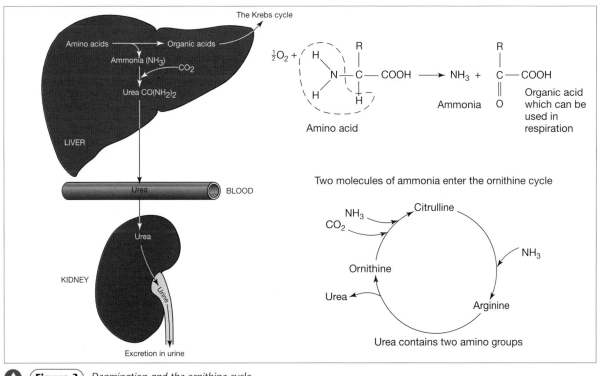

Figure 3 *Deamination and the ornithine cycle.*

Although urea is formed in the liver, the bloodstream carries it to the kidney where it is excreted.

The kidney

The human urinary system is shown in figure 4. You can see that it consists of two kidneys which produce urine. Urine passes from each kidney down tubes called **ureters** to the **bladder**. Urine is released out of the body from the bladder through the **urethra**.

The **renal arteries** carry blood to the kidneys from the rest of the body, and the **renal veins** carry blood away.

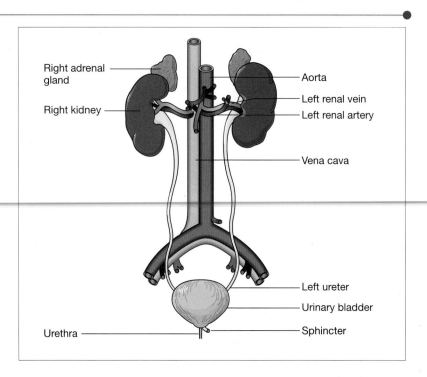

Right adrenal gland

Right kidney

Aorta

Left renal vein

Left renal artery

Vena cava

Left ureter

Urinary bladder

Sphincter

Urethra

 Figure 4 *The urinary system in humans.*

When a kidney is cut in half, two main layers are seen called the **cortex** and the **medulla**. The kidney is actually made up of over a million tiny tubes called **nephrons**. Only one nephron is shown in the diagram in figure 5. You can see that it starts in the cortex, enters the medulla and returns to the cortex. Urine produced in the nephron passes into a **collecting duct** and into the ureter.

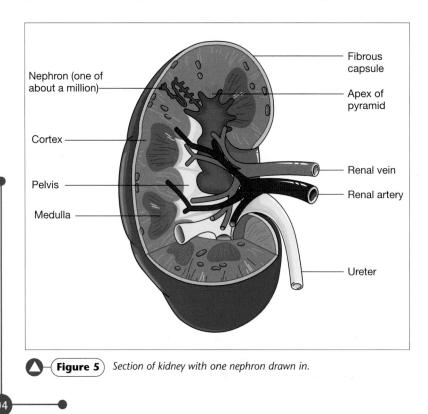

Nephron (one of about a million)

Cortex

Pelvis

Medulla

Fibrous capsule

Apex of pyramid

Renal vein

Renal artery

Ureter

Figure 5 *Section of kidney with one nephron drawn in.*

The nephron

In figure 6 you can see that the nephron has several parts. The **renal capsule**, **proximal convoluted tubule** and **distal convoluted tubule** all lie in the cortex of the kidney, while the **loop of Henle** and the collecting duct are positioned in the medulla. The distal convoluted tubules of several nephrons join together to form one collecting duct, and then bundles of collecting ducts form the **pyramids** which carry urine into a space called the **pelvis**. From the pelvis, urine is pushed along the ureters to the bladder by **peristalsis**.

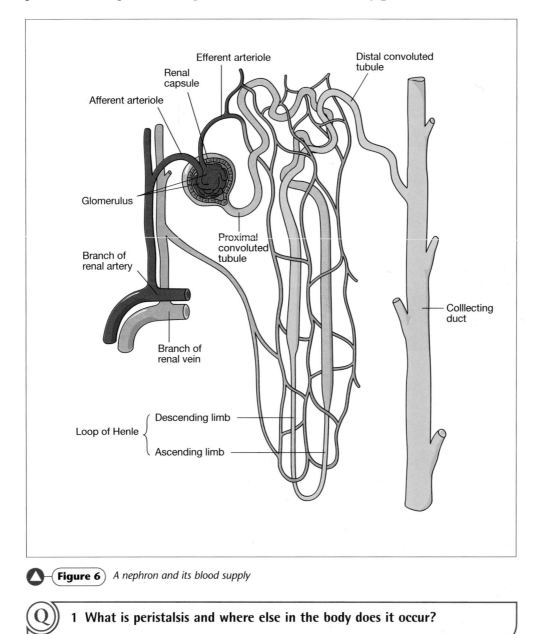

Figure 6 *A nephron and its blood supply*

Q 1 What is peristalsis and where else in the body does it occur?

Blood enters the nephron in an afferent arteriole. The arteriole forms a network of capillaries inside the renal capsule. An efferent arteriole leaves the renal capsule and forms a network of capillaries around the rest of the nephron.

Ultrafiltration in the renal capsule

Blood enters the kidney by the renal artery which divides into about a million branches, each supplying a **glomerulus**. Each glomerulus consists of a ball of capillaries and is enclosed in a cup-shaped structure called the **renal capsule**. You can see the renal capsule in figure 7.

Blood enters the glomerulus from the renal artery through a wide **afferent arteriole** (a blood vessel which carries blood towards the nephron). The blood is under pressure because the renal artery branches off the aorta. The **efferent arteriole**, which takes blood away from the renal capsule, is much narrower than the afferent arteriole, so this creates a high pressure in the capillaries of the glomerulus. As the blood passes through the glomerulus, the pressure forces some water, small molecules and ions across a filtering system into the renal space. This process is called **ultrafiltration**.

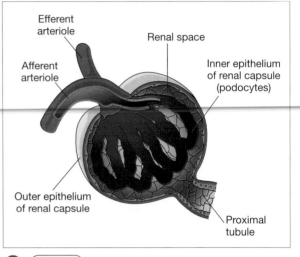

▲ **Figure 7** *The renal capsule.*

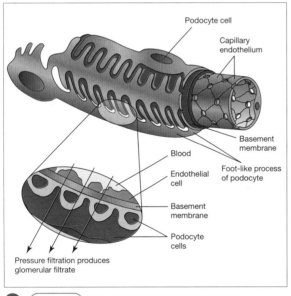

▲ **Figure 8** *The filtering system of the kidney.*

The filtering system is shown in figure 8. It has three layers.

1 The **capillary endothelium** contains large gaps which allow blood plasma through but not blood cells.
2 The **basement membrane**, which supports the capillary endothelium, acts as a fine filter allowing plasma proteins with a molecular mass of less than 68 000 to pass through, but not larger ones. This value of molecular mass is called the **renal threshold**.
3 The **podocytes**, which form the lining of the renal capsule, have large gaps between them which allow the glomerular filtrate through into the renal space.

Q **2 Explain why a person with a damaged basement membrane has large proteins in the urine.**

The ultrafiltration that takes place in the renal capsule is non-selective: all substances, whether they are waste products or useful, are filtered out of the blood if they are below the renal threshold. This means that substances such as glucose and amino acids are filtered out, as well as salts, water and urea. Useful substances are selectively reabsorbed in the proximal convoluted tubule.

The proximal convoluted tubule

Many of the substances in the glomerular filtrate, such as glucose, amino acids and mineral ions, are reabsorbed by active transport by the epithelial cells lining the proximal convoluted tubule, whereas urea is reabsorbed by diffusion. The structure of a cell from the proximal convoluted tubule is shown in figure 9.

Water is also absorbed in the proximal convoluted tubule. The active transport of glucose, amino acids and mineral ions lowers the water potential in the tissue fluid around the proximal convoluted tubule. Water enters the tissue fluid by osmosis. Glucose, amino acids and mineral ions diffuse into the blood in the capillaries around the proximal convoluted tubule and water enters the blood by osmosis. About half the urea in the filtrate is reabsorbed by diffusion. Usually all of the amino acids and glucose are reabsorbed. However, in diabetes mellitus, the glucose carrier proteins in the membrane cannot cope with the high level of glucose in the blood, so some is lost in the urine.

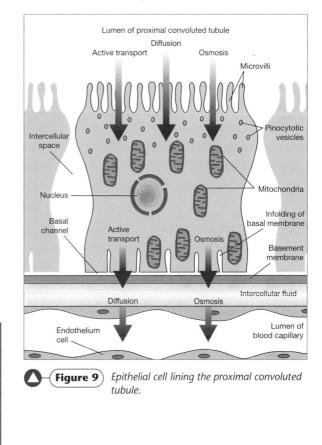

Figure 9 Epithelial cell lining the proximal convoluted tubule.

> **Q** 3 a) Give two ways in which the epithelial cell is adapted for reabsorption of glucose and other essential nutrients.
>
> b) Water is also reabsorbed from the tubule by osmosis. Describe how water is reabsorbed by osmosis in terms of water potential.

The loop of Henle

The loop of Henle creates a high concentration of salts, deep in the medulla of the kidney. It is the loop of Henle that allows humans to produce urine which is more concentrated than blood plasma. The descending limb of the loop of Henle is permeable to water but not very permeable to salts. The ascending limb has thicker walls which are impermeable to water. The thin ascending limb allows salts to move passively into the medulla, but the thick ascending limb actively transports sodium chloride into the medulla. It is in this way that the loop of Henle acts as a **countercurrent flow mechanism**. 'Countercurrent' means that the fluid in the descending limb is running the opposite way to the fluid in the ascending limb. The result is that the concentration gradient between the two limbs is maintained all the way along the loop.

Countercurrent flow

Look at figure 10. The loop of Henle is involved in creating a water potential gradient that allows water to be reabsorbed from the filtrate by osmosis. Some water has already been reabsorbed by osmosis in the proximal convoluted tubule, so the filtrate in the wide part of the descending limb (A) is isotonic with the fluid in the surrounding tissues. However, because the surrounding tissue fluid in the medulla of the kidney has a high concentration of salts, water is drawn out of the thin part of the descending limb (B) by osmosis as the filtrate passes down the loop of Henle. The salt concentration in the medulla increases towards the tip of the loop, so water can pass out along the whole length of the descending limb. This water is then carried away in the surrounding capillaries. As a result, the volume of the filtrate is now reduced and contains a higher concentration of salts. The ascending limb of the loop of Henle is permeable to sodium chloride but impermeable to water. As the filtrate travels up the thin part of the ascending limb (C), sodium chloride diffuses into the surrounding tissue fluid. Higher in the ascending limb (D) chloride ions are actively transported out of the limb and sodium ions follow into the tissue fluid. These processes maintain the high salt gradient in the surrounding tissue fluid that is needed for water reabsorption in the collecting ducts.

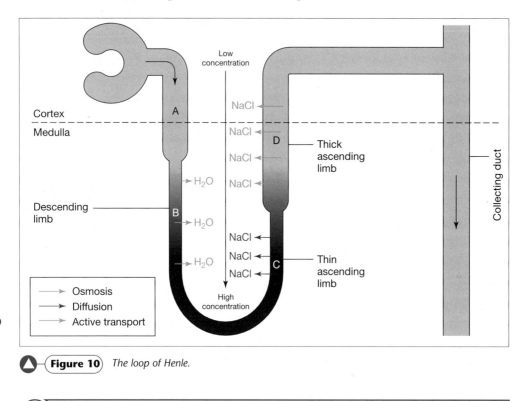

Figure 10 *The loop of Henle.*

Q

4 **What is meant by 'isotonic'?**

5 **Why does the high concentration of salts in the tissue fluid cause water to be drawn out of the thin part of the descending limb?**

6 **Suggest why the active transport of chloride ions out of the thick ascending limb causes sodium ions to follow.**

The distal convoluted tubule

Most of the useful substances, such as glucose and amino acids, have already been reabsorbed in the proximal convoluted tubule, but some salts and water remain. In the distal convoluted tubule some of the remaining salts and water are reabsorbed. Hormones control the amount of reabsorption by affecting the permeability of the distal convoluted tubule to salts and water. It is important that the amount of reabsorption is controlled because pH and water potential of the blood must be kept constant.

The remaining filtrate enters the collecting duct and is now called urine because it contains only waste products.

Regulating the water potential of the blood

Regulating the water potential of the blood is another example of homeostasis and is shown in figure 11.

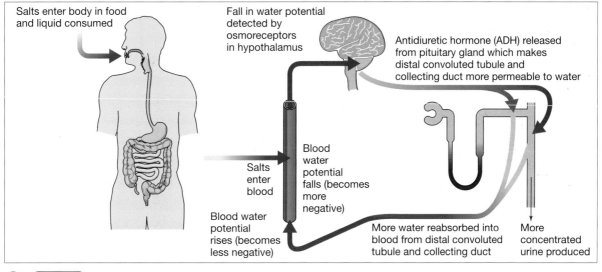

Figure 11 *The role of ADH in water reabsorption.*

There are special receptor cells in the hypothalamus of the brain called **osmoreceptors**. These receptors are sensitive to changes in the water potential of the blood. Salts and other solutes in food and drink cause the water potential of the blood to fall. When the water potential in the blood falls, these osmoreceptors stimulate the pituitary gland. The pituitary gland releases the hormone **ADH** (antidiuretic hormone) into the blood. ADH increases the permeability of the distal convoluted tubule and the collecting duct to water. As the water potential in the tubule is greater than the water potential in the blood, water is reabsorbed from the distal convoluted tubule and collecting duct. As some water has been reabsorbed from the tubule by osmosis, a smaller volume of more concentrated urine is produced.

Q   **7 Look at the control system shown in figure 11. Name a) the receptor, b) the co-ordinator, c) the effectors and d) the responses.**

High fluid intake

On the other hand, if fluid intake is high, the water potential of the blood rises. This is detected by the osmoreceptors in the hypothalamus, and ADH production in the pituitary gland is inhibited. This reduces the permeability of the distal convoluted tubule and the collecting duct to water, so less water is reabsorbed from the urine. Therefore a larger volume of dilute urine is produced.

Q   **8 Copy and fill in the flow chart in figure 12 to summarise the control of water potential by the kidney.**

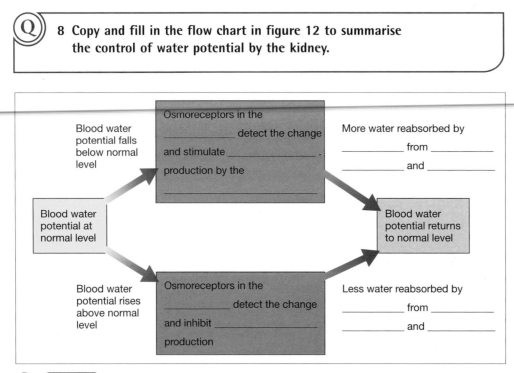

Figure 12 *Flow chart summarising the control of water potential by the kidney.*

Key ideas 92–100

- Waste products of metabolism are frequently toxic and must be removed from the body. Excess amino acids are deaminated, producing ammonia and an organic acid. The organic acid is respired and the ammonia converted to urea in the ornithine cycle.

- Urea and other waste products are excreted from the body in urine. Urine is formed in the kidney. The process of urine formation includes ultrafiltration in the renal capsule and selective reabsorption in the proximal convoluted tubule.

- The loop of Henle maintains a gradient of ions in the medulla. This is important in regulating blood water potential.

- The solute concentration of the blood is monitored by osmoreceptors in the hypothalamus.

- If blood solute concentration becomes too high, the pituitary gland secretes ADH which increases the permeability of the distal convoluted tubule and the collecting duct to water. This enables more water to be reabsorbed and more concentrated urine is produced.

4 The nervous system

All living things need to be able to respond to changes, either in their external environment or within their bodies. A change to which an organism can respond is called a stimulus. Being able to sense stimuli and respond to them increases the organism's chances of survival. For example, it allows organisms to avoid dangerous situations and to find sources of food.

Nervous tissue is composed of two types of cell: **neurones** and **glial cells**. Neurones transmit nerve impulses. Glial cells are in direct contact with neurones and often surround them. The neurone is the functional unit of the nervous system. A human has about 100 billion neurones in the brain alone. Neurones are variable in shape and size and they have three parts: **dendrites, cell body** and **axon.** Dendrites receive information from another cell and transmit nerve impulses to the cell body. The cell body contains the nucleus and other cell organelles. The axon conducts nerve impulses away from the cell body.

Memory joggers

- The nervous system works by using receptors to detect stimuli.
- Nerve impulses are sent from the receptor to a co-ordinator.
- The co-ordinator then sends impulses to effectors which brings about a response.

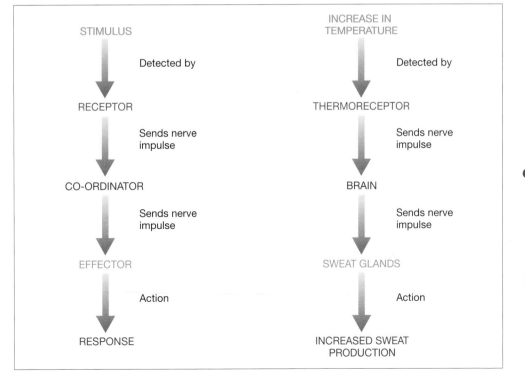

STIMULUS
Detected by
RECEPTOR
Sends nerve impulse
CO-ORDINATOR
Sends nerve impulse
EFFECTOR
Action
RESPONSE

INCREASE IN TEMPERATURE
Detected by
THERMORECEPTOR
Sends nerve impulse
BRAIN
Sends nerve impulse
SWEAT GLANDS
Action
INCREASED SWEAT PRODUCTION

Figure 1

Organisation of the nervous system

The nervous system can be divided into two parts as shown in figure 2.

1 The **central nervous system** (CNS) consists of the brain and spinal cord. These receive information from sense receptors, process the information, and send impulses to glands and muscles.
2 The **peripheral nervous system** consists of nerves leading to and from the brain and spinal cord. Sensory pathways carry nerve impulses from receptors to the CNS, and motor pathways carry nerve impulses from the CNS to effectors.

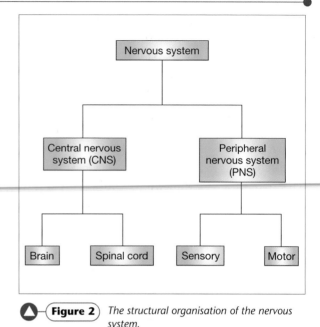

Figure 2 *The structural organisation of the nervous system.*

By means of the sensory pathways, the brain is kept informed of what is happening to the body's internal and external environments. The brain analyses, interprets, processes and stores the information it receives. It is the brain's association areas that may act on the information received by sending nerve impulses via motor pathways to effectors. The effectors then respond.

The nervous system can also be divided according to the functions it performs. This division is shown in figure 3.

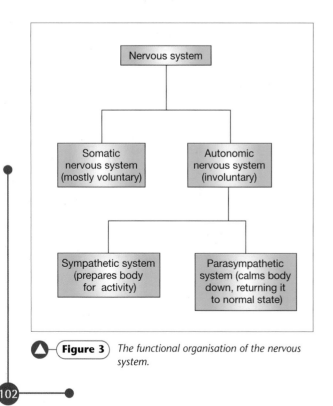

Figure 3 *The functional organisation of the nervous system.*

The somatic nervous system controls skeletal muscle and external sensory receptors. It is responsible for controlling voluntary actions and some involuntary reflex actions.

The **autonomic nervous system** usually works automatically and controls internal organs and structures, for example the heart. It can be split into two systems, the **sympathetic nervous system** and the **parasympathetic nervous system**. When the two systems affect the same organ or structure, they generally exert opposite effects. This is referred to as antagonistic action. For example the sympathetic nervous system increases heart rate and the parasympathetic nervous system decreases heart rate.

Neurones

Neurones are the basic unit of the nervous system. They are nerve cells that communicate with each other, receiving information and sending it on. They vary in size and shape depending on their function and position in the nervous system, but they all have the same basic structure. Two important types of neurone are sensory and motor neurones.

- **Sensory neurones** carry information from receptors to the central nervous system.
- **Motor neurones** carry information from the central nervous system to effectors.

The structure of a sensory neurone is shown in figure 4.

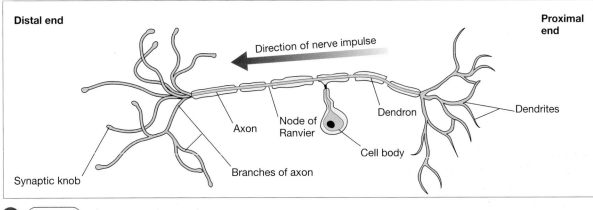

▲ (**Figure 4**) *The structure of a typical sensory neurone.*

Figure 5 shows the structure of a motor neurone. It has a cell body that contains a nucleus, most of the cytoplasm and cell organelles. There are many thin strands called dendrites leading to the cell body. These carry nerve impulses from the brain and spinal cord towards the cell body. The axon carries nerve impulses away from the cell body. Axons can be over a metre long. Many motor neurones have a **myelin sheath** around them. The end of the axon has branches with swollen endings. These endings communicate with effectors or with other neurones.

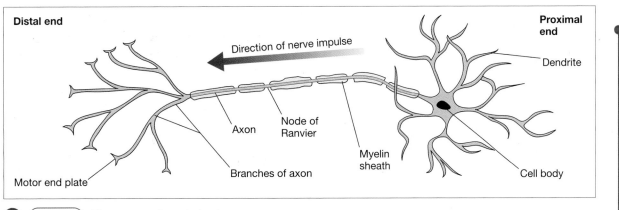

▲ (**Figure 5**) *The structure of a typical motor neurone.*

There are several other kinds of neurone, which are shown in figure 6.

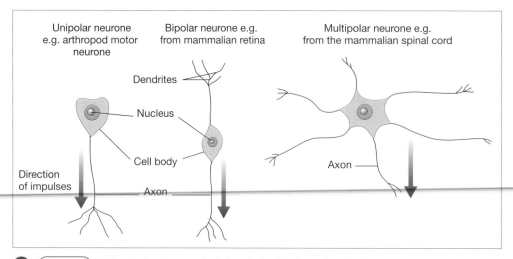

Figure 6 *Other kinds of neurone include unipolar, bipolar and multipolar neurones.*

Myelination

Another important type of cell found in the nervous system is a **Schwann cell**. A Schwann cell is a type of glial cell which wraps itself around the axon of a neurone and grows spirally, rather like a bandage wrapped around the axon. As the cell grows, the cytoplasm is flattened, so that many layers of cytoplasm are wrapped around the axon. This forms a lipid-rich insulating layer called the **myelin sheath**. There are small gaps of up to 1.5 mm between the Schwann cells; these are called **nodes of Ranvier**. They are important in transmitting nerve impulses, and in allowing the neurone to come into contact with the extracellular fluid. In humans, axons greater than 1 **micrometre** in diameter are myelinated. The process of myelination is shown in figure 7.

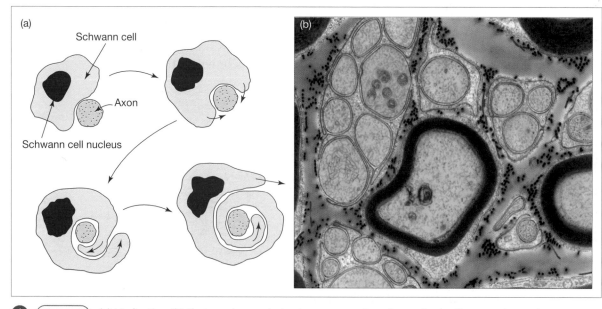

Figure 7 *(a) Myelination. (b) Electron micrograph showing a cross-section of a myelin sheath wrapped around an axon.*

Multiple sclerosis

Multiple sclerosis is a chronic, often disabling disease of the central nervous system. In multiple sclerosis, the patient's immune system gradually destroys the Schwann cells which form the myelin sheath around neurones, as shown in figure 8.

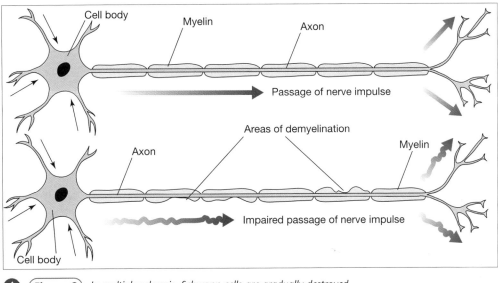

Figure 8 *In multiple sclerosis, Schwann cells are gradually destroyed.*

> **Q** **1 What effect will demyelination have on transmission of a nerve impulse?**

The first symptoms of the disease are usually problems with the sense organs such as eyesight difficulties, and numbness in the limbs. Gradually the neurones in the brain and spinal cord are affected. In many sufferers the disease worsens, giving more severe symptoms such as paralysis or loss of vision. The disease typically has periods of severe symptoms followed by periods of remission, when the symptoms become less severe or may even disappear.

Key ideas 101–105

- Neurones are the basic unit of the nervous system. There are several different kinds of neurone, including sensory neurones which carry impulses to the central nervous system, and motor neurones which carry impulses from the central nervous system to effectors.

- The nervous system also contains glial cells. The most important of these are the Schwann cells which form myelin sheaths around some nerve fibres.

- The nervous system can be subdivided into the central nervous system (the brain and spinal cord) and the peripheral nervous system (nerves leading to and from the central nervous system).

The nerve impulse

In 1786 Luigi Galvani discovered that nerves carry electrical signals. He applied an electric current to the nerves supplying dissected frog's legs, and found that this would make the legs twitch. It was difficult to find out more about nerves because they are so thin. However, in the 1930s Alan Hodgkin and Andrew Huxley found out that certain invertebrate animals, such as squid, have giant axons almost 1 mm in diameter. They dissected out the giant axons of squid and kept them in isotonic saline solution, which kept them alive for a short period of time. By inserting tiny electrodes into the axons, Hodgkin and Huxley found that there is an electrical potential difference between the outside and the inside of the axon of about −70 millivolts (mV). When an electrical stimulus was applied to the axon, the potential difference changed to +20 mV and then returned to about −70 mV.

Memory joggers

- Substances can pass into cells through both permanent and gated channel proteins in the cell surface membrane.

- There are proteins called carrier proteins in the cell surface membrane, which have a specific shape. They carry molecules with a complementary shape across the membrane using energy from ATP.

- Molecules may be helped to diffuse through membranes by specific channel proteins. This is called facilitated diffusion.

- The cell surface membrane of a neurone contains receptor proteins that control the permeability of the membrane.

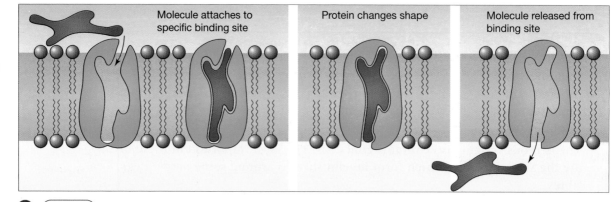

Molecule attaches to specific binding site   Protein changes shape   Molecule released from binding site

Figure 1 *Facilitated diffusion takes place through channel proteins.*

Being ready

When a neurone is not conducting a nerve impulse it is said to be 'resting'. However, the membrane of the neurone needs to be ready to conduct an impulse at any time. Experiments show that the membrane has a **resting potential** of about –70 mV, and it is said to be **polarised**. This means that the inside of the axon is negatively charged compared to the outside. This difference in charge is due to the distribution of ions between the inside and the outside of the axon, as shown in figure 2.

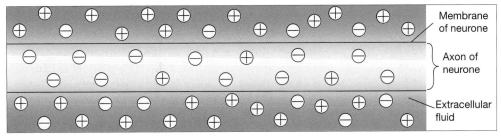

 Figure 2 *In a resting neurone there are more positive ions on the outside of the axon and fewer positive ions inside the axon.*

Neurone membranes contain specific proteins. One kind of protein in the membrane is called a **sodium–potassium pump**, shown in figure 3. This protein actively transports sodium ions out of the cell and potassium ions into the cell. Three sodium ions move out of the cell for every two potassium ions that move in.

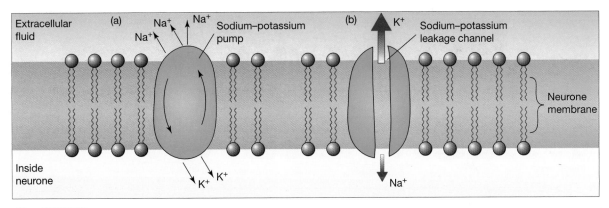

 Figure 3 *(a) The sodium–potassium pump uses energy from ATP to pump three sodium ions out of the axon in exchange for two potassium ions. (b) The membrane allows both sodium and potassium ions to diffuse through, but it is much more permeable to potassium ions than to sodium ions.*

There are also passive membrane channels called 'sodium–potassium leakage channels'. These are believed to be always open in a resting membrane. Both sodium and potassium ions diffuse through these channels, but about a hundred times more potassium ions leak out than sodium ions leak in. This means that the membrane is more permeable to potassium ions than to sodium ions. This is called **partial permeability**. It is this leakage of positively charged potassium ions together with the action of the sodium–potassium pump that is the cause of the resting potential.

> **Q** 1 What would happen if the axon membrane were not differentially permeable?

Starting an impulse

The membrane of a neurone also contains sodium gated channels and potassium gated channels. **Gated channels** only open when the potential difference across the membrane reaches a specific value. In a resting membrane, both types of gated channel are closed as shown in figure 4.

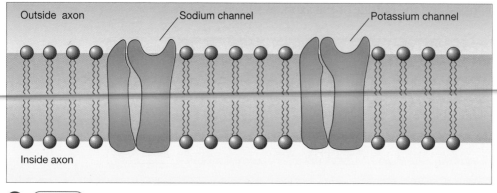

Figure 4 *The sodium and potassium gated channels are closed in a resting membrane.*

When a stimulus reaches the resting neurone, the sodium gated channels open at the point of stimulation, as shown in figure 5. Sodium ions move through the channels into the neurone. If sufficient sodium ions move in, more sodium gated channels open. This causes a reduction in the potential difference across the membrane which is called **depolarisation.**

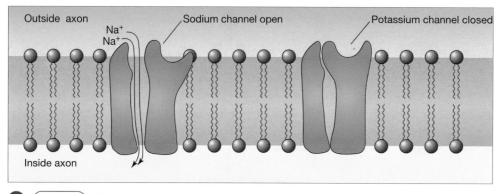

Figure 5 *The sodium channels open and sodium ions move into the axon along an electrical and concentration gradient.*

Sodium ions diffuse into the axon along a concentration gradient and also along an electrical gradient, because the inside of the axon is negatively charged compared to the outside. Because so many sodium ions move in, the inside of the axon becomes positively charged compared to the outside. The potential difference is now about +40 mV.

> Q   **2 Explain why it is possible for sodium ions to enter the axon along an electrical gradient.**

Recovery

Once the inside of the axon has become positively charged, the sodium gated channels close and the potassium gated channels open. This is shown in figure 6. Potassium ions can now diffuse out of the axon along a concentration and an electrical gradient. This repolarises the membrane and returns it to its original resting potential of about –70 mV.

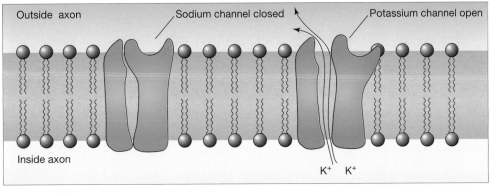

 Figure 6 *The sodium gated channels close and the potassium gated channels open. Potassium ions move out of the axon along an electrical and concentration gradient.*

In fact, the potassium channels stay open for a few milliseconds after repolarisation, so there is a brief period of **hyperpolarisation** when the potential difference across the membrane is more negative than the resting potential. There is a brief period after the sodium gated channels close when the neurone cannot respond to a stimulus. This is known as the **refractory period**.

This whole cycle of depolarisation and repolarisation is called an **action potential**. The changes in potential difference across the membrane during an action potential can be recorded using an oscilloscope, and are shown in figure 7.

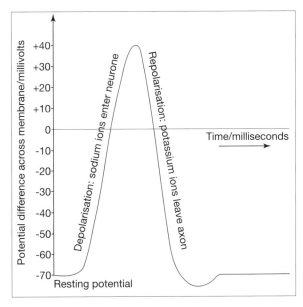

Figure 7 *The changes that take place during an action potential.*

As a result of the action potential, the extracellular fluid has gained some potassium ions and the cytoplasm inside the neurone has gained sodium ions. The balance of sodium and potassium ions is restored by the sodium–potassium pump.

Changes in permeability

Figure 8 shows the changes in permeability of the neurone membrane to sodium and potassium ions during an action potential.

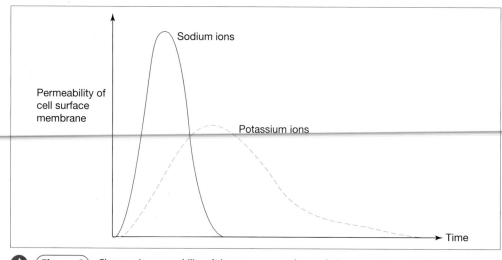

Figure 8 *Changes in permeability of the neurone membrane during an action potential.*

> (Q) **3 Use the graph in figure 8 to explain what happens during an action potential.**

All or nothing

A stimulus has to be above a certain **threshold value** if it is to cause an action potential. Figure 9 shows what happens if the stimulus is below the threshold value or **subthreshold**. However, all action potentials are the same size. This is called the **'all-or-nothing'** response. The way to distinguish between a weak and a strong stimulus is by the frequency of action potentials: a stronger stimulus will result in more frequent action potentials being produced in the neurone.

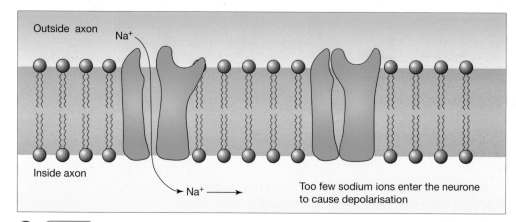

Figure 9 *An action potential occurs when a stimulus is above a threshold value. If the stimulus is below the threshold an action potential will not occur. This is the 'all-or-nothing' response.*

How impulses travel along the neurone

A nerve impulse is the passage of an action potential along a neurone. When sodium ions move into an unmyelinated neurone, a local flow of electrical current occurs. These local currents are caused by the sodium ions that have entered the neurone. Look at figure 10. The sodium ions diffuse along the neurone causing the next region of the membrane to depolarise. This brings about a further inflow of sodium ions. Each region of the neurone stimulates the next region to undergo an action potential, and so on, so that a nerve impulse passes all the way along the neurone.

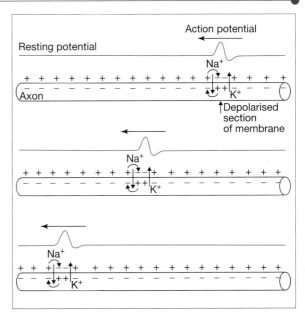

Figure 10 *The passage of an action potential along an unmyelinated neurone.*

Q 4 **In a neurone conducting at high frequency there is a small time gap between the action potentials. Use your knowledge of the action potential to explain this.**

Nerve impulses pass along a neurone at a constant speed. They do not speed up or slow down. However, wide neurones conduct impulses more quickly than narrow ones, and myelinated neurones tend to conduct impulses faster than unmyelinated ones.

Myelinated neurones

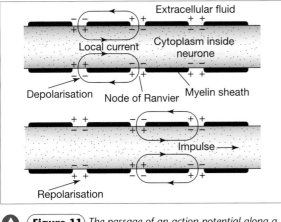

Figure 11 *The passage of an action potential along a myelinated neurone.*

Myelinated neurones conduct impulses more quickly because action potentials can only occur at the nodes of Ranvier. Local currents are set up in which sodium ions move from one node to the next, as shown in figure 11. This is described as **saltatory conduction**. It is more efficient than conducting impulses along unmyelinated neurones because ions are only exchanged at the nodes. This greatly reduces the energy needed for active transport of sodium and potassium ions. Wide myelinated neurones can carry impulses as quickly as $120 \, \text{m s}^{-1}$, while the unmyelinated giant axon of the squid carries impulses at about $25 \, \text{m s}^{-1}$.

Q 5 **Explain why, in myelinated fibres, ions can only be exchanged at the nodes of Ranvier.**

Key ideas 106–111

- When nerve cells are not conducting an impulse, they are said to be 'at rest'. The membrane of a nerve cell has a resting potential difference across it of approximately –70 mV. This is achieved by the membrane having differential permeability to sodium and potassium ions, and by the presence of a sodium–potassium pump in the membrane.

- When an action potential is initiated, the membrane becomes more permeable to sodium ions which flood into the axon, depolarising the membrane. Shortly afterwards, the membrane becomes more permeable to potassium ions, which move out of the membrane, repolarising it.

- Action potentials usually pass more quickly along myelinated nerve fibres because ion exchange only occurs at the nodes of Ranvier. Sodium ions 'jump' from node to node, which is described as saltatory conduction.

- After an action potential has occurred, there is a brief refractory period during which the membrane cannot conduct another action potential. This ensures that nerve impulses pass along the nerve fibre in one direction only, and ensures that one nerve impulse does not merge with another.

- If a stimulus is below a certain threshold value, an action potential will not occur. Action potentials obey the 'all-or-nothing' law. All action potentials are the same size.

- The intensity of a stimulus is conveyed by the frequency of action potentials.

Synapses

Each neurone communicates with more than one other neurone. Most neurones communicate with hundreds or even thousands of other neurones, creating complex networks. The point where one neurone communicates with another is called a **synapse**. Therefore a synapse is the junction between two neurones. Some neurones may form more than one synapse. For example some neurones in the brain form several hundred synapses.

Memory joggers

- Diffusion is the overall movement of molecules from an area of high concentration to an area of lower concentration.
- Substances can pass through cell membranes by diffusion.
- Action potentials pass along a neurone from the proximal to the distal end.
- Action potentials pass along a neurone in one direction only.

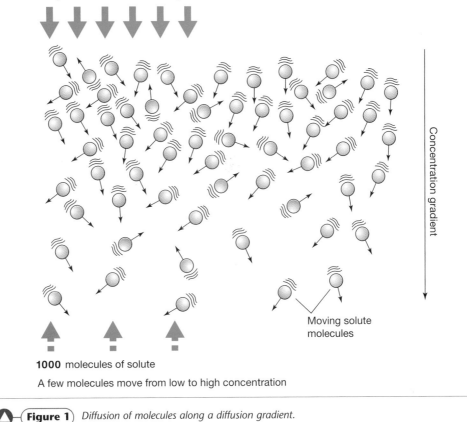

100 000 molecules of solute

Many molecules move from high to low concentration

Concentration gradient

Moving solute molecules

1000 molecules of solute

A few molecules move from low to high concentration

Figure 1 *Diffusion of molecules along a diffusion gradient.*

Synapses

At a synapse, a **presynaptic neurone** communicates with a **postsynaptic neurone** as shown in figure 2. At the end of the axon of the presynaptic neurone there are **synaptic knobs**. These come very close to the dendrites and cell body of the postsynaptic neurone, but they do not actually touch. There is a tiny gap about 20 nanometres wide, called the **synaptic cleft**. The basic structure of a synapse is shown in figure 2.

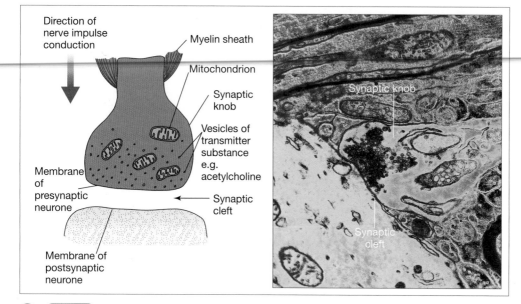

Figure 2 *The structure of a synapse.*

Nerve impulses cannot travel directly across this gap. Instead, communication is by means of a chemical, called a **neurotransmitter**. The best known neurotransmitter is a substance called **acetylcholine**, but there are many others, for example noradrenaline and dopamine. The neurotransmitter is stored in **synaptic vesicles** inside the synaptic knob of the presynaptic neurone. These are small, temporary membrane-bound sacs which contain neurotransmitter. The synaptic knob also contains many mitochondria to provide ATP, which is needed for active transport and synthesis of the neurotransmitter.

The membrane of the postsynaptic neurone contains gated channels that can allow ions into the cell. Normally these channels are closed, but they open when a neurotransmitter binds to them.

Q 1 **Explain how gated channels open when a neurotransmitter binds to them.**

The sequence of events at a synapse is described below.

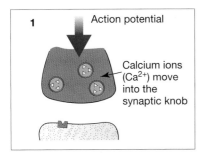

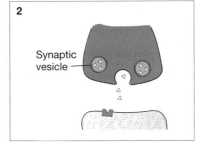

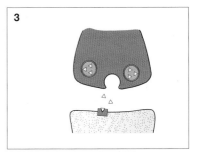

1 An action potential arrives at the synaptic knob. This causes calcium channels to open in the presynaptic membrane, allowing calcium ions to enter the synaptic knob from the extracellular fluid.

2 The calcium ions cause the synaptic vesicles to fuse with the presynaptic membrane and release acetylcholine into the synaptic cleft.

3 The acetylcholine diffuses across the synaptic cleft and binds to specific receptor sites in the membrane.

> **Q 2** What is meant by specific receptor sites?

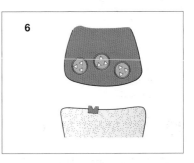

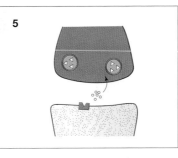

4 This causes the sodium channels in the postsynaptic membrane to open. Sodium ions diffuse into the postsynaptic neurone which produces a small reduction in the membrane potential called an **excitatory postsynaptic potential** or EPSP.

5 When the acetylcholine has bound to the receptors on the postsynaptic membrane, it is immediately broken down into choline and ethanoic acid by an enzyme on the postsynaptic membrane called **acetylcholinesterase**. Once the acetylcholine has broken down, the sodium channels close.

6 The choline and ethanoic acid diffuse back into the presynaptic neurone where they are used to resynthesise acetylcholine using ATP from the mitochondria.

> **Q 3** What would happen if the enzyme acetylcholinesterase were not present?

In some synapses the release of the transmitter causes the postsynaptic membrane to be hyperpolarised. These are **inhibitory postsynaptic potentials** (IPSP) and prevent impulses passing to the next nuerone.

Neurotransmitters

The first neurotransmitter to be discovered was acetylcholine. Neurones that release acetylcholine as a transmitter are called **cholinergic nerves**. However, there are other neurotransmitters. Noradrenaline is the transmitter released at the endings of most sympathetic neurones. These are called **adrenergic nerves**. Other neurotransmitters include dopamine and serotonin. Amino acids can also act as neurotransmitters, for example glycine, glutamate and gamma-amino butyric acid (GABA).

Drugs and synapses

A dentist, when extracting or filling a tooth, uses a local anaesthetic such as procaine, as shown in figure 3. This acts mainly on sensory nerves. It binds to the sodium gated channels in the neurone membrane while they are open, blocking the flow of sodium ions and so preventing an action potential from being set up. Procaine is particularly useful as a local anaesthetic because its effects are short-term. Enzymes quickly break down procaine in the extracellular fluid.

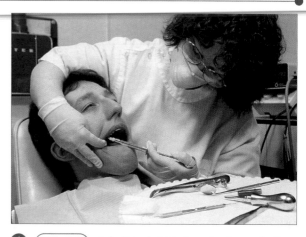

Figure 3 *A dentist administering a local anaesthetic.*

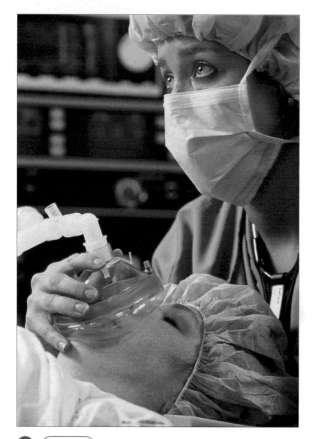

Figure 4 *An anaesthetist administering general anaesthetic drugs during surgery.*

Many other drugs operate on synapses. Diazepam stimulates GABA receptors in the postsynaptic membrane. GABA is an inhibitory neurotransmitter, so diazepam stimulates inhibitory synapses. It has a number of uses, for example as a tranquilliser and in the treatment of epilepsy.

Botulinum toxin is produced by the bacterium *Clostridium botulinum*. It is a powerful toxin which prevents acetylcholine being released by the presynaptic neurone. *Clostridium botulinum* causes a very serious, often fatal form of food poisoning in which the patient suffers from progressive paralysis.

Some drugs, such as tubocurarine, 'compete' with acetylcholine for receptor proteins in the postsynaptic membrane. If the drug binds to the receptor protein it prevents the opening of sodium gated channels. Anaesthetists use tubocurarine to relax skeletal muscles during surgical operations; see figure 4.

Myasthenia gravis is an autoimmune disorder characterised by fluctuating, sometimes fatal, muscle weakness. Symptoms vary according to the amount of activity undergone, as well as the presence of infection or stress of any kind. The sufferer may seem perfectly normal one moment, but within a few hours or even minutes is droopy and listless. At times, sufferers find it difficult or impossible to eat, speak or laugh. The disorder causes sufferers to produce antibodies targeted against certain acetylcholine receptors so that they have fewer acetylcholine receptors on their muscle cells. Therefore myasthenia gravis is treated with inhibitors of acetylcholinesterase, such as prednisolone. This stops acetylcholine breaking down, so the effects of acetylcholine are prolonged.

Malathion and certain other organophosphates are acetylcholinesterase inhibitors used as insecticides. They are rapidly metabolised to inactive products in birds and mammals, but not in insects, and so are considered by the general public to be safe to use. However, fish are not able to break down malathion, and fish have often been killed when malathion has been used on or near lakes, streams and rivers; see figure 5.

Figure 5 *Malathion is an insecticide but it can also kill fish.*

Schizophrenia is a serious personality disorder in which the sufferer may have auditory hallucinations, delusions, thought disorders and behavioural disturbances. One theory is that schizophrenia results from increased dopamine activity in certain areas of the brain. It is usually treated with drugs that block dopamine receptors, such as chlorpromazine.

Q **4 List the different ways in which drugs can act on synapses.**

Key ideas 113–117

- A synapse is the point where two nerve cells meet. There is a tiny gap called the synaptic cleft.

- A chemical transmitter substance is released from the presynaptic neurone, diffuses across the synaptic cleft and fits into receptors on the postsynaptic membrane. This may cause depolarisation of the postsynaptic neurone and set up an action potential.

- Where a motor neurone connects with a muscle fibre, a neuromuscular junction is formed. This is similar to a synapse.

- Many drugs affect synapses.

The mammalian eye

The simplest receptors are single nerve cells that respond directly to a stimulus. Other receptors are grouped in more complex sense organs. The eye is an example of a sense organ.

Mammals depend very much on vision. The eye is a spherical structure made up of three layers. The tough outer **sclera** protects the eye. Inside there is the **choroid**, which contains blood vessels, and the light-sensitive receptor cells are in the inner **retina**.

Memory joggers

- The eye comprises the sclera, cornea, iris, pupil, lens, ciliary muscles, suspensory ligaments, retina and optic nerve.
- The tough outer sclera has a transparent region at the front called the cornea.
- The muscular iris controls the size of the pupil and hence the amount of light reaching the retina.
- The lens is held in position by suspensory ligaments and ciliary muscles.
- The retina contains the receptor cells which are sensitive to light.
- Light from an object enters the eye through the cornea. The curved cornea and the lens produce an image on the retina.
- The receptor cells in the retina send impulses to the brain along sensory neurones in the optic nerve.

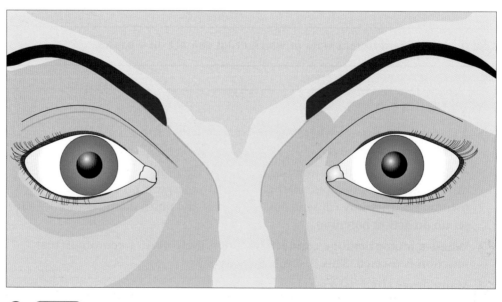

▲ Figure 1

The structure of the human eye

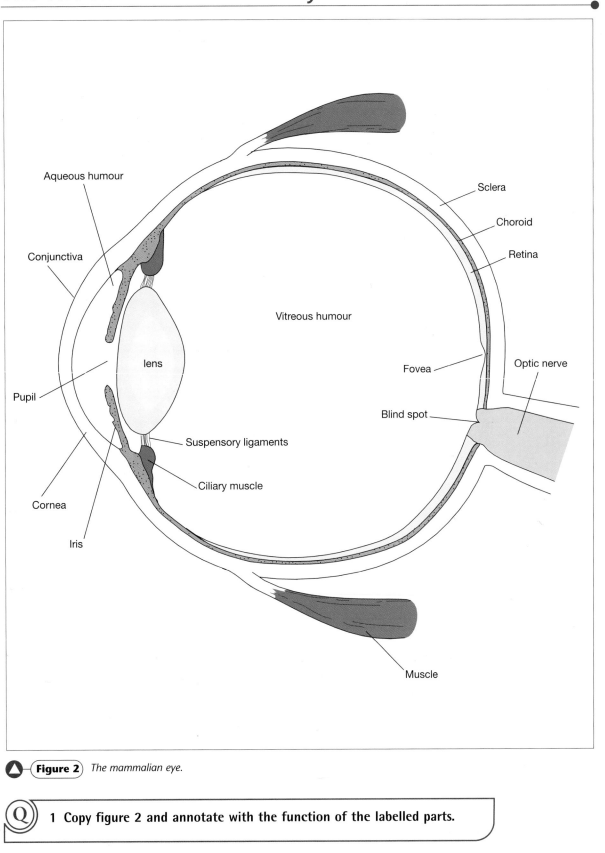

Figure 2 *The mammalian eye.*

Q 1 Copy figure 2 and annotate with the function of the labelled parts.

The retina

The retina is a layer at the back of the eye which is sensitive to light. The structure of the retina is shown in figure 3. It contains two kinds of light-sensitive receptor cells: the **rods** and the **cones**. They connect to **bipolar neurones**, which in turn connect with **ganglion cells**. The fibres of the ganglion cells join together to form the **optic nerve**, which carries impulses to the brain. Notice that the receptor cells are next to the choroid layer. This means that light has to pass through the neurone layer to reach the receptor cells.

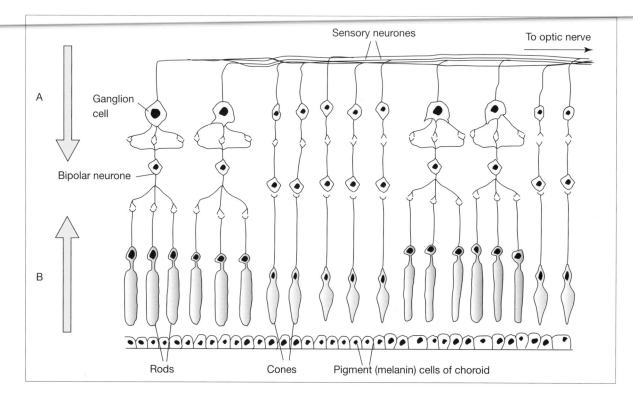

Figure 3 *Component cells of the retina.*

Q
2 **Which arrow, A or B, on figure 3 shows (a) the direction of light entering the eye and (b) the direction of the nerve impulse to the optic nerve?**

The nerve cells and blood vessels on the surface of the retina are not visible because the brain interprets the image you see and ignores the nerve cells and blood vessels.

The choroid

The choroid, shown in figure 4, is a layer containing many blood vessels. These supply the cells of the eye with oxygen and nutrients, and remove waste. The cells of the choroid are very dark in appearance because they contain a high concentration of the pigment **melanin**. This absorbs any light that has not been absorbed by the rod and cone cells.

> **Q** 3 **What do you think would happen if the choroid cells did not contain melanin?**

At the front of the eye, the choroid forms the **ciliary muscle**. This contains smooth muscle which alters the shape of the **lens**. The ciliary muscle also secretes the **aqueous humour**, a watery fluid that fills the front of the eye. The choroid also forms the **iris**. This contains radial and circular muscles, which control the size of the **pupil**. The pupil is the hole in the middle of the iris that allows light into the eye. The muscles in the iris control the amount of light entering the eye.

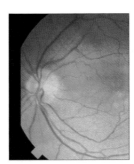

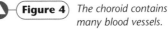
Figure 4 *The choroid contains many blood vessels.*

The sclera

The sclera is the tough outer layer of the eye, containing many collagen fibres. Most of the sclera is white in colour, but part of it forms the cornea which is transparent and colourless. The cornea is transparent to allow light to enter the eye and it is curved to focus light.

There are six external muscles that attach the outside of the sclera to the eye socket of the skull. These move the eyeball, allowing you to look from side to side or up and down. Fine movements of the eyeball allow focusing of both eyes on an object.

Inside the eye

The inside of the eye contains an elastic lens. Its shape is described as 'biconvex'. The part of the eye in front of the lens is filled with aqueous humour, but the region behind the lens is filled with **vitreous humour**. This is a transparent gel-like fluid that supports the retina and keeps the eyeball spherical.

How light enters the eye

Light enters the eye through the cornea. It then passes through the pupil, the aqueous humour, the lens and the vitreous humour, before reaching the retina. For the eye to function efficiently in different light conditions, the amount of light reaching the retina must be controlled.

Changing pupil diameter

The iris – the coloured part of the eye – controls the size of the pupil and contains a pigment which reduces the passage of light. The pupil forms an aperture within the centre of the iris through which light can pass. Radial and circular muscles in the iris control the size of the pupil. Figure 5 shows how this is achieved.

In bright light the pupil gets smaller (**constricts**) because the radial muscles relax and the circular muscles contract. In dim light the radial muscles contract and the circular muscles relax, causing the pupil to widen (**dilate**).

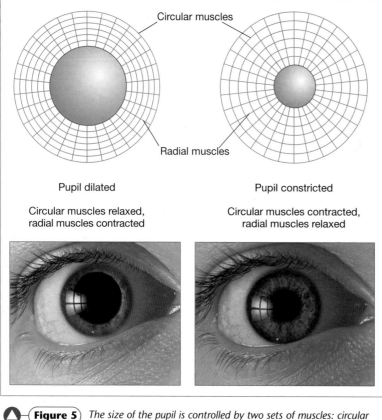

Circular muscles

Radial muscles

Pupil dilated

Circular muscles relaxed, radial muscles contracted

Pupil constricted

Circular muscles contracted, radial muscles relaxed

Figure 5 *The size of the pupil is controlled by two sets of muscles: circular muscles and radial muscles.*

The muscles of the iris are controlled by the nervous system. Changing the size of the pupil is a reflex response that is not under the conscious control of the brain.

Focusing an image

When you look at an object, it forms an inverted image on the retina which is smaller than the actual object. You can see this in figure 6.

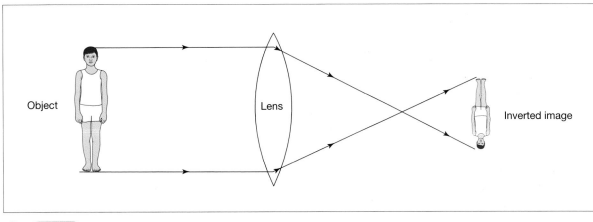

Figure 6 *Formation of an inverted image.*

Light passing through the cornea is refracted or bent because of the cornea's curvature. When light rays enter the eye the greatest refraction occurs at the cornea, although light is also refracted by the lens. The light rays then converge (travel towards each other) towards the retina. The lens focuses the image precisely onto the retina because it is able to change shape due to its elasticity. When you focus on a distant object the lens becomes thinner and when you focus on a near object the lens becomes fatter. The events that occur when focusing on an object are shown in figure 7.

Focusing on a distant object

1 The light rays that reach the eye from a distant object are nearly parallel.
2 The ciliary muscles relax. The suspensory ligaments are pulled and become tense. The suspensory ligaments, in turn, pull on the lens causing it to become thinner.
3 The image then focuses on the retina.

Focusing on a near object

1 The light rays that reach the eye from a near object are diverging (travelling away from each other).
2 The ciliary muscles contract, reducing the tension on the suspensory ligaments. This reduced tension allows the lens to become fatter.
3 The image then focuses on the retina.

Figure 7 *Focusing on (a) a distant object and (b) a near object.*

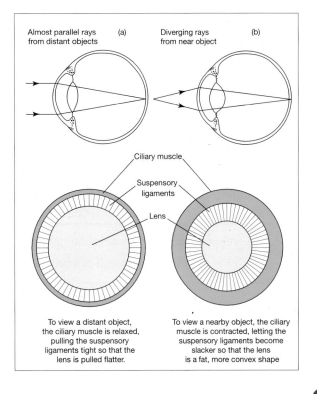

Receptor cells

The retina of the eye contains millions of light-sensitive **photoreceptor** cells. There are two types of photoreceptor cells: rods and cones. These are shown in figure 8.

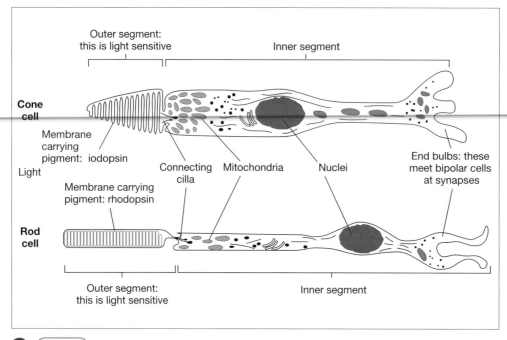

Figure 8   *Rod and cone cells are found in the retina of the eye and are so named because of their shapes.*

Rods and cones are specialised neurones that detect light intensity. Embedded in the outer segment membrane are photopigments that absorb light. When the pigments absorb light, a cascade of events occurs leading to a change in the electrical state of the rod or cone cell membrane. This change is conducted to other neurones in the retina and via the optic nerve to the brain.

Unlike other receptors, stimulation of a photoreceptor leads to a decrease in the permeability of the cell membrane to sodium ions. The membrane becomes hyperpolarised resulting in a decrease in the amount of neurotransmitter released at the synapses with adjacent neurones. The adjacent neurones are called bipolar neurones. They are also unusual because, like photoreceptors, the bipolar cells respond by depolarising. Bipolar neurones synapse (form junctions) with ganglion cells. Ganglion cells respond by producing an action potential.

(Q)
  4 What is meant by 'hyperpolarisation'?
  5 How does a ganglion cell produce an action potential?

Rods and cones

The graph in figure 9a shows the distribution of rod and cone cells in the retina.

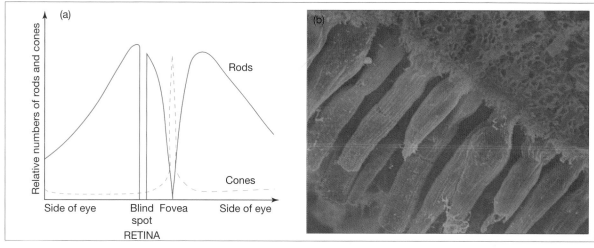

Figure 9 (a) The distribution of rod and cone cells in the retina. (b) Electron micrograph showing rod cells (blue) and less numerous cone cells (green-blue) in the retina.

The cells are partially embedded in the choroid and they synapse with bipolar neurones. Bipolar neurones synapse with ganglion cells which in turn synapse with neurones in the optic nerve. Rod cells outnumber cone cells: there are about 120 million rod cells and about 6 million cone cells in each human retina.

Several rod cells connect with a single bipolar neurone, increasing the ability of the brain to detect a small amount of light. This is called **convergence**; it allows weak stimuli to be amplified giving rod cells great **sensitivity**. However, the brain is unable to determine in which rod cell the stimulus originated. Only one cone cell converges with each bipolar neurone. The ability of the eye to distinguish two or more stimuli as separate stimuli is known as **visual acuity**.

Table 1 lists the differences between rod and cone cells.

Rods:	Cones:
• are more numerous in the retina than cones (about 20 times more)	• are less numerous in the retina than rods
• are spread approximately evenly across the retina, although there are none in the fovea	• are more numerous in the fovea than elsewhere in the retina
• contain the light-sensitive pigment rhodopsin	• contain the light-sensitive pigment iodopsin
• occur as only one type of cell	• occur as three types of cell, each with a different form of iodopsin sensitive to red, green and blue light
• are unable to detect colour	• are able to detect colour
• are sensitive to low light intensities	• are only sensitive to high light intensities
• provide low visual acuity because several rods share a connection to the optic nerve	• provide high visual acuity because each cone has its own connection to the optic nerve

Table 1 The differences between rod and cone cells.

Rods function in dim light

In dim light you use your rod cells. Figure 10 shows how a rod cell functions in the dark and in the light.

In the outer segment of each rod cell there are thousands of vesicles containing a pigment called **rhodopsin**. Rhodopsin is composed of two parts: **retinal** (a derivative of vitamin A) and **opsin** (a protein). When light is absorbed by rhodopsin it splits into retinal and opsin. This is sometimes called '**bleaching**'. Opsin causes a chemical called **cyclic GMP** (cGMP) to be broken down. The cyclic GMP-controlled membrane channels close in the rod cell so that the negative charge inside the rod cell increases. This causes the membrane of the rod cell to **hyperpolarise** (i.e. the potential difference across the membrane increases), resulting in a decrease in the amount of neurotransmitter released at the synapses with bipolar neurones. The bipolar neurones respond by depolarising. Bipolar neurones synapse with ganglion cells. Ganglion cells respond by producing an action potential causing nerve impulses to pass along the optic nerve to the brain.

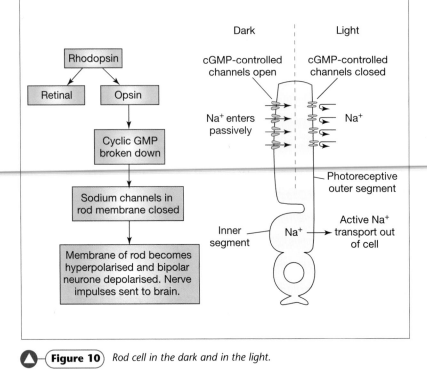

Figure 10 Rod cell in the dark and in the light.

Before the rod cell can be stimulated again, the opsin and retinal must recombine to reform rhodopsin.

Night sight

Rhodopsin is very sensitive to light, so rod cells are used mainly in dim light. In bright light, rhodopsin is broken down faster than it can be reformed. In other words, our eyes are light-adapted. However, in dim light, rhodopsin is not broken down so quickly. It can be reformed at a fast enough rate for us to see clearly, and we say our eyes are dark-adapted.

Q 6 When you go from a brightly lit area to a dark room, you cannot see very much at first. However, when you have been in the dark room for ten minutes or so, you can see much more clearly. Explain this in terms of the way rod cells function.

Cones

Your vision in bright or moderate light is brought about by the functioning of cone cells. Cone cells provide vision in colour as well as in black and white, and enable you to see fine detail (visual acuity).

Cone cells contain a pigment called **iodopsin** and retinal. There are three types of iodopsin, but only one type is found in each cone cell. Each type of iodopsin absorbs most strongly in a particular part of the visible spectrum, as shown in figure 11. The way in which cone cells respond to light is very similar to the way in which rod cells respond. However, cone cells are able to respond to different colours of light. The brain perceives colour as a result of the relative stimulation of each type of iodopsin. This is the **trichromatic theory of colour vision**. Look at table 2. You can see that if red-sensitive and green-sensitive cones are stimulated, the colours perceived by the brain are orange and yellow.

Light stimulates			Colour perceived by brain
Red-sensitive cones	Green-sensitive cones	Blue-sensitive cones	
✓	✓	✓	white
✓			red
✓	✓		orange
✓	✓		yellow
	✓		green
		✓	blue
✓		✓	magenta
			black

▲ **Table 2** *Perception of colour.*

Q 7 Use table 2 to explain how cone cells can detect black and white objects.

Problems with colour vision

There is an overlap in the range of light absorbed by the three types of iodopsin. Look at figure 11. You can see that all three types of cone cell can absorb green light.

Very few people cannot distinguish colours at all. Most 'colour blind' people actually have abnormal colour vision such as red-green colour blindness, in which the red and green on traffic lights can be confused. Some males have an inherited defect in their ability to discriminate reds and greens. The genes for the red-absorbing iodopsin and the green-absorbing iodopsin are on the X chromosome.

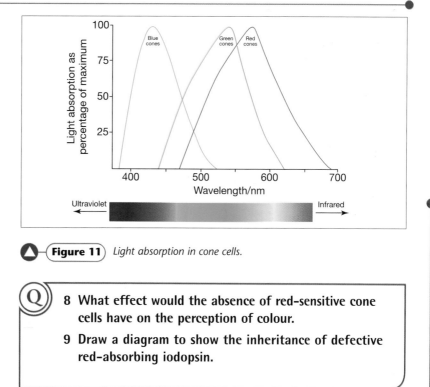

▲ **Figure 11** *Light absorption in cone cells.*

Q 8 What effect would the absence of red-sensitive cone cells have on the perception of colour.

9 Draw a diagram to show the inheritance of defective red-absorbing iodopsin.

Visual acuity

Cone cells are found throughout the retina, but they are much more closely packed at a point called the **fovea**. Each cone cell in the fovea synapses with only one bipolar neurone as shown in figure 12. This allows the brain to determine where the stimulus originated, so you can see in detail. The fovea is the area of greatest visual acuity.

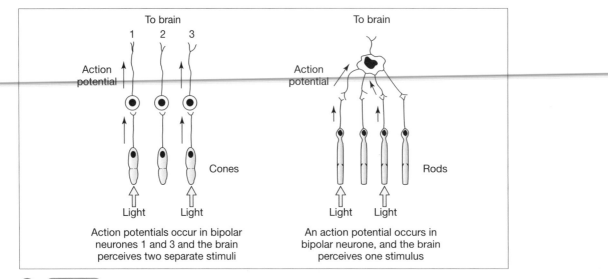

Action potentials occur in bipolar neurones 1 and 3 and the brain perceives two separate stimuli

An action potential occurs in bipolar neurone, and the brain perceives one stimulus

Figure 12 *Cone cells allow you to see in great detail.*

If you keep your head still and fix your eyes on an object about four metres away, you are able to see it in great detail. This is because the image of that object is falling on the fovea. While you are looking directly at that object, you can see others things around you but in much less detail. The reason why we see a very clear picture of everything around us all the time is because we keep moving our eyes, shifting the image that falls on the fovea and allowing our brains to build up a detailed picture of the environment around us.

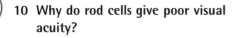

Q 10 **Why do rod cells give poor visual acuity?**

Cone cells are only stimulated by high light intensities, so they are used in day vision.

Rod cells are used in dim light and at night. Both types of cell can operate at the same time under certain conditions. For example, in dim or dark conditions rod cells are more sensitive, but cone cells respond to stimuli that are sufficiently bright. This is why you can see the colours of neon lights on dark nights, as in figure 13.

Figure 13 *Rod and cone cells can operate at the same time to allow coloured light to be seen in the dark.*

Disappearing from view

There is a point on the retina where there are no rod or cone cells. This is the **blind spot**. At this point the optic nerve leaves the retina. Try the simple tests below to investigate your blind spot.

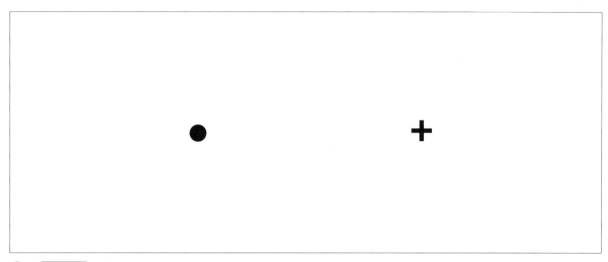

△─(**Figure 14**) *Investigating your blind spot.*

Hold the book at arm's length and close your left eye. With your right eye, look at the dot in figure 14. Slowly bring the book towards you, looking straight at the dot all the time. At a certain distance, the cross will disappear from view. This is when the cross falls on the blind spot of your retina. Repeat the procedure, but this time close your right eye and look at the cross with your left eye. The dot will disappear at a certain distance from your eye.

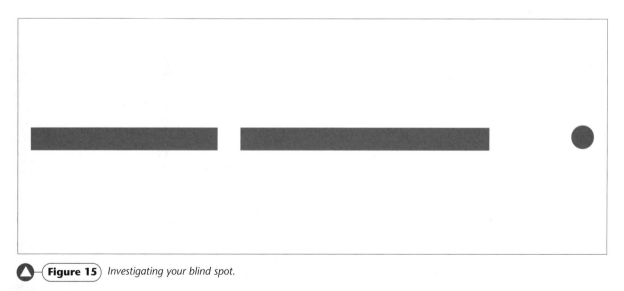

△─(**Figure 15**) *Investigating your blind spot.*

Hold the book at arm's length and close your right eye. With your left eye, look at the red circle in figure 15. Slowly bring the book towards you. At a certain distance, the blue line will not look broken. This is because the gap is falling on the blind spot, so the brain is 'filling in' the missing information.

Seeing is believing

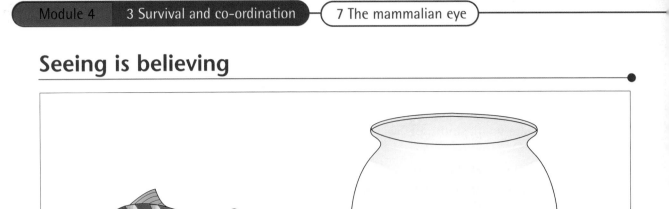

Figure 16 *Put the fish in the fish bowl.*

Stare at the yellow stripes in the middle of the fish in figure 16 for about 15 to 30 seconds. Then move your gaze to the fish bowl. Can you see an image of a fish in the bowl? The explanation of this is that when you look at the stripes on the fish, some of your cone cells become adapted as all the iodopsin is broken down. When you look at the bowl the cone cells that are adapted do not respond until the iodopsin has reformed. Therefore, the information from all of the different cone cells is not in balance, giving you a colour 'after-image'.

Key ideas 118–130

- The iris is a circular muscle that controls the amount of light entering the eye.
- The cornea is a transparent layer at the front of the eye and it plays a part in focusing an image on the retina of the eye. However, the main part of the eye responsible for the focusing of light is the lens. The lens can be adjusted by the ciliary muscles and suspensory ligaments to focus an image on the retina.
- The retina contains two kinds of photosensitive cells: the rods and the cones.
- Rods contain a photosensitive pigment called rhodopsin. This is bleached by light.
- Cones are able to detect colour. According to the trichromatic theory of colour vision, there are three different kinds of cones, each responding to a different wavelength of light. It is the stimulation of these different kinds of cone cell that enables humans to see in colour.
- Cones have individual connections to the optic nerve, while rods share connections to the optic nerve. This means that cones have much greater visual acuity than rods. However, rods are more sensitive to low light intensities than cones.

Analysis and integration

8

The brain is the control centre of the body. It is composed of billions of neurones. It keeps the body working and is also responsible for your thoughts, feelings and memory. Different parts of the brain have different functions; for example the medulla oblongata controls involuntary activities such as breathing and heart rate. The largest area of the brain is the **cerebrum** which controls conscious feelings and voluntary movements. It is also responsible for intelligence and learning.

Memory joggers

- The medulla of the brain controls the rate of breathing.
- The medulla of the brain receives impulses from receptors in the lungs, aortic and carotid bodies. This can lead to an increase in breathing rate in response to increased muscular activity.
- Pressure receptors and chemoreceptors in the walls of the aorta and carotid sinuses send impulses to the medulla. This can bring about an increase in heart rate in response to increased muscular activity.

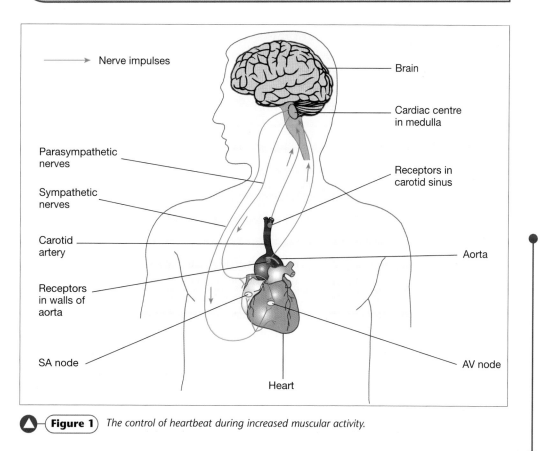

Figure 1 *The control of heartbeat during increased muscular activity.*

Brain

There are three parts to the brain: the **hindbrain**, **midbrain** and **forebrain**. Look at figure 2. It is much easier to see this division in the brains of primitive vertebrates. The human brain is divided up into these three regions too, but in humans the forebrain is so large that it hides the other parts of the brain.

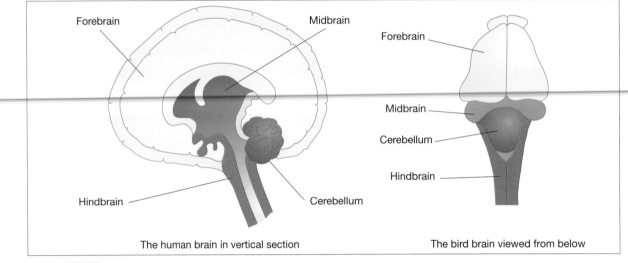

The human brain in vertical section

The bird brain viewed from below

△ **Figure 2** *The division of forebrain, midbrain and hindbrain in humans compared with a primitive vertebrate brain.*

The hindbrain

The **medulla oblongata** is part of the hindbrain. It controls vital functions such as heart and ventilation rates, peristalsis and blood pressure. The **cerebellum** is also part of the hindbrain and controls balance and muscle co-ordination.

> (Q) **1 Describe the role of the medulla oblongata in the control of heart and ventilation rates.**

The midbrain

In mammals, the midbrain is quite small. It contains nerve fibres that connect the forebrain and hindbrain.

The forebrain

The forebrain is made up of the **cerebrum**, the **thalamus** and the **hypothalamus**. The cerebrum controls the body's voluntary behaviour, learning, reasoning, personality and memory. The thalamus relays sensory information from the sense organs to the correct part of the cerebrum. The hypothalamus receives a great deal of sensory information. It contains centres that control factors such as body temperature and blood solute concentration. It causes the pituitary gland to release certain hormones, such as ADH (antidiuretic hormone).

> (Q) **2 Describe the role of the hypothalamus in thermoregulation.**

Cerebral hemispheres

The cerebrum is split by a deep cleft to form two halves called the left and right **cerebral hemispheres**, shown in figure 3. The left cerebral hemisphere controls the right side of the body and the right hemisphere controls the left side of the body. The two hemispheres are connected by a large number of neurones called the **corpus callosum**. The corpus callosum allows information to be transferred between the hemispheres.

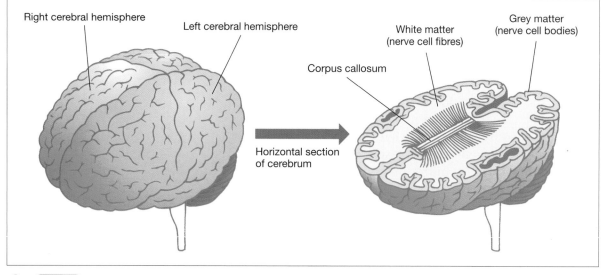

Right cerebral hemisphere

Left cerebral hemisphere

White matter (nerve cell fibres)

Grey matter (nerve cell bodies)

Corpus callosum

Horizontal section of cerebrum

Figure 3 *The cerebral hemispheres and corpus callosum.*

The cerebral hemispheres have an outer layer called the **cerebral cortex** which contains nerve cell bodies (grey matter) and an inner area containing nerve fibres (white matter). In humans, the cortex is very highly folded to give it a larger surface area, and most of your conscious thought occurs here.

Look at figure 4. You can see that folds divide the cortex into four lobes.

1 The **occipital** lobe receives and processes information from the eyes.
2 The **temporal** lobe receives and interprets information from the ears, processing language and the meaning of words.
3 The **parietal** lobe is associated with the sensory cortex and interprets sensory information about touch, taste, pressure, pain, heat and cold.
4 The **frontal** lobe has three functions: it controls conscious motor movement, speech and thought processes.

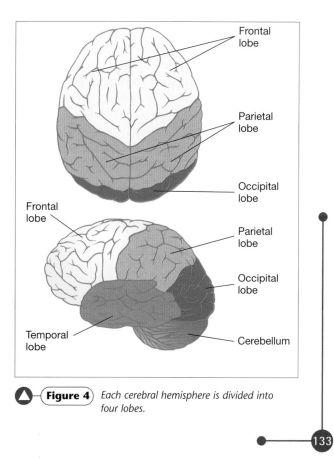

Frontal lobe

Parietal lobe

Occipital lobe

Frontal lobe

Parietal lobe

Occipital lobe

Temporal lobe

Cerebellum

Figure 4 *Each cerebral hemisphere is divided into four lobes.*

Functional areas

On each cerebral hemisphere, three discrete areas have been identified according to the functions their cells perform. These are:

1 **sensory areas** which receive nerve impulses from receptors
2 **association areas** which analyse and interpret the nerve impulses received from receptors
3 **motor areas** which send nerve impulses to appropriate effectors.

The areas are interconnected and nerve impulses are constantly passing between them. This allows the different areas to function in a co-ordinated way, with no area working in complete isolation.

Figure 5 shows the location of the visual (seeing), auditory (hearing), somatosensory, motor and speech regions of the left cerebral hemisphere. Each region shown, except speech, is duplicated (in mirror image) on the right cerebral hemisphere. Each person has only one speech area which is situated on the left hemisphere in about 90% of the human population. You can see that several of the association areas are adjacent to their related sensory area.

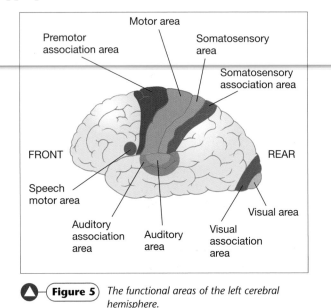

Figure 5 The functional areas of the left cerebral hemisphere.

Sensory areas

Mapping of the sensory areas of the brain shows that they can be functionally divided. Mapping of the **somatosensory area** shows that it can be functionally subdivided according to the areas of the body from which it receives sensory information as shown in figure 6. The size of the sensory area devoted to any one part of the body is not in proportion to the actual size of the body part. The mapping reflects the relative sensitivity of the different body parts. Some parts of the body contain more sensory receptors than others, so they will have a larger area of cerebral cortex to receive impulses from these receptors.

Q 3 **Using the information in figure 6, list in order of sensitivity, starting with the most sensitive, the following parts of the body: hand, lips, hip, tongue.**

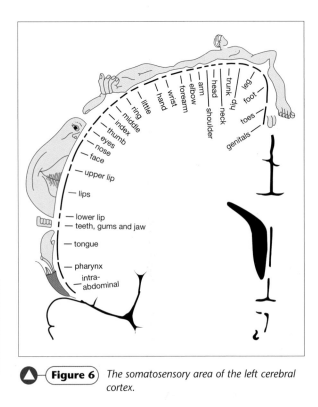

Figure 6 The somatosensory area of the left cerebral cortex.

Association areas

The association areas form a link between the sensory and motor areas. They associate the sensory information they receive with previously perceived information that is stored as memory. This allows the information received to be recognised. The sensory information is interpreted and given meaning. Association areas are also responsible for initiating appropriate responses which are passed to the relevant motor area. Therefore association areas are involved in thinking, reasoning, decision making, memory, emotion and learning.

Motor areas

Each motor area of the brain consists of motor neurones which transmit nerve impulses to initiate the voluntary movement of skeletal muscle. The motor area can be mapped in a similar way to the somatosensory area. Figure 7 shows the extent of motor area that is devoted to each body part.

The larger the region of motor area, the more mobile that part of the body is.

> **Q 4** Using the information in figure 7, list in order of mobility, starting with the most mobile, the following parts of the body: hand, lips, hip, tongue.

Figure 8 shows two imaginary figures, 'sensory homunculus' and 'motor homunculus'. The body parts of sensory homunculus are shown in proportion to their sensitivity, not to their actual size. The body parts of motor homunculus are shown in proportion to their mobility, not to their actual size.

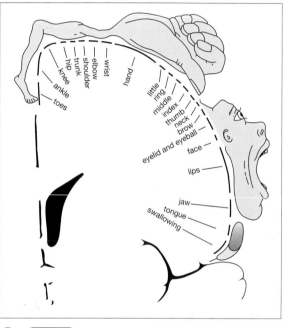

Figure 7 The motor area of the right cerebral cortex.

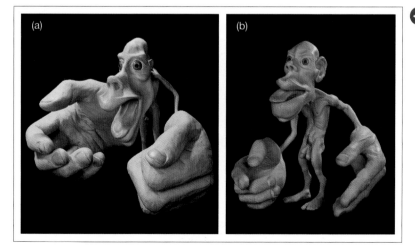

Figure 8 (a) Sensory homunculus and (b) motor homunculus.

(a)   (b)

The visual pathway

Each eye collects light from a region of the environment called the **visual field**. Because both your eyes point forward, the visual fields of each eye overlap as shown in figure 9. This is called **binocular vision**. Light from the right side of each visual field focuses on the left side of each retina and light from the left side of each visual field focuses on the right side of each retina.

Sensory information (nerve impulses) from the retina travels along the optic nerve to the **visual cortex**. This is in the occipital lobe at the back of the brain as shown in figure 10. The right and left optic nerves meet at the **optic chiasma**. At the optic chiasma about half the sensory fibres from each eye cross to the other side of the brain. Therefore sensory information from both eyes passes to each cerebral hemisphere.

Because each eye is looking at the environment from a different position, the images received from each eye will be subtly different. These different images are processed in the visual cortex of the cerebral hemisphere to produce a single perceived image.

The visual cortex is the part of the brain that enables you to interpret what you see, although it is not recognised until impulses have passed to the visual association area. The frequency at which action potentials are received tells the visual cortex the strength of the stimulus. Each part of the visual cortex is devoted to a part of the retina, therefore the brain is able to tell from which part of the retina the sensory neurone originated. The analysis of visual information by the visual cortex is called **visual processing**.

Q 5 What would happen if the corpus callosum were cut?

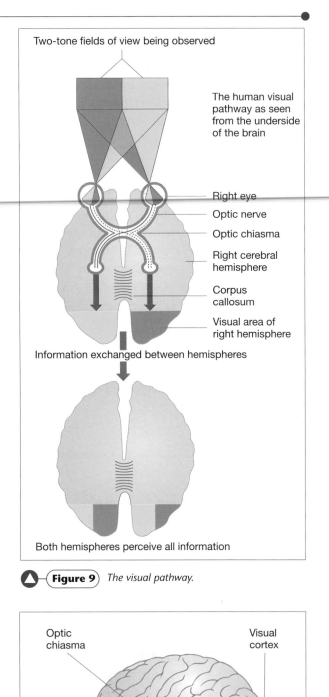

Two-tone fields of view being observed

The human visual pathway as seen from the underside of the brain

Right eye
Optic nerve
Optic chiasma
Right cerebral hemisphere
Corpus callosum
Visual area of right hemisphere

Information exchanged between hemispheres

Both hemispheres perceive all information

Figure 9 *The visual pathway.*

Optic chiasma   Visual cortex

Figure 10 *The location of the visual cortex in the human brain.*

Speech

Brain scans can be used to identify those areas of the brain that have the highest levels of activity during a particular action. Most people who have been studied have their language and speech areas on the left cerebral hemisphere. The process of speech is complex and involves several specific regions of the brain. These areas are highlighted in figure 11.

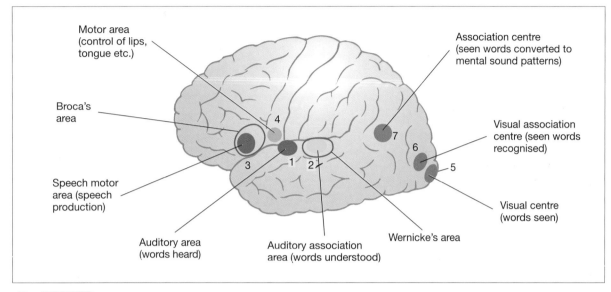

Figure 11 *The location of Wernicke's and Broca's areas on the left cerebral hemisphere.*

Language comprehension is found in Wernicke's area. This area also initiates the choice of sounds needed for producing meaningful speech. For example area 1 is very active when words are being heard and area 2 is very active when words are being understood. Speaking ability is located in Broca's area. Broca's area is linked to Wernicke's area and it is important for co-ordinating the muscular responses that produce speech. Lips, tongue and vocal cords are all involved in the production of speech. Area 3 is highly active when words are being prepared for speech and area 4 is highly active when words are being spoken.

Areas 5, 6 and 7 have high activity while a person is seeing words.

Q 6 Why are areas 5 and 6 active when words are being read?

Area 6 is very active when words are being converted into mental sound patterns.

Damage to Broca's area causes speech impairment but not impairment of language comprehension, whereas damage in Wernicke's area impairs the ability to comprehend written and spoken words but not speech.

Autonomic nervous system

The **autonomic nervous system** (ANS) controls involuntary actions. It is made up of two separate parts: the **sympathetic** and the **parasympathetic** systems, as shown in figure 12.

In general, the sympathetic system is concerned with responses to stress, such as exercise, physical threat, exposure to cold or severe blood loss. Think how you feel just before an examination, or when you are walking down a quiet road late at night and you are afraid someone is following you. Your heart rate speeds up, your pupils dilate, your hair 'stands on end', you sweat more and you breathe more deeply. All of these prepare your body either to face the thing that is threatening you, or to run away from it. For this reason, it is called the 'fight or flight' reaction. On the other hand, the parasympathetic nervous system is concerned with the body's normal activities, such as digestion and lowering the heart and breathing rates.

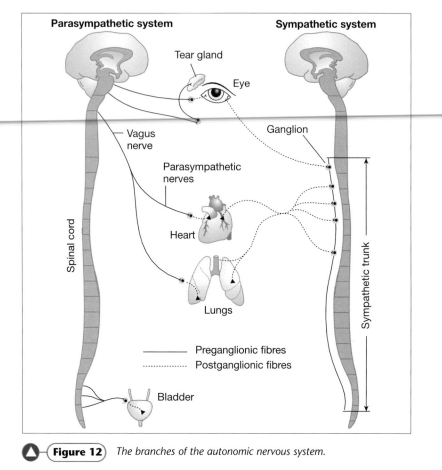

Figure 12   *The branches of the autonomic nervous system.*

Q

7 **Is the sympathetic division always excitatory and the parasympathetic division inhibitory? Give a reason for your answer.**

8 **Copy and complete table 1.**

	Sympathetic	Parasympathetic
1. Where do preganglionic neurones leave the CNS?		
2. Are preganglionic neurones short or long?		
3. Are ganglia interconnected or discrete?		
4. Are postganglionic neurones short or long?		

Table 1

Sympathetic and parasympathetic

The sympathetic and parasympathetic nervous systems are alike in that they are both two-neurone systems. However, they differ in their organisation and in their transmitter substances. These differences are summarised in figure 13.

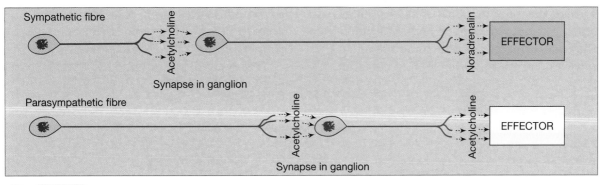

Figure 13 *The autonomic nervous system.*

A chain of **ganglia** (collections of neurone cell bodies) lies close to the spinal cord.

Many organs of the body are supplied by both sympathetic and parasympathetic neurones. In general, they have opposite effects, one stimulating the effector and the other inhibiting it. Some of these effects are shown in table 2.

Target	Sympathetic effect	Parasympathetic effect
Iris of eye	Dilation	Constriction
Bronchi	Dilation	Constriction
Heart	Increase in rate	Decrease in rate
Sphincters of gut	Constriction	Dilation
Urinary bladder	Dilation	Constriction
Tear glands of eye	—	Tear production
Salivary glands	—	Secretion of saliva
Stomach	—	Secretion of gastric juice
Pancreas	—	Secretion of pancreatic juice
Genitalia	—	Vasodilation of erectile tissue
Blood vessels	Vasoconstriction	—
Sweat glands	Secretion of sweat	—

 Table 2 *The major effects of sympathetic and parasympathetic nerves.*

Q **9** In emergencies, a co-ordinated response of the whole body is needed. Which division of the ANS is designed for this type of response?

10 Which division of the ANS would be most active during physical exercise?

Controlling pupil diameter

Both sympathetic and parasympathetic nerves supply the iris. When impulses pass along the sympathetic nerves to the iris, the circular muscles relax and the radial muscles contract causing the pupil to dilate. When impulses pass along the parasympathetic nerves to the iris, the circular muscles contract and the radial muscles relax causing the pupil to constrict.

The pupil adapts very quickly to changing light conditions because of the pupil reflex. When light hits the retina, impulses pass along the optic nerve to a specific part of the brain. From here, impulses pass along parasympathetic nerves to the iris, where the circular muscles contract and the radial muscles relax. In darkness the reflex is inhibited so that the pupil dilates. The pupil reflex is shown in figure 14.

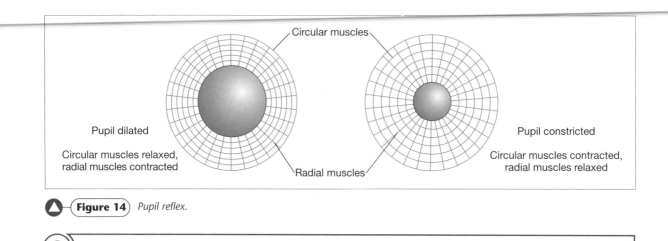

Circular muscles

Pupil dilated

Circular muscles relaxed, radial muscles contracted

Radial muscles

Pupil constricted

Circular muscles contracted, radial muscles relaxed

Figure 14 *Pupil reflex.*

Q 11 The pupil diameter is about 1.5 mm when it is fully constricted, and about 8 mm when it is fully dilated. Using the formula for the area of a circle (area = πr^2), calculate the area of a fully constricted pupil and a fully dilated pupil. By how much does the reflex decrease the amount of light entering the eye when the pupil changes from fully dilated to fully constricted?

Problem pupils

Some diseases, such as central nervous system syphilis or alcoholism, block the parasympathetic pupil reflex. The pupils stay partly constricted and are unable to respond to light.

When impulses pass along the sympathetic nerves to the iris, the radial muscles contract and the pupil dilates. There is a condition called **Horner's syndrome** in which the sympathetic nerves are interrupted. This means that the pupil of the affected eye remains more constricted than the pupil of the other eye. The upper eyelid droops because this is also controlled by the sympathetic nerves. These effects can be seen in figure 15.

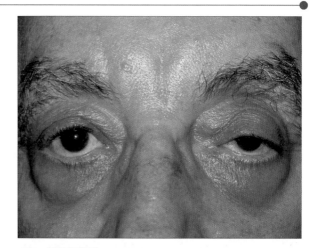

Figure 15 *A person with Horner's syndrome, showing narrowing of the pupil and drooping of the eyelid of the affected eye (here the left eye).*

> **Q** **12** Two other symptoms of Horner's syndrome are that blood vessels on the affected side of the head are permanently dilated, and sweating cannot occur on the affected side. Explain why this happens.

Control of tear production

Tears flow from tear glands into your eyes through tiny **tear ducts**. You can see this in figure 16. There is a parasympathetic nerve connected to the tear ducts, but not a sympathetic nerve. The tear glands are located under your upper lids. When they are stimulated by the parasympathetic nervous system, they produce tears to form a thin film over your eyeballs. Every time you blink the film spreads over your eyes to keep them moist and free of dust and other irritants. Whether you are awake or asleep, happy or sad, this fluid is always flowing from the tear glands.

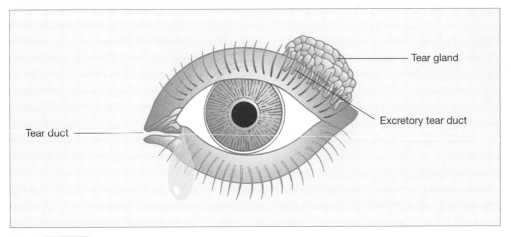

△ Figure 16 *The position of the tear glands in the eye.*

Tears contain mucin and fatty substances which lubricate the surface of the eye, and lysozyme, an enzyme that destroys bacteria. Besides protecting your eyes in normal conditions, the tear glands produce more fluid when your eyes are irritated. These extra tears are called **reflex** or **irritant tears**. When something makes you happy or sad, the parasympathetic nerve sends more impulses to the tear glands, causing them to produce **emotional tears**. Used tears then drain down into two tiny openings on the edge of your upper and lower eyelids, at the inner margin of your eyes. These lead to tear ducts next to the bridge of your nose. From there, they are channelled into the nasal cavity where they are swallowed or blown out with other nasal fluids. If there are too many tears, they will overflow your lower lid and run down your cheeks.

> **Q** **13** What will be the effect of a reduced number of impulses along the parasympathetic nerve to the tear ducts?

When you cut or peel an onion, a chemical is released that reacts with tears on the surface of your eyes. The chemical reaction produces sulphuric acid which irritates your eyes.

Control of the urinary bladder

Control of the urinary bladder is an example of a reflex action controlled by the autonomic nervous system. Urine passes from the kidneys, along the ureters and into the bladder by a peristaltic action of smooth muscle. Smooth muscle in the bladder wall relaxes to accommodate the increasing volume of urine. Normally urine does not leak out of the bladder because of two rings of muscle: the internal **sphincter** and the external sphincter. Sympathetic and parasympathetic nerves supply the bladder and internal sphincter. You can see these in figure 17. In addition, the external sphincter is controlled voluntarily by a motor nerve originating in the spinal cord; this is also shown in figure 17.

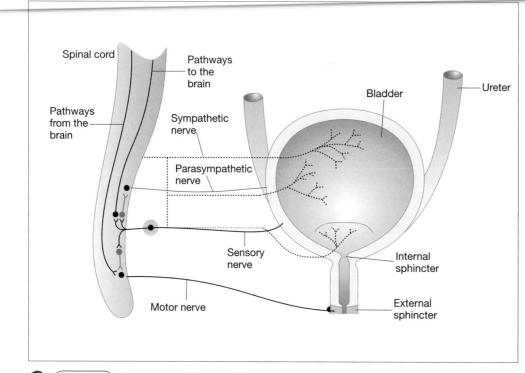

Figure 17 *Innervation of the urinary bladder.*

As the bladder fills, **stretch receptors** in the bladder muscle are stimulated. These send nerve impulses to the spinal cord, which causes a reflex contraction of the bladder muscle and relaxation of the internal sphincter. Nerve impulses also reach the brain, giving the sensation of fullness.

In adult humans, once a certain volume is reached (about 400 cm³) the reflex contraction is strong enough to open the internal sphincter. As this occurs, the motor nerve that normally keeps the external sphincter contracted is inhibited. This results in relaxation of the external sphincter. Once both sphincters are open, the contraction of the bladder muscles forces urine out of the **urethra**. The emptying of the bladder is called **micturition**.

Although the reflex is a spinal reflex involving the autonomic nervous system, it can be overruled by higher centres in the brain. These partly inhibit the reflex until the person finds it convenient to urinate. These higher centres can prevent urination occurring even if the reflex does occur. However, when the person wishes to urinate, the higher centres of the brain can send impulses to the external urinary sphincter so that it relaxes.

Q   **14 Draw a flow chart of the events described above.**

Voluntary control of the external sphincter is learned during childhood. By activation of pathways descending from the brain, you can initiate or prevent urination. Loss of voluntary control of urination can occur if the spinal cord is injured. Childbirth can lead to a temporary loss of the mother's voluntary control. This can also occur with ageing.

Key ideas 131–143

- The cerebral hemispheres are large folded areas of the brain.
- Sensory areas of the cerebral hemispheres receive input from receptors, and motor areas send impulses to control effectors.
- One side of the body is controlled by the opposite hemisphere.
- Speech appears to be located mainly in the left hemisphere.
- Association areas interpret sensory input. For example, the visual association area receives impulses from the retina and interprets the images in relation to previous experience.
- The autonomic nervous system is made up of the sympathetic and the parasympathetic nervous system.
- The autonomic nervous system controls involuntary activities of the body, for example pupil diameter and tear production in the eye, and emptying of the bladder.

Muscles

Your bones move because of joints, but your muscles cause the actual movement. When muscles contract they pull your bones to make your body move. Muscles contract when they receive impulses from your nerves. Muscles are made up of many muscle fibres arranged in bundles. They can only pull, not push. For this reason most muscles are arranged in pairs that work together.

Memory joggers

- Glucose, glycogen and fatty acids are sources of energy for muscle contraction.
- ATP is the immediate source of energy for muscle contraction.
- Under different exercise conditions, sources other than the aerobic respiration of glucose may be used.

▲ Figure 1

Types of muscle

There are three types of muscle in the body, shown in figure 2.

Smooth muscle

This is also called **involuntary muscle**. It is called smooth muscle because you cannot see any stripes when you look at it through the microscope, and it is called involuntary muscle because you cannot make it contract and relax through conscious control. Smooth muscle contracts and relaxes automatically. This muscle is found in such places as the gut and in the iris of the eye.

Cardiac muscle

The muscle of your heart is also involuntary, but it looks different under the microscope because it has a striped appearance and many interconnecting bridges. Cardiac muscle contracts and relaxes automatically without you having to think about it. Cardiac muscle is myogenic.

Skeletal muscle

Skeletal muscle is also called **voluntary muscle** or **striped muscle**. It is called striped muscle because it has a striped appearance when viewed through a microscope. It is called voluntary muscle because you have direct control over this type of muscle when you want to make a movement.

Skeletal muscle is the muscle attached to your bones. You have direct control over these muscles and can make a large range of movements. Skeletal muscle is also found in your face and jaws, so it is used when you smile or frown and when you talk, eat or drink.

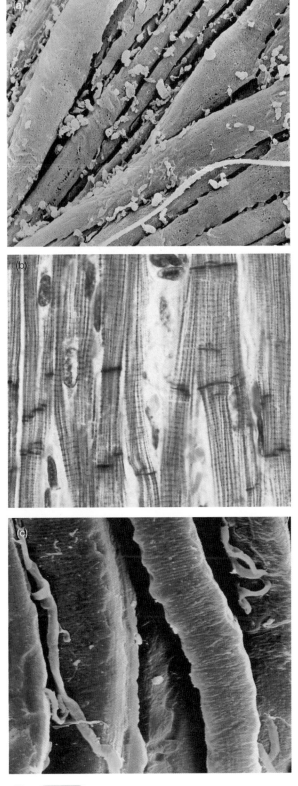

Figure 2 (a) Smooth muscle, (b) cardiac muscle and (c) skeletal muscle.

Working in pairs

Muscles can contract and relax but they cannot push. For this reason, muscles work in pairs. This is true for skeletal muscle, smooth muscle and cardiac muscle. You will remember from AS that the intestines have a muscle layer containing circular muscles and longitudinal muscles. When the circular muscles contract they make the intestines longer (and thinner) and when the longitudinal muscles contract they make the intestines shorter (and fatter). These muscles work in a co-ordinated way to move food along the gut by peristalsis and to help mix food with digestive juices.

Skeletal muscles need to work in pairs or you would not be able to move your joints. A good example of muscles working in pairs is the movement of the forearm. You will see in figure 3 that two muscles control the bending of the arm at the elbow, the biceps and triceps.

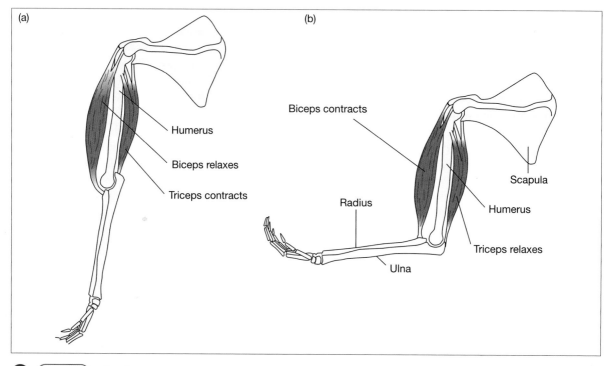

Figure 3   *The elbow joint (a) straightened and (b) bent.*

When the biceps contracts, the elbow joint bends. At the same time the triceps relaxes and becomes longer because the biceps pulls it. When the triceps contracts it straightens the elbow joint, and at the same time it pulls the biceps to make it longer. These two muscles have to work together to move the arm because the muscle can only contract and pull on a bone. To allow movement of the elbow joint in two directions there has to be a muscle on each side of the joint pulling in opposite directions. This is called an **antagonistic pair**. As one muscle contracts the other relaxes.

(Q) 1 **What would happen if both the biceps and the triceps contracted at the same time?**

The structure of skeletal muscle

When you eat meat, you are eating skeletal muscle. You will have noticed that it is made up of many fibres. You can see the structure of skeletal muscle in figure 4.

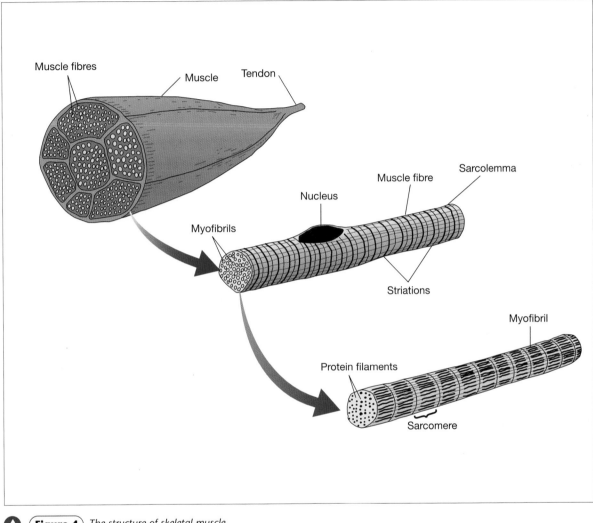

Figure 4 *The structure of skeletal muscle.*

The cell surface membrane forms the **sarcolemma**. This is like an axon membrane along which an action potential can pass and cause the muscle fibre to contract. The cytoplasm inside the muscle fibre is called the **sarcoplasm**. This contains many smaller fibres called **myofibrils** and many mitochondria. Myofibrils are multinucleate cells, because each myofibril is made up of many cells that have fused together.

The myofibrils are only 1–2 micrometres wide, and they have a banded appearance. They are made up of units called **sarcomeres**.

Thick and thin

The sarcomeres contain two kinds of protein: **actin** and **myosin**. Myosin forms thick filaments and actin forms thin filaments, and these overlap in places to give dark bands. This is what gives myofibrils their banded appearance, as shown in figures 5 and 6.

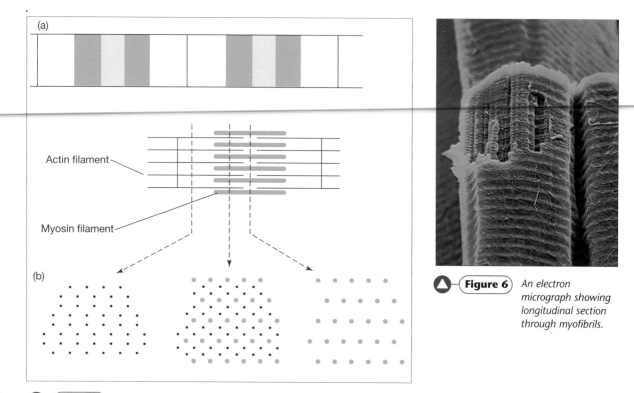

Actin filament

Myosin filament

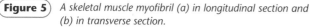

Figure 6 An electron micrograph showing longitudinal section through myofibrils.

Figure 5 A skeletal muscle myofibril (a) in longitudinal section and (b) in transverse section.

Figure 7 shows the appearance of a sarcomere in a muscle fibre.

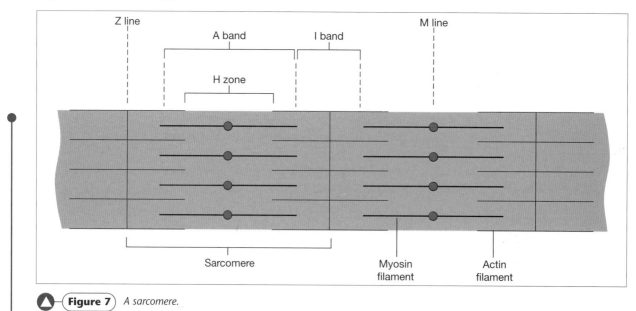

Figure 7 A sarcomere.

Muscle contraction

Actin and myosin are involved in muscle contraction.

Myosin forms thick filaments. The myosin molecule resembles a tadpole with two heads. The filament is formed by the myosin 'tails' wrapping around each other. The 'heads' always face the end of the filament, so the centre of the filament has no 'heads', as shown in figure 8.

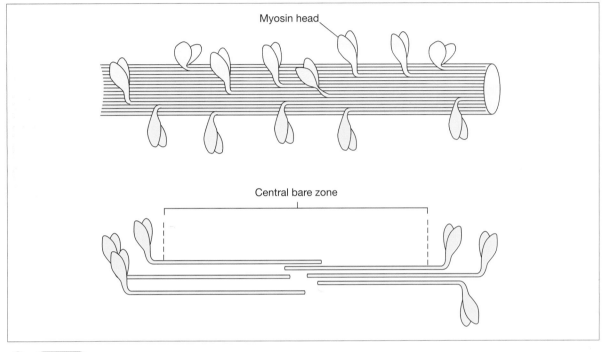

Myosin head

Central bare zone

Figure 8 *Myosin filament.*

The 'head' of the myosin molecule has **ATPase** enzyme activity. This means it can break down ATP and release the energy contained by it.

The thin filaments are made of actin, but two other proteins are also present, as shown in figure 9. They are called **troponin** and **tropomyosin** and are involved in switching muscle contraction on and off.

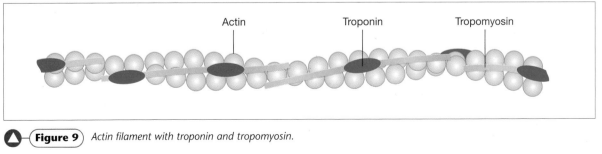

Actin   Troponin   Tropomyosin

Figure 9 *Actin filament with troponin and tropomyosin.*

Sliding filaments

The way muscles contract is explained by the **sliding filament hypothesis**.
Figure 10 shows the appearance of the actin and myosin filaments in a relaxed
and a contracted sarcomere.

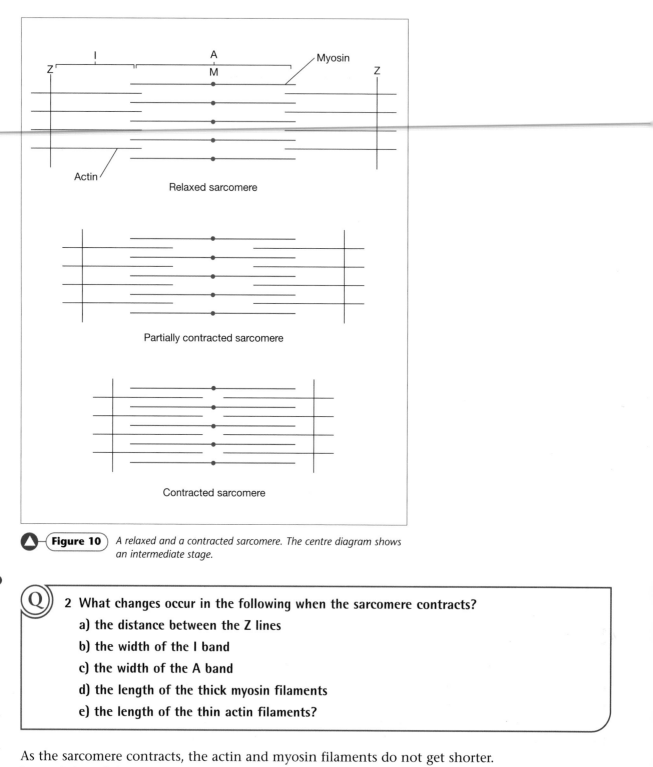

Figure 10 *A relaxed and a contracted sarcomere. The centre diagram shows
an intermediate stage.*

Q **2 What changes occur in the following when the sarcomere contracts?**

    a) the distance between the Z lines

    b) the width of the I band

    c) the width of the A band

    d) the length of the thick myosin filaments

    e) the length of the thin actin filaments?

As the sarcomere contracts, the actin and myosin filaments do not get shorter.
Instead they slide over each other and overlap to a greater extent.

Moving filaments

The actin and myosin filaments slide over each other because the myosin filaments 'walk' along the actin filaments. The way this happens is shown in figure 11.

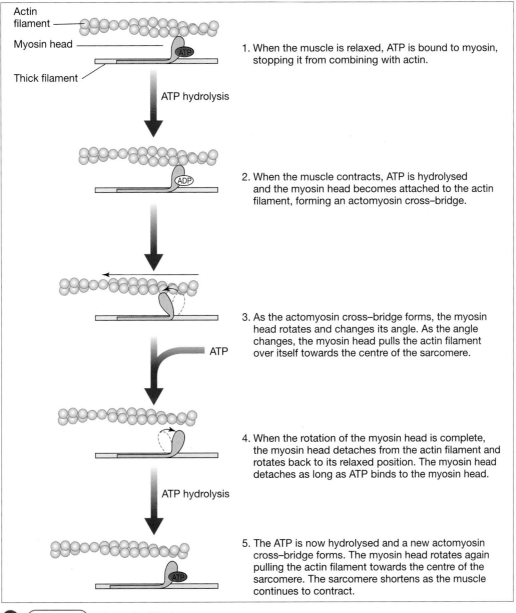

Actin filament
Myosin head
Thick filament

ATP hydrolysis

1. When the muscle is relaxed, ATP is bound to myosin, stopping it from combining with actin.

2. When the muscle contracts, ATP is hydrolysed and the myosin head becomes attached to the actin filament, forming an actomyosin cross–bridge.

ATP

3. As the actomyosin cross–bridge forms, the myosin head rotates and changes its angle. As the angle changes, the myosin head pulls the actin filament over itself towards the centre of the sarcomere.

4. When the rotation of the myosin head is complete, the myosin head detaches from the actin filament and rotates back to its relaxed position. The myosin head detaches as long as ATP binds to the myosin head.

ATP hydrolysis

5. The ATP is now hydrolysed and a new actomyosin cross–bridge forms. The myosin head rotates again pulling the actin filament towards the centre of the sarcomere. The sarcomere shortens as the muscle continues to contract.

Figure 11 *Myosin 'walking'.*

You will notice that ATP is needed to break the cross-bridges between actin and myosin. If there is insufficient ATP, the muscle stays contracted. Without ATP, myosin stays locked onto actin, even if the muscle is trying to relax. After death, the ATP in the muscles slowly breaks down, so rigor mortis develops. Rigor mortis starts about four hours after death and lasts about 24 hours.

Controlling contraction

Muscle contraction is not useful unless it can be switched on and off. Muscle contraction starts when a nerve impulse reaches the muscle. This causes the actin and myosin filaments to slide past each other.

Each motor neurone synapses with several muscle fibres in different places in the muscle. These act together and are called a motor unit.

The neuromuscular junction

A **neuromuscular junction** is where a nerve communicates with a muscle fibre. It is very similar to a synapse. The axon terminal (called a **motor end plate**) has many vesicles which contain the neurotransmitter acetylcholine. There is a gap between the nerve and the muscle at the neuromuscular junction. However, the nerve and muscle membranes are very highly folded to increase the surface area. Although the neuromuscular junction and a synapse are very similar, there are some significant differences. First, a muscle fibre is supplied by only one nerve fibre. Second, there is no threshold for stimulation of a muscle fibre. If an impulse arrives at the motor end plate, it will always stimulate the muscle fibre.

The structure of the neuromuscular junction is shown in figure 12.

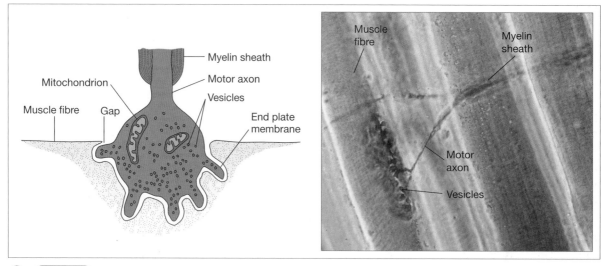

Figure 12   *The structure of a neuromuscular junction.*

Neuromuscular junctions differ from synapses in that the release of acetylcholine *always* sets up an action potential in the membrane surrounding the muscle fibre (the sarcolemma). The impulse moves in both directions from the neuromuscular junction.

T-system

There are two sets of tubules in the muscle fibre. The **transverse system**, or **T-system**, spreads across the fibre, as shown in figure 13. It is made up of infoldings of the sarcolemma that spread inside the fibre. The **sarcoplasmic reticulum** has tubules that spread lengthways along the fibre. In a resting muscle, the tubules of the sarcoplasmic reticulum accumulate calcium ions by active transport from the sarcoplasm. The level of calcium ions in the sarcoplasm is therefore very low.

As the nerve impulse arrives at the neuromuscular junction it causes acetylcholine to be released. The acetylcholine initiates a wave of depolarisation which spreads across the sarcolemma and enters the T-tubules and sarcoplasmic reticulum. This causes the sarcoplasmic reticulum to release calcium ions into the sarcoplasm. The calcium ions activate myosin which hydrolyses the bound ATP. These calcium ions also join to troponin causing its shape to change. The troponin displaces the tropomyosin, allowing the myosin heads to attach to the actin filament.

Acetylcholine is destroyed at the neuromuscular junction by the enzyme acetylcholinesterase. This stops the stream of action potentials along the sarcolemma. The sarcoplasmic reticulum stops releasing calcium ions, and calcium ions are once again pumped back into the sarcoplasmic reticulum. As the level of calcium ions in the sarcoplasm falls, the proteins troponin and tropomyosin move back to their original positions. Here, they block the action of the myosin molecule heads so that they cannot reach the actin filaments any more, and contraction ceases.

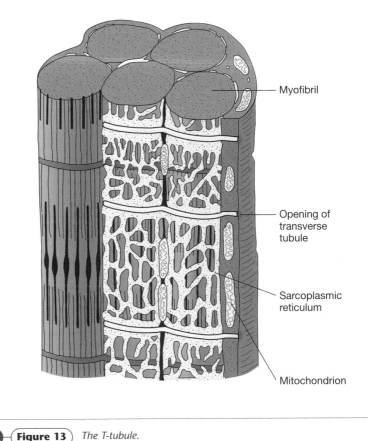

Figure 13 The T-tubule.

Labels: Myofibril; Opening of transverse tubule; Sarcoplasmic reticulum; Mitochondrion

Key ideas 144–153

- Muscles are only able to contract or relax; they cannot push. For this reason, muscles required to move a joint are arranged in antagonistic pairs.
- Skeletal muscle is made up of subunits called sarcomeres.
- Sarcomeres contain thick filaments of myosin and thin filaments of actin. When muscle contraction occurs, the myosin filaments slide over the actin filaments and form cross-bridges, using ATP.
- Muscle contraction is inhibited by troponin and tropomyosin. These are displaced by calcium ions when a muscle fibre is stimulated, causing muscle contraction.

Unit 3 – Questions

(10)

(1) The graph in figure 1 shows the effect of the loss of liver and kidney function on the amount of urea in the blood. A cross marks the time when the liver function was lost and a circle marks the time when the kidney function was lost.

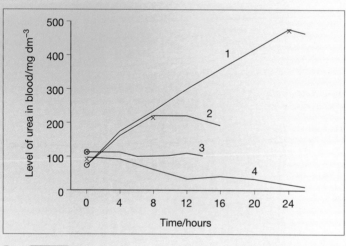

Key to figure:

1 Kidney function lost at time 0, liver function lost 24 hours later

2 Kidney function lost at time 0, liver function lost 8 hours later

3 Kidney and liver function lost at time 0

4 Liver function lost at time 0, kidney function not affected.

▲ Figure 1

a) i) Explain why the amount of urea in the blood rises steadily over 24 hours in 1. (3 marks)

ii) Explain the shape of the graph in 2. (3 marks)

b) i) Explain why the amount of urea in the blood stays approximately the same for 14 hours in 3. (2 marks)

ii) Explain why the amount of urea in the blood falls steadily in 4. (2 marks)

(Total 10 marks)

(2) **a)** Explain how the connections between rod and cone cells and neurones in the retina give rise to differences in:

i) sensitivity

ii) acuity. (3 marks)

b) Explain why it is difficult to see when you first move from a well-lit area into a dark room, but after about ten minutes you can see much more clearly. (3 marks)

c) Explain the roles of the sensory and association areas of the forebrain in processing information from the optic nerves. (2 marks)

(Total 8 marks)

3 The graph in figure 2 shows the changes in permeability of a neurone membrane to potassium (K^+) and sodium (Na^+) ions during the course of an action potential.

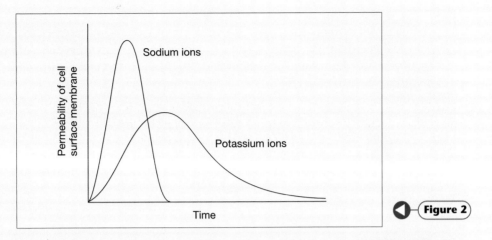

Figure 2

a) During the course of an action potential, the potential difference across the neurone membrane changes from –70 mV to +40 mV and back to –70 mV. Using the information in the graph and your own knowledge, explain what causes these changes. **(4 marks)**

b) i) What is meant by the 'all-or-nothing' nature of a nerve impulse?
(1 mark)

ii) Neurones can respond to both strong and weak stimuli. Describe how a neurone conveys information about the strength of a stimulus. **(1 mark)**

(Total 6 marks)

4 Figure 3 shows the appearance of a sarcomere in a relaxed muscle.

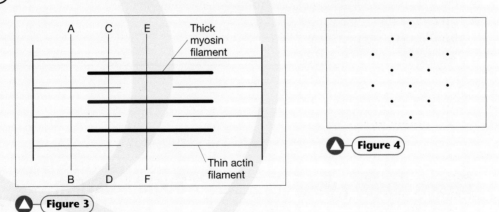

Figure 4

Figure 3

a) Draw a diagram to show the appearance of the sarcomere in a contracted muscle. **(3 marks)**

b) The diagram in figure 4 represents a transverse section through the sarcomere at **A–B**. Sketch the appearance of a transverse section through the sarcomere at:

(i) **C–D**;

(ii) **E–F**. **(2 marks)**

(Total 5 marks)

Energy supply

Energy exists in many forms, but the majority of biological processes use the chemical energy in the bonds of an ATP molecule. ATP is synthesised during the processes of photosynthesis and respiration, so all the energy in living organisms is either directly or indirectly obtained from solar energy. Energy is needed for active transport and synthesis of large molecules, both of which you met in Module 1. Other uses include muscle contraction and driving chemical reactions in cells. When ATP is used, some of its energy is released as heat and is lost to the environment. Mammals and birds use energy to maintain a constant body temperature, which allows them to survive in a range of environmental temperatures.

Memory joggers

- Green plants use solar energy, carbon dioxide and water to make food by photosynthesis.
- Photosynthesis occurs in chloroplasts.
- Animals and saprophytes obtain food by feeding on other organisms. Some energy is transferred by feeding.
- Respiration uses oxygen to release energy from sugars.
- Respiration occurs in mitochondria.
- The carbon cycle summarises the processes by which carbon is transferred between living organisms and the environment.
- Photosynthesis brings carbon into living things; respiration returns it to the environment.

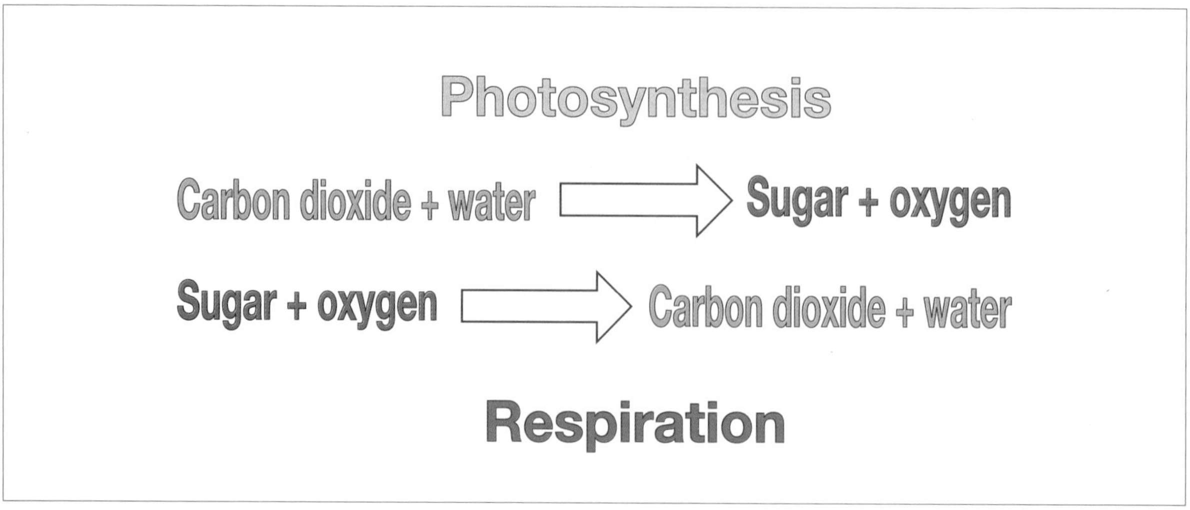

Photosynthesis

Carbon dioxide + water ⟹ Sugar + oxygen

Sugar + oxygen ⟹ Carbon dioxide + water

Respiration

△ Figure 1

Energy sources

Energy exists in many forms, some of which can be used by living organisms. Figure 2 summarises the main changes in energy as it is used by living organisms. During photosynthesis, **solar energy** is converted to **chemical energy** and is stored in the bonds that hold sugar molecules together. These sugar molecules can be used to synthesise other molecules, which also contain chemical bond energy. This chemical bond energy is **potential** (stored) **energy**.

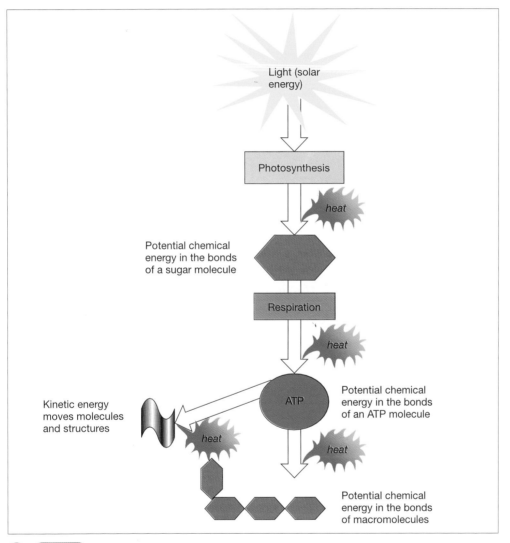

Figure 2 *Energy changes in living organisms.*

During respiration, chemical bonds are broken releasing **free energy**, some of which is used to form chemical bonds in the energy carrier molecule **ATP**. Enzymes can use the potential energy in ATP to drive reactions in living organisms. As ATP is broken down, free energy is released. In some reactions the energy may be used to form chemical bonds in other molecules. In other reactions, some of the free energy is converted to **kinetic** (movement) **energy**. In all cases, when potential energy is released, some is converted to **heat energy** and may be lost to the environment.

ATP – the energy carrier

ATP is a free nucleotide. Its molecule is organised in the same way as the nucleotides in nucleic acids. The term ATP is an abbreviation of adenosine triphosphate. Figure 3 shows the structure of an ATP molecule.

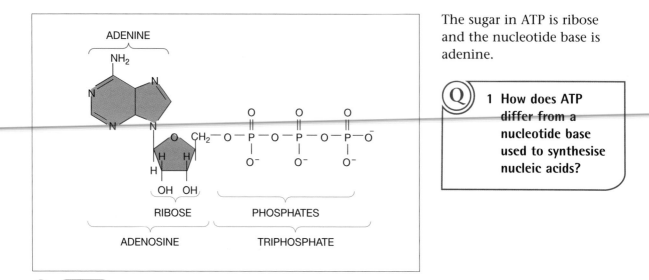

The sugar in ATP is ribose and the nucleotide base is adenine.

Q 1 **How does ATP differ from a nucleotide base used to synthesise nucleic acids?**

Figure 3 *The structure of an ATP molecule.*

Cells use ATP as an energy carrier. When ATP is hydrolysed, energy is released. Enzymes can use this energy to drive chemical reactions. The hydrolysis of ATP forms ADP (adenosine diphosphate) and a phosphate group. ATP can be reformed during photosynthesis and respiration. In a cell there is a pool of ATP which is constantly being used and resynthesised. Figure 4 shows the ATP–ADP cycle.

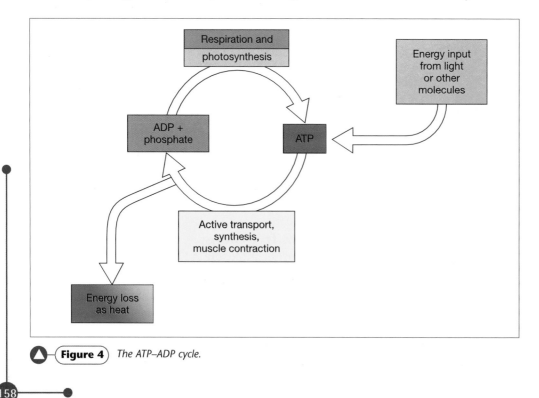

Figure 4 *The ATP–ADP cycle.*

ATP synthesis

The synthesis of most ATP molecules occurs in two types of reaction:

- **substrate** level – energy released during a reaction is used directly in the synthesis of ATP
- **electron transfer** – kinetic energy from the movement of electrons from one molecule to another is used to synthesise ATP.

The majority of ATP in both photosynthesis and respiration is synthesised during electron transfer.

The transfer of electrons uses complex organic molecules called electron carriers. These are bound to membranes in chloroplasts and mitochondria. The structure of these molecules allows them to both accept and donate electrons. When a carrier accepts an electron it reaches a higher energy level (gains energy) and becomes reduced as shown in Figure 5.

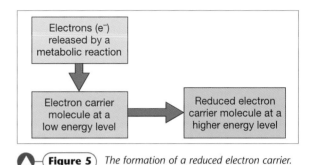

Figure 5 *The formation of a reduced electron carrier.*

As an electron carrier donates an electron it becomes **oxidised**. The next carrier in the chain becomes **reduced**. During the transfer of the electron, some energy is released and may be used in ATP synthesis. Thus the next carrier in the chain gains less energy. The transfer of an electron from one molecule to another is sometimes called a **redox** reaction. This is because as one molecule is **red**uced, another molecule reacting with it becomes **ox**idised. These reactions are written as shown in figure 6. Reduced carrier 1 reacts with oxidised carrier 2. As electrons are transferred, carrier 1 is oxidised and carrier 2 is reduced.

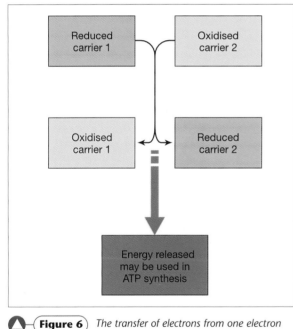

Figure 6 *The transfer of electrons from one electron carrier to another.*

Q 2 Copy figure 6. Add another carrier to the chain and draw arrows to show the transfer of electrons to this carrier.

Other reactions involving reduction or oxidation occur by adding or removing **hydrogen ions (protons)** and electrons. **Coenzymes** (which 'cowork' with enzymes) are used to accept or donate hydrogen ions and electrons. Both respiration and photosynthesis include redox reactions of this type.

Q 3 Draw a diagram like figure 5 to show a redox reaction involving hydrogen transfer from a metabolic reaction to a coenzyme.

Obtaining energy in living organisms

Green plants are **photoautotrophs** (photo = light, auto = self, troph = feeding). They trap solar energy and convert it into chemical energy in ATP molecules during the process of photosynthesis.

Other organisms, apart from some bacteria and viruses, are **heterotrophs** (hetero = others, troph = feeding). This means they use the energy trapped by photoautotrophs either directly, by feeding on green plants, or indirectly, by eating other animals. This transfer of energy through organisms is shown in figure 7.

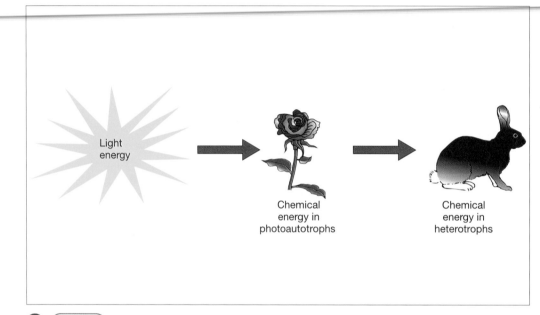

Light energy

Chemical energy in photoautotrophs

Chemical energy in heterotrophs

Figure 7 *Energy transfer through living organisms.*

During respiration, glucose is oxidised by removing hydrogen ions and electrons. The energy released from the chemical bonds by oxidation is used to synthesise ATP. Most heterotrophs can also oxidise other organic molecules, such as proteins, to synthesise ATP.

Energy-containing molecules

All molecules in living organisms contain potential energy, but some molecules contain more energy than others. Carbohydrates and proteins contain approximately the same amount of energy per kilogram whereas lipids have about twice as much energy per kilogram. Energy is more readily available from some molecules, so living organisms use different energy-containing molecules for different purposes. Animals and plants both synthesise energy storage molecules: in animals these are lipid and glycogen; in plants these are lipid and starch. Carbohydrate, protein and lipid can all be used in respiration. Carbohydrates are the easiest to use, as they require the least oxygen and are readily converted to glucose. Almost all enzymes use ATP as an energy source because it releases sufficient free energy to drive most metabolic activities.

A balancing act: photosynthesis and respiration

Investigations show that six carbon dioxide molecules and six water molecules are needed to synthesise one molecule of glucose during photosynthesis. During this process six molecules of oxygen are released.

In respiration, six molecules of oxygen are needed to oxidise one molecule of glucose. During this process six molecules of water and six molecules of carbon dioxide are released. Thus, in theory, the consumption of carbon dioxide by photosynthesis is balanced by the production of carbon dioxide in respiration.

  4 Write out a chemical equation for photosynthesis and respiration.

Key ideas 156–161

- Living organisms need chemical energy to drive reactions in cells.
- ATP makes energy available to cells.
- All energy in living organisms is obtained from sunlight energy.
- Photosynthesis converts light energy to chemical energy in organic molecules.
- Respiration transfers chemical energy in organic molecules to ATP.
- Most ATP is synthesised using energy released by electron transport.

② Respiration

The process of respiration involves a series of reactions during which energy in the chemical bonds of glucose is transferred into ATP molecules. The process involves the **oxidation** of glucose by removing hydrogen, which is then used to obtain **electrons (e⁻)** and **hydrogen ions (H⁺)**. The transfer of electrons by **electron carriers** allows energy to be used in ATP synthesis. The whole process occurs by three interconnected, enzyme-catalysed, metabolic pathways.

Memory joggers

- All living cells respire.
- During respiration a chemical reaction occurs in which sugars are oxidised to release energy. Carbon dioxide and water are released during these reactions.
- Glucose enters cells by diffusion and facilitated diffusion.
- Glucose has six carbon atoms and is very similar to another sugar called fructose.
- Glucose and fructose can be converted into one another.
- When there is a shortage of oxygen, muscles produce lactate in respiration.
- Mitochondria consist of a double layer of membrane surrounding a central matrix. The inner membrane is folded to form cristae.
- Coenzymes are complex organic molecules that are used by enzymes to accept or donate molecules involved in a reaction.
- An electron is a negatively charged particle surrounding the nucleus of an atom.
- A proton is a positively charged particle found in the nucleus of an atom.

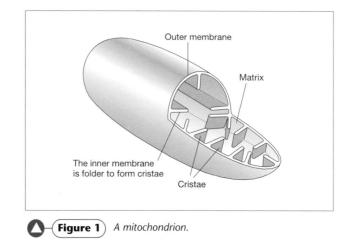

Figure 1   *A mitochondrion.*

Organised pathways

The first pathway of respiration, called **glycolysis** (glyco = carbohydrate, lysis = split), takes place in the cytoplasm of cells. The other two pathways, called **the Krebs cycle** and **electron transport**, occur in different regions of mitochondria. As these metabolic pathways take place in different parts of the cell, coenzymes are used to transfer substrates between the three pathways. The coenzyme **NAD** (nicotine adenine dinucleotide) is used as an acceptor for hydrogen ions and electrons during the first two pathways of respiration. The reduced NAD formed is used as a donor of hydrogen ions and electrons for the last pathway during which most of the ATP is synthesised.

Figure 2 shows the way in which the three metabolic pathways are organised.

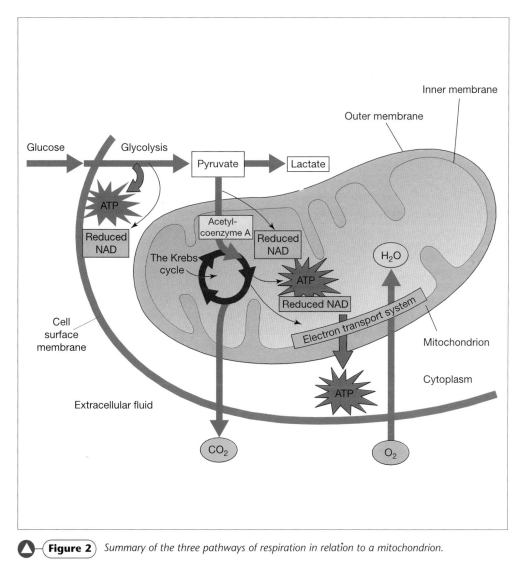

Figure 2 *Summary of the three pathways of respiration in relation to a mitochondrion.*

Q **1 Where in a mitochondrion do the Krebs cycle and electron transport occur?**

Glycolysis – splitting glucose

Glucose is made more reactive using ATP. It is then split into two sugars, each with three carbon atoms. Each of these molecules is then oxidised to **pyruvate** by removing hydrogen ions and electrons. Enzymes called **dehydrogenases** (de = remove, hydrogen, ase = enzyme) catalyse the oxidation. NAD becomes reduced as it accepts the hydrogen ions and electrons that have been removed. Although NAD accepts both hydrogen ions and electrons, it is commonly referred to as a hydrogen acceptor.

Glycolysis involves several reactions involved in:

- activation and splitting of glucose
- oxidation and conversion of glucose to pyruvate.

Activation and splitting

Figure 3 shows the activation and splitting of glucose; only the main steps are shown.

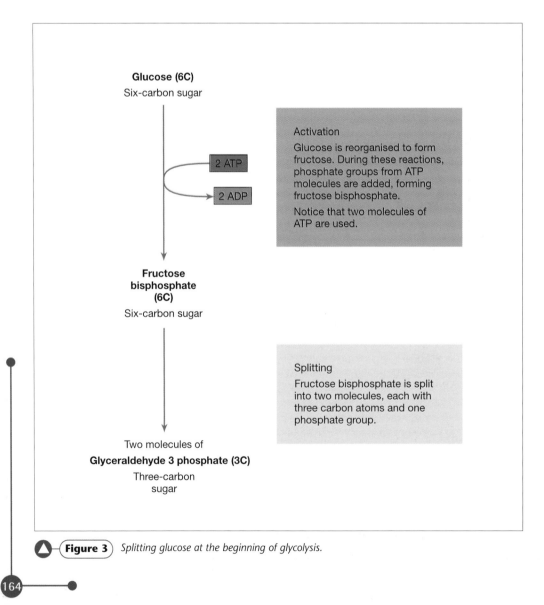

Glucose (6C)
Six-carbon sugar

2 ATP

2 ADP

Activation
Glucose is reorganised to form fructose. During these reactions, phosphate groups from ATP molecules are added, forming fructose bisphosphate.

Notice that two molecules of ATP are used.

Fructose bisphosphate (6C)
Six-carbon sugar

Splitting
Fructose bisphosphate is split into two molecules, each with three carbon atoms and one phosphate group.

Two molecules of
Glyceraldehyde 3 phosphate (3C)
Three-carbon sugar

Figure 3 *Splitting glucose at the beginning of glycolysis.*

Oxidation and conversion to pyruvate

Figure 4 shows the oxidation and conversion of the three-carbon sugars to pyruvate.

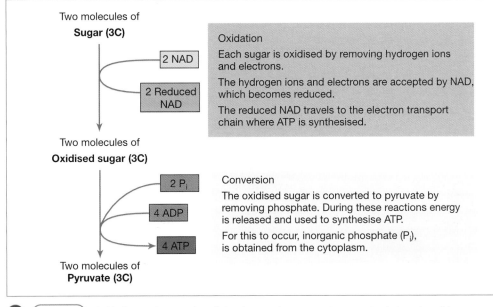

Figure 4 *Oxidation and conversion of the three-carbon sugars to pyruvate during glycoylsis.*

Notice that at the end of this pathway there is a net gain of two molecules of ATP and two molecules of reduced NAD. Pyruvate is the final product of glycolysis. The two molecules of pyruvate are then available for the next stage of respiration.

> Q
> 2 Why is there a net gain of only two molecules of ATP?
> 3 A cell has only a limited number of molecules of NAD. Some toxins can prevent NAD transferring hydrogen ions and electrons during the later stages of respiration. Explain what will happen to glycolysis in this situation.

Remember from Module 3 that when there is a shortage of oxygen, muscles make lactate. This is done by adding the hydrogen ions and electrons from reduced NAD to pyruvate, as shown in figure 5.

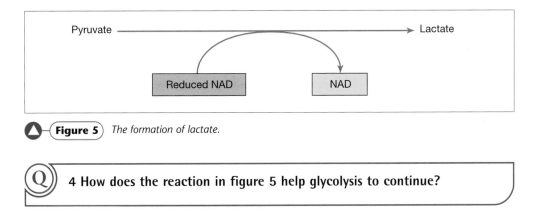

Figure 5 *The formation of lactate.*

> Q
> 4 How does the reaction in figure 5 help glycolysis to continue?

Link reaction

Pyruvate from glycolysis enters the matrix of a **mitochondrion**. Here, pyruvate is converted into a molecule that can enter the Krebs cycle. This is known as the link reaction and is shown in figure 6. Often the link reaction is included as part of the Krebs cycle.

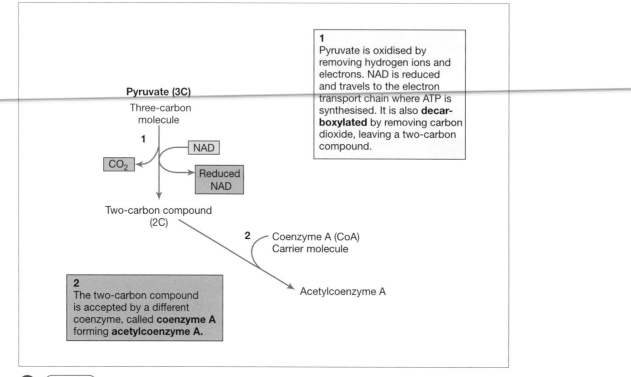

1
Pyruvate is oxidised by removing hydrogen ions and electrons. NAD is reduced and travels to the electron transport chain where ATP is synthesised. It is also **decarboxylated** by removing carbon dioxide, leaving a two-carbon compound.

Pyruvate (3C)
Three-carbon molecule

NAD

CO_2

Reduced NAD

Two-carbon compound (2C)

2
Coenzyme A (CoA)
Carrier molecule

Acetylcoenzyme A

2
The two-carbon compound is accepted by a different coenzyme, called **coenzyme A** forming **acetylcoenzyme A.**

▲ (**Figure 6**) *The link reaction, shown for one molecule of pyruvate.*

Acetylcoenzyme A, formed during the link reaction, carries the two-carbon compound into the Krebs cycle, where further oxidation occurs.

(Q) **5 How many carbons are removed from each molecule of pyruvate in the link reaction?**

  6 Write out the redox reaction occurring during the link reaction. Label the molecule that has been reduced and the molecule that has been oxidised.

The Krebs cycle – obtaining hydrogen

A four-carbon acceptor molecule reacts with acetylcoenzyme A to form a six-carbon molecule. Coenzyme A is reformed so it can be reused. During the Krebs cycle, the six-carbon compound is further oxidised. As the molecule is broken down, hydrogen ions and electrons are accepted by coenzymes and carbon dioxide is formed as a waste product. Figure 7 shows these reactions. For each glucose molecule, two acetylcoenzyme A molecules enter the Krebs cycle.

Main events in the Krebs cycle

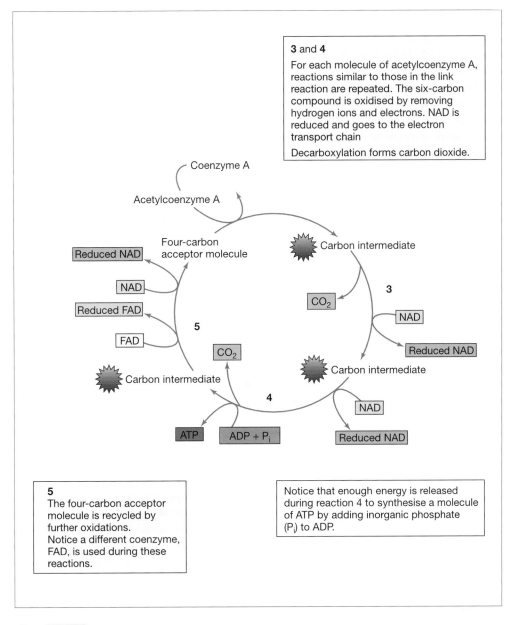

3 and 4

For each molecule of acetylcoenzyme A, reactions similar to those in the link reaction are repeated. The six-carbon compound is oxidised by removing hydrogen ions and electrons. NAD is reduced and goes to the electron transport chain

Decarboxylation forms carbon dioxide.

5
The four-carbon acceptor molecule is recycled by further oxidations.
Notice a different coenzyme, FAD, is used during these reactions.

Notice that enough energy is released during reaction 4 to synthesise a molecule of ATP by adding inorganic phosphate (P_i) to ADP.

Figure 7 Main events in the Krebs cycle, shown for one molecule of acetylcoenzyme A.

Q

7 Copy and complete figure 7 by filling in the number of carbon atoms each intermediate molecule has.

8 What happens to the carbon dioxide produced in this cycle?

9 How many redox reactions happen during the link reaction and the Krebs cycle? List where they occur.

10 How many reduced NAD and reduced FAD molecules will be formed from one glucose molecule during the link reaction and the Krebs cycle?

Electron transport – ATP synthesis

Reduced coenzymes are reoxidised on the cristae of mitochondria by passing hydrogen ions and electrons to other carriers. The electrons (e^-) and hydrogen ions (H^+) are separated and transferred into different pathways. Electrons pass along an electron transport chain in the membranes of cristae. Hydrogen ions move through the inner membrane of the cristae in a separate set of reactions. Hydrogen ions and electrons are both passed to oxygen, which is reduced to form water. The movement of hydrogen ions and electrons allows energy to be released, which can be used by enzymes to synthesise ATP molecules. This method of synthesising ATP is called **oxidative phosphorylation**.

Oxidation of reduced NAD

Figure 8 shows the reoxidation of NAD. Notice that this oxidation releases energy, which is used to synthesise ATP from ADP and inorganic phosphate.

- Reduced NAD is oxidised to NAD by passing hydrogen ions and electrons to other coenzymes.
- A complex of enzymes and coenzymes called **Q** separates electrons and hydrogen ions. These hydrogen ions are now commonly referred to as protons.
- The electrons are passed through a series of electron carriers which use **iron** (**Fe**) to accept electrons when they are reduced. Reduced iron is written as **Fe^{2+}** and oxidised iron is written as **Fe^{3+}**.
- Hydrogen ions are pumped through the crista membrane using enzymes and energy from the movement of electrons.
- As hydrogen ions move through the membrane, energy is released and used to synthesise ATP.

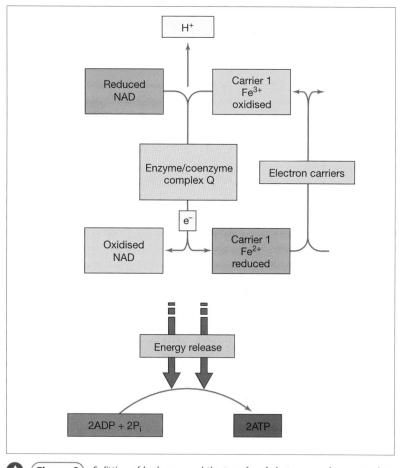

Figure 8 *Splitting of hydrogen and the transfer of electrons to electron carriers.*

(Q) **11 Draw your own diagram to show the transfer of electrons to the next electron carrier.**

Oxidation of reduced FAD

Reduced FAD feeds into a similar reaction at a later stage, releasing sufficient energy to synthesise one molecule of ATP. In many diagrams of the electron transport chain, FAD is shown following NAD. These diagrams show the synthesis of one molecule of ATP between NAD and FAD and one between FAD and the electron carriers.

Reduction of oxygen – reforming oxidised carriers

Figure 9 shows the reduction of oxygen.

- The last electron carrier in the electron transport chain passes electrons to an oxygen molecule.
- In the same reaction, hydrogen ions are passed to the same oxygen molecule and water is formed as a waste product.
- Energy released during the reduction of oxygen is used to synthesise another molecule of ATP.

Oxygen is the **terminal** (final) **acceptor** for hydrogen from the oxidation of glucose. The water produced as a waste of respiration is often called **metabolic water**.

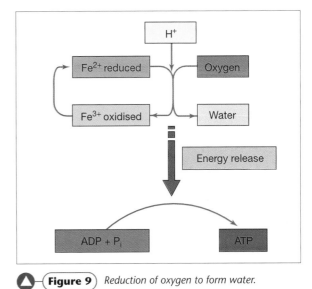

Figure 9 Reduction of oxygen to form water.

Using other molecules in respiration

Glycolysis in the cytoplasm is only one pathway that links to the Krebs cycle. There are other pathways in the cytoplasm that also produce acetylcoenzyme A, allowing other substrates to be used in respiration. These other routes are shown in figure 10. In exercise, for example, which you studied in Module 3, fatty acids are used. Proteins can also be used to produce acetylcoenzyme A.

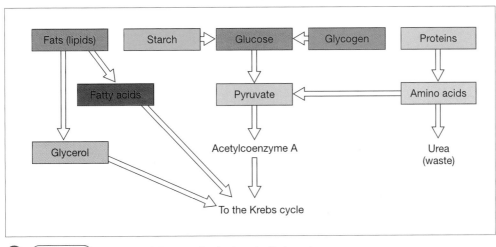

Figure 10 Routes for different molecules into the Krebs cycle.

Getting it all together

The organisation of the respiratory pathways improves their effectiveness. The mitochondrion keeps the Krebs cycle and oxidative phosphorylation close together, allowing coenzymes to transfer hydrogen ions and electrons efficiently between the two pathways. The membrane of the cristae provides a surface that holds electron carriers in position and allows movement of hydrogen ions. The location of glycolysis in the cytoplasm allows glucose to be readily obtained as it diffuses into a cell, or from storage compounds in the cytoplasm.

Figure 11 shows how all these pathways interact.

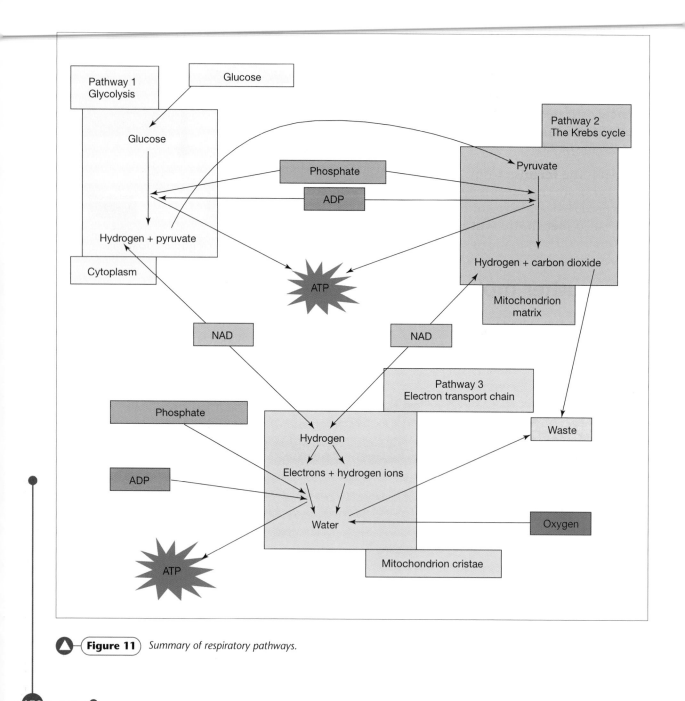

Figure 11 *Summary of respiratory pathways.*

Key ideas 162–170

- Respiration releases energy from glucose by oxidation.

- Glycolysis involves the oxidation of glucose to pyruvate with a net gain of ATP and reduced NAD.

- Pyruvate combines with coenzyme A to produce acetylcoenzyme A. This is effectively a two-carbon molecule that combines with a four-carbon molecule to produce a six-carbon molecule, which enters the Krebs cycle.

- The Krebs cycle involves a series of oxidation reactions and the release of carbon dioxide, leading to the production of ATP and reduced coenzyme.

- Coenzymes are reoxidised by donating hydrogen ions and electrons to a membrane-bound set of coenzymes and electron carriers in the membrane of cristae formed by mitochondria.

- Electrons are transferred through electron carriers to oxygen. Energy released is used to synthesise ATP.

- The waste products of respiration are water and carbon dioxide.

- Glucose is the usual substrate for respiration.

- A variety of organic molecules can be oxidised in the cytoplasm and fed into the Krebs cycle.

Photosynthesis

The process of photosynthesis involves a series of reactions during which solar energy is converted into chemical energy, which other living organisms can use. The process involves using light energy to obtain hydrogen ions and electrons from water. These are then used in the synthesis of ATP and reduced **NADP**. Carbon dioxide is used to synthesise sugars using reduced NADP and ATP. The whole process occurs by two interconnected, enzyme-catalysed metabolic pathways: the **light-dependent** reaction and the **light-independent** reaction.

Memory joggers

- Green plants photosynthesise when there is light.
- During photosynthesis, light energy is absorbed by chlorophyll.
- Chlorophyll is found in chloroplasts, which occur mainly in the mesophyll cells of leaves and the stems of some plants.
- Chloroplasts consist of a double membrane surrounding a central **stroma**. Stacks of thylakoid membrane inside the stroma form **grana** (singular **granum**).
- Light energy is used to convert carbon dioxide and water into glucose, releasing oxygen as a by-product.
- Water is taken up by the roots and transported in the xylem.
- Carbon dioxide enters leaves by diffusion through stomata.
- The glucose produced in photosynthesis may be converted into insoluble starch for storage.
- The rate of photosynthesis may be limited by low temperature, shortage of carbon dioxide and shortage of light.

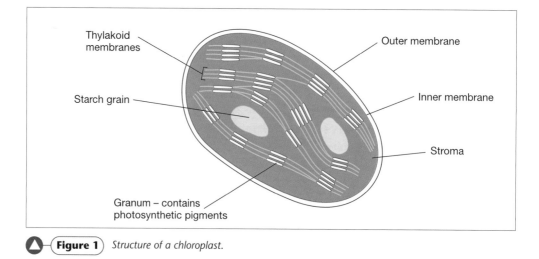

Figure 1 Structure of a chloroplast.

Linked pathways

As in respiration, the pathways of photosynthesis are organised to allow the most efficient transfer of hydrogen ions, electrons and ATP. The light-dependent reaction occurs in the thylakoid membrane (grana) of the chloroplasts. The light-independent reaction takes place in the stroma. The coenzyme NADP (nicotine adenine dinucleotide phosphate) is used as an acceptor for hydrogen ions and electrons in the light-dependent reaction. The reduced NADP formed is used as a donor of hydrogen ions and electrons in the light-independent reaction to synthesise sugars. ATP synthesised in the light-dependent reactions is also used to synthesise sugars.

Figure 2 shows the way in which the pathways are organised.

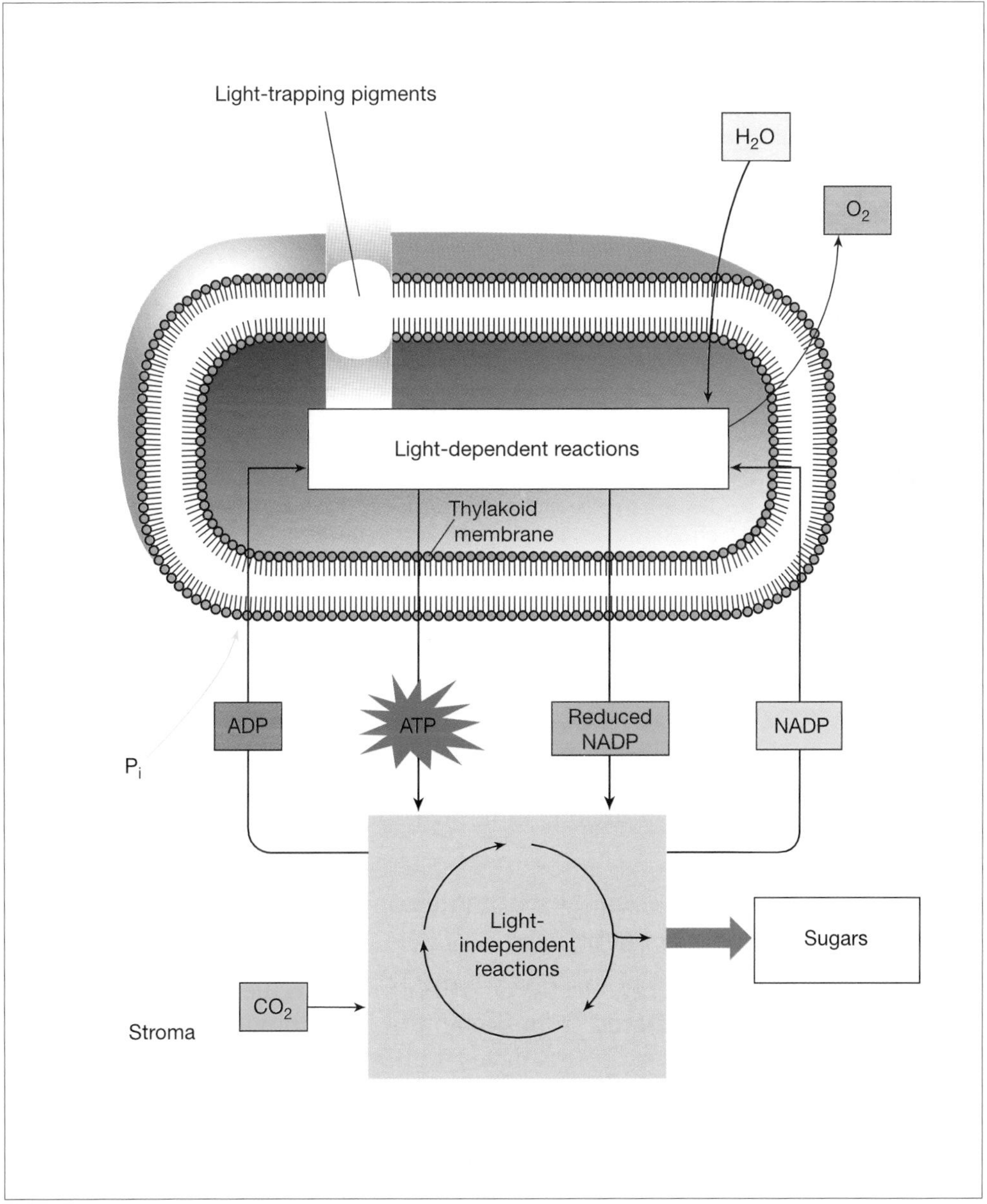

Figure 2 *The organisation of photosynthesis pathways in a granum.*

The light-dependent stage

Which light?

Light is made up of packets of energy called **photons**. Some photons have more energy than others. Light can be thought of as a wave, which has different wavelengths with different types of photon. Light with a short wavelength has high-energy photons. Light with a long wavelength has lower-energy photons. Only certain wavelengths of light are visible to the human eye. This range of wavelengths is called the **visible spectrum** and contains light that is coloured. Photosynthesis can only use light within the visible spectrum, red and blue light being the most effective. Wavelength is measured in **nanometres** (nm). Figure 3 shows the total spectrum of light and the visible spectrum, and the action spectrum for chlorophyll.

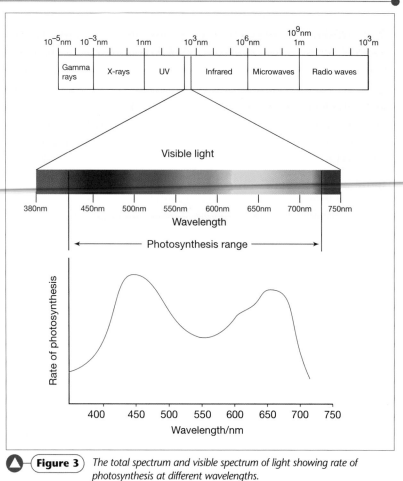

Figure 3 *The total spectrum and visible spectrum of light showing rate of photosynthesis at different wavelengths.*

Trapping light energy

The light-dependent reaction has two products, both of which are used in the light-independent reaction.

- ATP provides energy for the synthesis of sugars.

- Reduced NADP is used for the reduction of organic molecules formed using carbon dioxide.

Both of these products are synthesised in a complex set of interconnecting reactions during which chlorophyll absorbs light.

As a chlorophyll molecule absorbs light energy, electrons within the molecule become 'excited'. 'Excited' electrons are **emitted** from (leave) the chlorophyll molecule and are accepted by electron carriers. Plants have additional pigments to direct light energy to chlorophyll.

(Q) **1 Explain why chlorophyll is oxidised when it is excited by light.**

As electrons are transferred along a chain of electron carriers, some energy is used to synthesise ATP. The arrangement of chlorophyll molecules and electron carriers is very complex and results in the electrons travelling between two chlorophyll molecules, referred to here as chlorophyll (I) and chlorophyll (II), at different points in the thylakoid membrane. Some of the electrons, together with hydrogen ions, are used to reduce the coenzyme NADP.

Synthesising ATP

Figure 4 shows the events that occur during ATP synthesis. 'Excited' electrons from chlorophyll (II) are transferred along a chain of electron carriers to chlorophyll (I). Chlorophyll (I) has also been excited by light and has lost electrons. Notice that as electrons are transferred, energy is released and used to synthesise ATP. This is called **photophosphorylation** (photo = light, phosphorylation = adding phosphate).

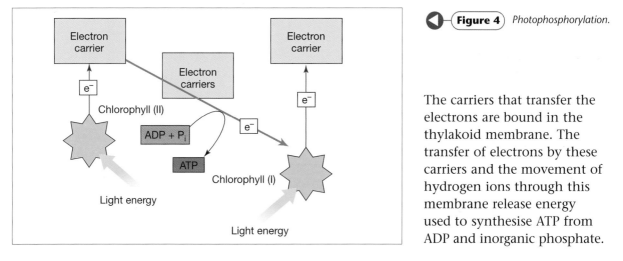

Figure 4 *Photophosphorylation.*

The carriers that transfer the electrons are bound in the thylakoid membrane. The transfer of electrons by these carriers and the movement of hydrogen ions through this membrane release energy used to synthesise ATP from ADP and inorganic phosphate.

Forming reduced NADP

This requires two different sets of reactions involving electrons from chlorophyll (I) and hydrogen ions from water.

Photolysis

The 'excited' electrons lost from chlorophyll (I) are replaced by electrons from chlorophyll (II). Electrons taken from water molecules replace the electrons lost from chlorophyll (II). The activity of chlorophyll (II) causes this to happen and releases hydrogen ions and oxygen gas. This is called **photolysis** and is shown in figure 5.

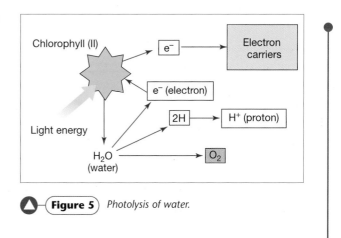

Figure 5 *Photolysis of water.*

Reduction

The 'excited' electons from chlorophyll (I) are accepted by an electron carrier and transferred to NADP. Hydrogen ions from water move through the thylakoid membrane and are also transferred to NADP. As a result, reduced NADP is formed. This is shown in figure 6.

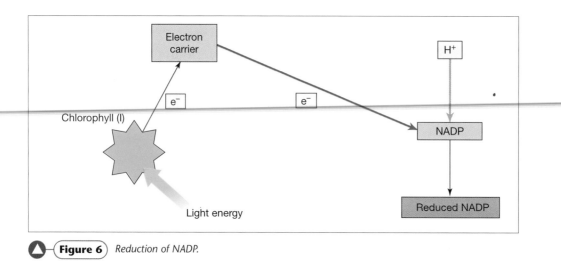

Electron carrier

H⁺

e⁻   e⁻

Chlorophyll (I)

NADP

Reduced NADP

Light energy

Figure 6 *Reduction of NADP.*

Q **2 Write a word equation to show the reduction of NADP.**

All the events described – photophosphorylation, photolysis and the reduction of NADP – are happening at the same time. Thus the light-dependent reaction consists of three interdependent sets of reactions. The overall effect is as follows.

- Light energy excites electrons so they leave chlorophyll molecules.
- Some of these electrons are passed to NADP and go into the light-independent reaction.
- The chlorophyll electrons are replaced in two different ways: in one system, electron carriers transfer electrons from one chlorophyll molecule to another; in the other system, photolysis of water provides electrons.
- ATP is synthesised during the transfer of electrons from one chlorophyll to the other and goes into the light-independent reaction.
- Hydrogen ions are passed to NADP and go into the light-independent reaction.

Look at figure 7, which shows how these sets of reactions interact.

Q **3 a) Copy figure 7 and draw boxes around the three sets of reactions.**
   b) Which reaction is part of both photolysis and photophosphorylation?
   c) Which reaction is part of photophosphorylation and the reduction of NADP?
   4 Explain why reduction of NADP depends upon photolysis.

Moving electrons to synthesise ATP

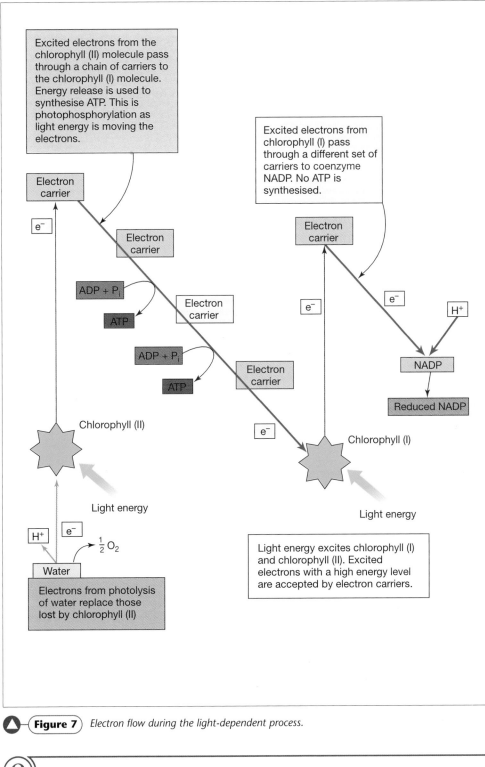

Excited electrons from the chlorophyll (II) molecule pass through a chain of carriers to the chlorophyll (I) molecule. Energy release is used to synthesise ATP. This is photophosphorylation as light energy is moving the electrons.

Excited electrons from chlorophyll (I) pass through a different set of carriers to coenzyme NADP. No ATP is synthesised.

Electron carrier

e^-

Electron carrier

ADP + P_i

ATP

Electron carrier

ADP + P_i

ATP

Electron carrier

Electron carrier

e^-

e^-

H^+

NADP

Reduced NADP

e^-

Chlorophyll (II)

Chlorophyll (I)

Light energy

Light energy

H^+ e^- $\frac{1}{2} O_2$

Water

Electrons from photolysis of water replace those lost by chlorophyll (II)

Light energy excites chlorophyll (I) and chlorophyll (II). Excited electrons with a high energy level are accepted by electron carriers.

Figure 7 *Electron flow during the light-dependent process.*

Q 5 Write a description of the light–dependent reaction without using diagrams.

Light-independent reactions – the Calvin cycle

The products of the light-dependent reaction (reduced NADP and ATP) are used in the stroma, together with carbon dioxide, to make sugars.

An enzyme starts the pathway by adding carbon dioxide to a five-carbon sugar, **ribulose bisphosphate** (RuBP), forming two molecules of **glycerate-3-phosphate** (GP). GP is reduced using reduced NADP and energy from ATP forming glyceraldehyde phosphate (GALP). Some of the GALP is used to reform RuBP using ATP. Figure 8 shows the Calvin cycle.

Forming sugars

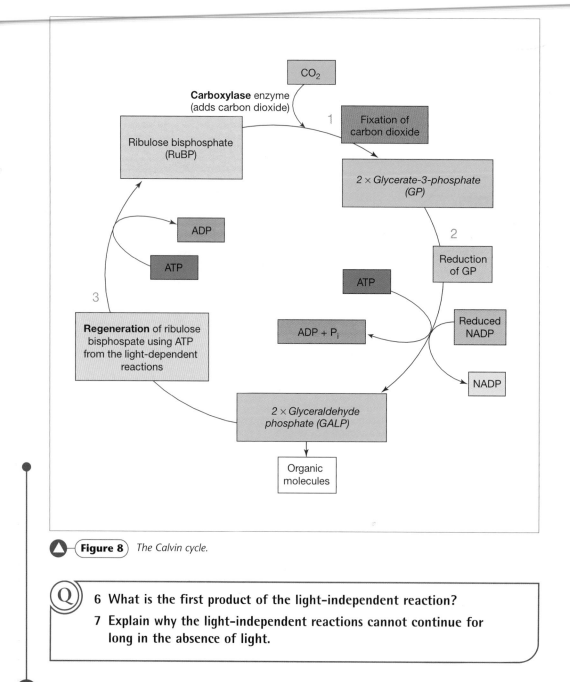

Figure 8 The Calvin cycle.

Q
6 What is the first product of the light–independent reaction?

7 Explain why the light–independent reactions cannot continue for long in the absence of light.

Synthesising organic molecules

Once GALP has been formed, there are two sets of reactions it can enter. One set of these reactions leads to the recycling of RuBP as shown in the Calvin cycle. The other set of reactions leads to the formation of new organic molecules. Figure 9 summarises the range of different molecules that can be synthesised from GALP.

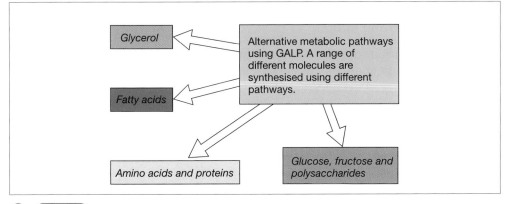

Figure 9 *Alternative pathways to synthesise new organic molecules.*

Q) 8 **Explain how a carbon dioxide molecule can end up in a starch grain in a chloroplast.**

The reactions in the Calvin cycle are not the only way in which carbon dioxide is 'fixed'. Many important crop plants are grasses, which use another pathway called the **Hatch and Slack pathway**. Figure 10 shows this pathway.

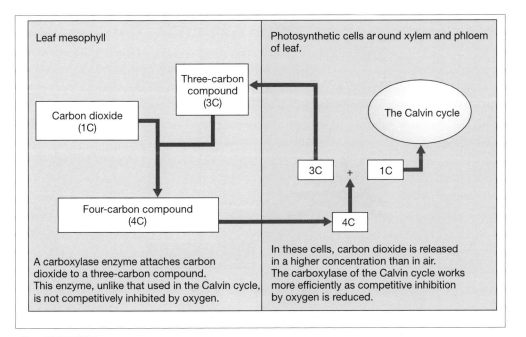

Figure 10 *The Hatch and Slack pathway.*

Getting it all together

As in respiration, the interacting stages of photosynthesis are organised to allow the most efficient transfer of reduced NADP and ATP between the two pathways in a chloroplast. The membranes of the thylakoids provide a surface for the light-dependent reaction. These membranes are needed to:

- allow electrons to be transferred by carriers for ATP synthesis
- hold the electron carriers in position
- hold the light-trapping pigments in position.

The enzymes of the Calvin cycle are in the stroma of a chloroplast, as are many of the enzymes used to synthesise new organic molecules. Figure 11 shows how these pathways interact.

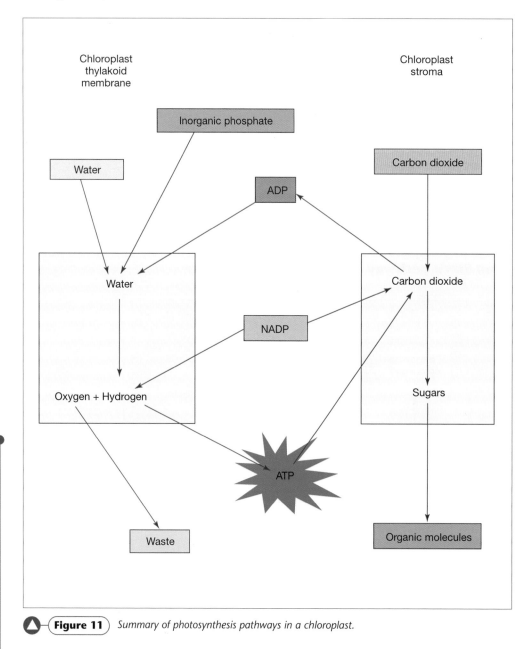

Figure 11 *Summary of photosynthesis pathways in a chloroplast.*

Key ideas 172–180

- Photosynthesis has two sets of reactions, one light-dependent and the other light-independent.
- The light-dependent reaction uses light energy and can only occur when light of the correct wavelength is present.
- The thylakoid membranes of the chloroplast hold the electron carriers, chlorophyll and other light-trapping pigments in place.
- The enzymes of the Calvin cycle are in the stroma of a chloroplast.
- Light energy excites electrons in chlorophyll, causing them to be emitted.
- The energy from excited electrons is used to generate ATP and reduced NADP.
- The photolysis of water makes hydrogen ions available for the light-independent reaction and releases oxygen gas.
- The light-independent reaction does not require light energy, but ATP and reduced NADP from the light-dependent reaction are needed.
- Carbon dioxide is accepted by RuBP to form two molecules of GP.
- ATP and reduced NADP are used to reduce GP to GALP.
- GALP can be used to recycle RuBP or to synthesise new organic molecules.

Unit 4 – Questions

1 Complete the following passage about respiration.

Respiration is a process by which organisms release ....from organic molecules. Respiration can be divided into stages, each of which occurs in a different part of the cell. Glycolysis takes place in the .... of the cell and produces .... which passes into the next stage, ... cycle. This compound is broken down in the .... of a mitochondrion to form reduced .... and ATP.

(6 marks)

2 Figure 1 summarises the biochemical pathways involved in photosynthesis.

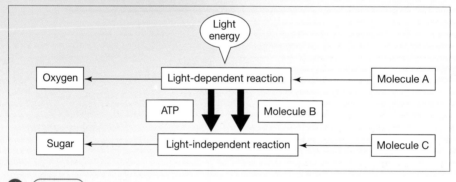

◢ **Figure 1**

a) Name the molecules **A**, **B** and **C**. (3 marks)

b) i) Describe how ATP is produced in the light-dependent reaction.

(4 marks)

ii) What part does ATP play in the light-independent reaction?

(3 marks)

(Total 10 marks)

3 a) Give *two* similarities in structure between mitochondria and chloroplasts.

(2 marks)

b) Describe:

i) the similarities in the ways in which ATP is produced in respiration and photosynthesis

ii) the differences in the ways in which ATP is produced in respiration and photosynthesis. (6 marks)

c) Describe how ATP is used in *one* metabolic reaction during respiration. (2 marks)

(Total 10 marks)

4 a) Give the location in the chloroplast of:
  i)   the light-dependent reactions
  ii) the light-independent reactions.   (2 marks)

b) In an investigation, single-celled algae were supplied with labelled carbon dioxide and allowed to photosynthesise. After 10 minutes the light was switched off and the algae were left in the dark. The concentration of glycerate-3-phosphate (GP), ribulose bisphosphate (RuBP) and glucose were measured during the time the algae were in the dark. The results are shown in figure 2.

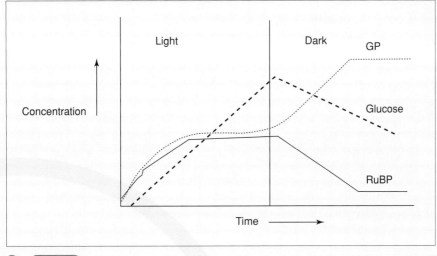

Figure 2

  i)   Explain the change that occurred in the concentration of RuBP and GP after the light was switched off.   (4 marks)
  ii) Give *two* ways in which the algae may be using the glucose while they are in the dark.   (2 marks)

(Total 8 marks)

5 Figure 3 shows details of the link reaction.

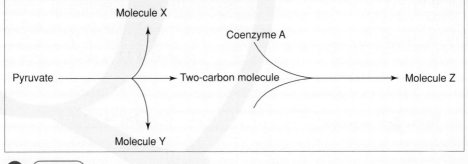

Figure 3

a) Name the molecules **X**, **Y** and **Z** in figure 3.   (3 marks)
b) Describe what happens to molecule **Z** during the Krebs cycle.   (4 marks)
c) Explain why the production of molecule **Z** cannot take place in anaerobic conditions.   (3 marks)

(Total 10 marks)

Module 4 – Test yourself

1. Figure 1 shows the structure of a synapse between two neurones.

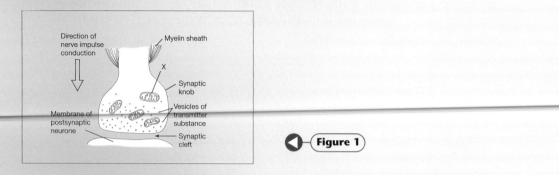

Figure 1

a) Describe the sequence of events occurring between the arrival of an action potential at the presynaptic membrane and the generation of an action potential in the postsynaptic neurone. (5 marks)

b) Name organelle **X** and explain why large numbers of these organelles are found in the presynaptic neurone. (2 marks)

c) Table 1 gives some information about certain drugs that affect the nervous system.

Substance	Effect
Nicotine	Acts on the membrane of the postsynaptic neurone by mimicking the effect of acetylcholine
Strychnine	Inhibits the breakdown of acetylcholine at the postsynaptic membrane

Table 1

Explain the effect each of these drugs will have on the nervous system:
    i) nicotine
    ii) strychnine. (4 marks)

(Total 11 marks)

2. a) Identify A, B and C in table 2. (3 marks)

Table 2

Part of the brain	Function
A	Control of breathing and heart rate
Hypothalamus	B
C	Understanding speech

b) Explain how a person who has had damage to a small part of the brain may be unable to speak but can still understand what is said. (4 marks)

(Total 7 marks)

3 Insulin production can be assessed in hospitals by using a test called the glucose tolerance test. A patient must not eat any food for several hours before the test. At the start of the test, the patient swallows 50g of glucose in 150cm³ water. The concentration of glucose in the patient's blood is then measured immediately and at 30-minute intervals over a period of two to three hours. The graph in figure 2 shows changes in the blood glucose concentration of three patients who have taken this test.

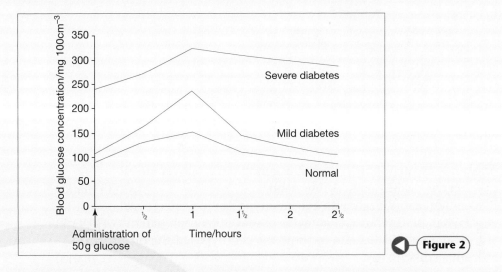

Figure 2

a) Explain why patients must not eat for several hours before the test is carried out. (1 mark)
b) Explain the changes that take place in blood glucose concentration of the non-diabetic over the period shown in the graph. (4 marks)
c) What do the results of this test show about insulin production in the two diabetic patients? Explain the evidence for your answer. (3 marks)

(Total 8 marks)

4 The diagram in figure 3 shows how blood water potential is controlled.

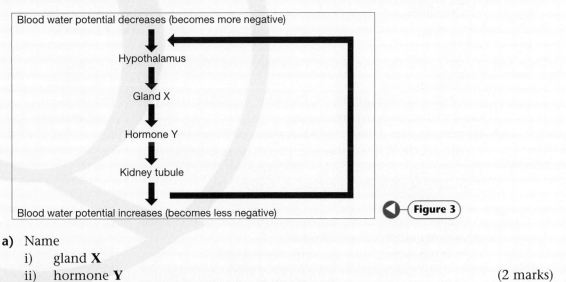

Figure 3

a) Name
    i) gland **X**
    ii) hormone **Y** (2 marks)
b) What effect does hormone **Y** have on the kidney? (2 marks)
c) Explain how the blood water potential increases when hormone **Y** is secreted. (3 marks)
d) Use the diagram to explain what is meant by 'negative feedback'. (2 marks)

(Total 9 marks)

(5) Some forms of clover, called 'cyanogenic', produce poisonous cyanide gas when their tissues are damaged. Acyanogenic clover cannot produce cyanide.

The production of cyanide gas occurs using a metabolic pathway controlled by two enzymes. A different gene controls the synthesis of each of these enzymes.

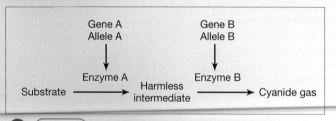

Figure 4

a) Explain why the following possible genotypes of clover are all acyanogenic: aaBB, aaBb, AAbb, Aabb. (3 marks)
b) Two clover plants, each with the genotype AaBb, were crossed.
   i) What are the possible gametes produced by each parent? (1 mark)
   ii) Use a genetic diagram to show the genotypes of the offspring of this cross. (2 marks)
   iii) What proportion of the offspring are likely to be acyanogenic? (1 mark)
c) Clover is an important food source for a variety of insect that eats the leaves. These insects occur more commonly at low altitude where the temperature is higher. In the low temperatures at high altitude, clover cells may freeze which causes damage leading to cyanide release.

   Use the information above to explain why the frequency of the alleles for cyanogenesis is different in clover populations growing at high and low altitudes. (6 marks)
   (Total 13 marks)

(6) a) Explain why the gametes of a woman are all genetically different from each other. (2 marks)
   b) Use a genetic diagram to explain how approximately half of the children produced in humans are female. (2 marks)
   c) In humans, the gene for red-green colour blindness is sex-linked and is carried on the X chromosome. The allele **n** is recessive and prevents a pigment necessary to detect red light being synthesised. The allele **N** allows normal colour vision.

   A couple, neither of whom suffers from colour blindness, have a son who suffers from colour blindness.
   i) What is meant by the term 'recessive'?
   ii) What are the likely genotypes of the female partner and the male partner?
   iii) Explain why this couple is unlikely to have a colour blind daughter. (4 marks)
   (Total 8 marks)

7 a) i)   Describe the five-kingdom model of classification.   (2 marks)
       ii) Describe the principles on which this classification of living organisms
            is based.   (5 marks)
    b) Read the following passage.

        This organism consists of a mass of microscopic tubular structures. Each tube has a
        wall surrounding cytoplasm containing scattered nuclei.
        There are no obvious cross cell walls. Chemical analysis shows the presence of chitin
        in the walls. The mass of tubes is found just below the surface of dead wood. Food is
        absorbed from the environment. Reproductive structures arise by fusion of the tubular
        body mass and produce large numbers of spores.

        i)   To which kingdom does this organism belong?
        ii) Give *two* reasons for your answer.   (3 marks)
                                                                      (Total 10 marks)

8 The diagram in figure 5 shows the structure of a chloroplast.

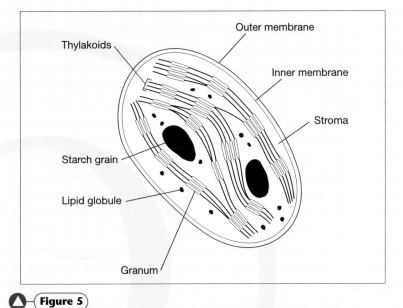

Figure 5

    a) On the diagram give the location of the light-dependent and the light-
        independent processes.   (2 marks)
    b) Describe the role of each of the following in photosynthesis:
        i)   water
        ii)   light
        iii) NADP.   (7 marks)
    c) Describe how carbon dioxide is fixed during the light-independent
        processes of photosynthesis.   (2 marks)
                                                                      (Total 11 marks)

Module 5

Environment

There are two main areas of this module which build upon some parts of GCSE. There are also links to Module 4 and AS. The content of these areas, as they are organised in this book, is summarised below.

Sections 1 to 4 are concerned with the ecosystem and how natural processes maintain it. Feeding relationships and energy flow are studied from a different perspective from Module 4, and are linked to the role of micro-organisms in the cycling of materials. Sections 5 and 6 are concerned with the factors that determine the nature of the living organisms which live in a particular ecosystem. The nature of an ecosystem is discussed in relation to the non-living component and the living component. The various methods used to study ecosystems are discussed in section 7 and used to introduce statistical analysis of results of these studies.

Sections 8 to 10 are concerned with human influences on the environment. The main emphasis is on the impact of farming in relation to fertilisers and pesticides. This is linked to farming practice and the development of sustainable techniques that conserve ecosystems.

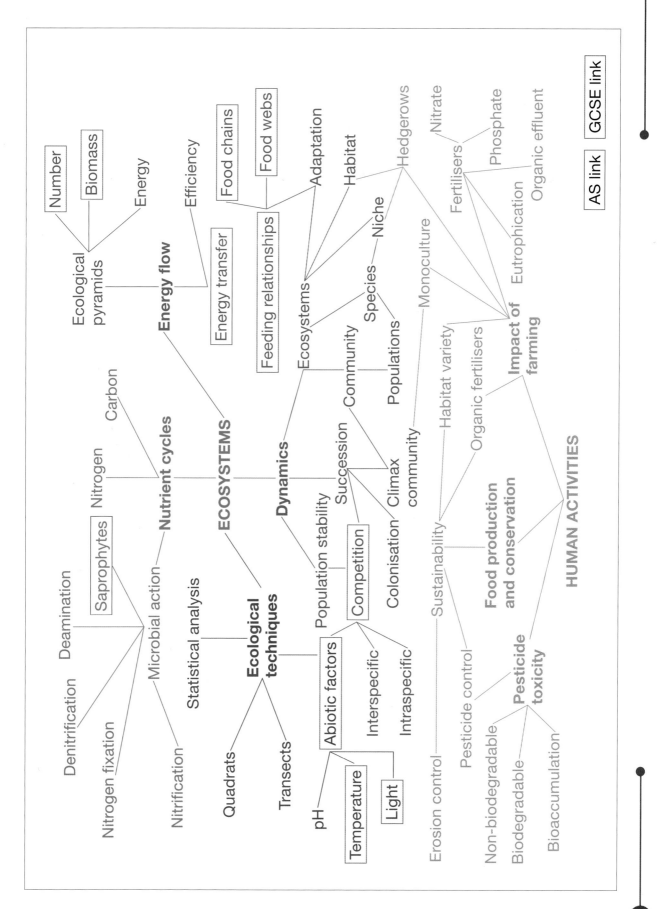

ECOSYSTEMS

Energy flow

Ecological pyramids
- Number
- Biomass
- Energy

Efficiency

Energy transfer

Food chains

Food webs

Feeding relationships
- Adaptation
- Habitat

Ecosystems
- Species
- Niche
- Community
- Populations

Monoculture

Nutrient cycles
- Carbon
- Nitrogen

Saprophytes

Microbial action
- Denitrification
- Deamination
- Nitrogen fixation
- Nitrification

Statistical analysis

Ecological techniques
- Quadrats
- Transects

Dynamics

Population stability

Succession
- Competition
- Colonisation
- Climax community

Abiotic factors
- pH
- Temperature
- Light
- Interspecific
- Intraspecific

Impact of farming
- Hedgerows
- Fertilisers
  - Nitrate
  - Phosphate
- Organic effluent
- Eutrophication
- Habitat variety
- Organic fertilisers

HUMAN ACTIVITIES

Food production and conservation
- Sustainability
- Erosion control
- Pesticide control

Pesticide toxicity
- Non-biodegradable
- Biodegradable
- Bioaccumulation

AS link   GCSE link

189

Environment

Ecology is the study of the relationships between organisms and their surroundings. Ecologists carry out this study by examining **ecosystems**; these are areas in which organisms interact with each other and with their physical environment. The influences that act upon organisms are called the **environment**. An ecosystem can be split into two components:

- the **biotic** – the living component which is the effect all other living organisms have on an individual, such as predation, competition and parasitism
- the **abiotic** – the non-living component, such as climate, soil structure and water currents.

Each organism has its own specific abiotic requirements and its success depends on how it interacts with its physical environment.

Memory joggers

- Only members of the same species are capable of breeding to produce fertile offspring.
- A group of individuals of the same species which occupy a particular area is called a population.
- In a community, a number of different populations occupy a particular area at the same time.
- Organisms live, grow and reproduce in places where, and at times when, conditions are suitable.
- Physical factors, such as temperature, amount of light and the availability of water, carbon dioxide and oxygen, may affect organisms.

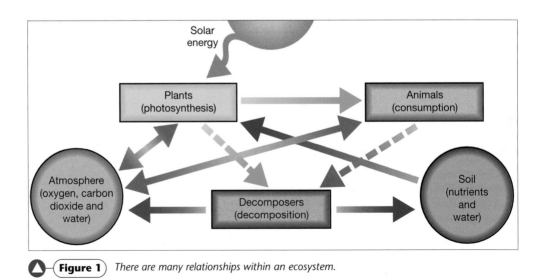

Figure 1 *There are many relationships within an ecosystem.*

Ecosystems

The parts of Earth that support life are known as the **biosphere**. The organisms of the biosphere depend on one another and on Earth's physical environment, which consists of the **atmosphere** (the gases surrounding Earth), the **hydrosphere** (Earth's water supply) and the **lithosphere** (the soil and rock of Earth's crust).

The biosphere is made up of many parts that have different environmental conditions; these are known as **biomes**. Biomes that exist on land are called **terrestrial biomes**; an example is temperate deciduous forest. Biomes that exist in water are called **aquatic biomes**; examples are lakes and ponds.

Look at the examples shown in figure 2.

Figure 2 *(a) Temperate deciduous forests are found where there are hot summers and cold winters. They are dominated by broad-leaved deciduous trees such as oak. (b) Freshwater lakes support a wide variety of organisms.*

Ecological organisation

The field of ecology is very broad and can be studied at many different levels. You have already learnt how atoms are organised into molecules which are then organised into cells, and how cells are organised into organisms. Ecologists are interested in those levels of biological organisation that are above the level of the individual organism. Ecologists study not just a particular organism in an ecosystem, but also the environment in which it lives.

Levels of biological organisation

Organisms are grouped into **populations**. A population is a group of organisms of the same **species** that live together in the same area at the same time. A species is a group of individuals with similar features that can interbreed to produce fertile offspring. Different populations are arranged into a **community**. A community is, therefore, all the populations of different species that live and interact together in the same area at the same time. The community is the biotic component (i.e. the living organisms) of the ecosystem. The different levels of biological organisation are shown in figure 3.

Figure 3   *Levels of organisation above the level of the individual organism in an ecosystem.*

Levels of environmental organisation

A community and its physical environment form an ecosystem. The physical environment can also be subdivided. The **habitat** of an organism is the physical environment it is found in (i.e. where it lives). Each ecosystem contains a number of different habitats. The oak woodland shown in figure 4 provides a habitat for a whole range of different species including the fox, whose natural habitat is a mixed landscape with abundant woodlands. Within the total habitat there will be areas with specific conditions known as **microhabitats**, for example the area under a rotting log.

Figure 4 *(a) Oak woodland showing oak in the foreground and beech in the background. (b) English oak.*

When describing the habitat of an organism it is important to include all the abiotic and biotic factors that enable the organism to thrive.

The general habitat of English oak (*Quercus robur*) is deciduous woodland; trees that are deciduous shed their leaves in winter. English oak grows best where there is fertile, heavy (clay) soil with a pH between 4.5 and 7.5. Mature trees can tolerate flooding even from seawater. Most oak woodlands are made up of a mixture of species including sessile oak, birch, rowan, hazel, holly and occasionally beech. The ground flora (plants) is generally rich in mosses and ferns. Bramble and bracken often carpet low-lying oak woodland on level ground. Soils with a high nutrient content also produce bluebells. There are many invertebrate animals including wood ants, blue ground beetles, wood crickets and many different butterfly and moth species. A range of small mammals such as badgers and squirrels are present. The bird community is characterised by pied flycatchers, wood warblers and redstarts.

The ecological niche

Within a habitat a species occupies an **ecological niche**. A species' niche is determined by its adaptations to food and the abiotic factors that are present. The ecological niche can be described as the position an organism fills in its environment, comprising its habitat, the resources it uses and the time at which it occurs there.

The ecological niche of the red fox (*Vulpes vulpes*)

The red fox, shown in figure 5, is the largest fox in its genus. It is characterised by a large bushy tail often tipped with a white splash. Although commonly known as the red fox, many colour variants exist. The most common colour is a rust red to flame red. The backs of the ears are black and the lower leg parts, known as the socks, are often black.

The red fox is found throughout the Northern Hemisphere, from the Arctic Circle to North Africa, Central America and the Asiatic Steppes, excluding Iceland, the Arctic islands and some parts of Siberia and the extreme desert.

Figure 5　*Being highly adapted, the red fox is found in nearly all habitats from salt marshes and sand dunes to the tops of mountains. In Britain, foxes have also adapted to life in urban surroundings. This photo shows a young fox stealing through a garden.*

Key ideas 190–194

- An ecosystem is an area in which organisms interact with each other and with their physical environment.
- The biotic component of the environment is the effect all other living organisms have on an individual, such as predation, competition and parasitism.
- The abiotic component of the environment is the effect of physical factors such as climate, soil structure and water currents.
- Each organism has its own specific abiotic requirements and its success depends on how it is adapted to, and how it interacts with, its physical environment.
- A population is all the organisms of one species in a habitat.
- Populations of different species form communities.
- Communities are found in a particular habitat and are based on dynamic (changeable) feeding relationships.
- Within a habitat a species occupies an ecological niche governed by adaptation to food and abiotic forces.

Energy and the environment

Energy exists in many forms: heat, radiant energy (e.g. light energy), chemical energy (stored in chemical bonds of molecules), mechanical energy and electrical energy. An ecosystem can only survive if energy is provided. Plants obtain their energy from the sun. Animals get their energy by eating either plants or other animals. Energy flows through an ecosystem in one direction, from the sun via plants to animals. Living organisms need **energy** for survival. In living organisms energy is transferred into a form suitable for growth, movement, reproduction and repair. During this transfer, some of the energy becomes unsuitable for use by organisms and is lost to the environment as heat.

Memory joggers

- Food chains show which organisms eat other organisms.
- Food chains always begin with green plants (producers), which provide food for other organisms (consumers).
- Radiation from the sun is the source of energy for all communities. Green plants capture a small part of the solar energy that reaches them. This energy is stored in the substances that make up the cells of plants.
- Food chains are interconnected to form food webs.
- Food chains and food webs show the transfer of energy and materials from one type of organism to another.

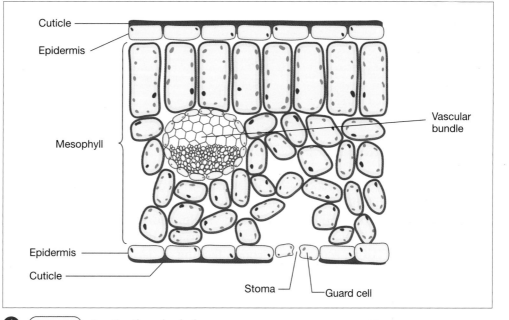

Figure 1 A section through a leaf.

Energy

In most ecosystems the initial source of energy is the sun; this is **solar energy**. Plants use solar energy for **photosynthesis**, which is used to make organic molecules as shown in figure 2.

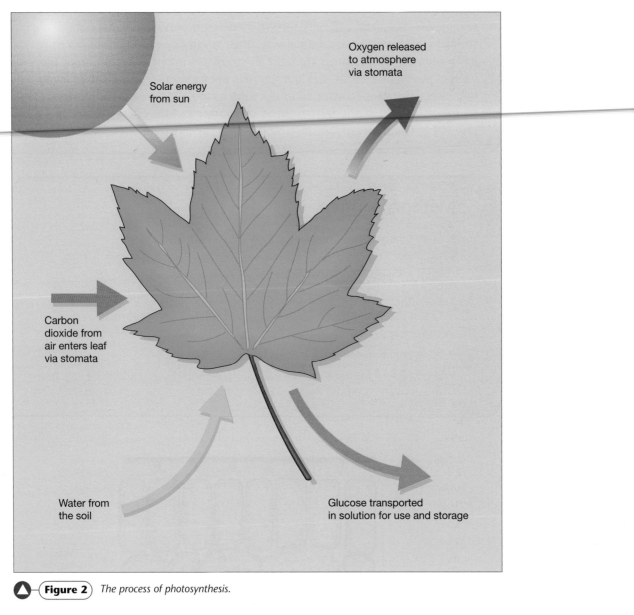

Solar energy from sun

Oxygen released to atmosphere via stomata

Carbon dioxide from air enters leaf via stomata

Water from the soil

Glucose transported in solution for use and storage

Figure 2 *The process of photosynthesis.*

The chemical energy that plants store in organic molecules is released within the cells of plants, animals or other living organisms through **cellular respiration**. Therefore photosynthesis is the major route by which energy enters an ecosystem. The energy of photosynthesis can be passed on to other living components of an ecosystem through feeding or decomposition.

Q
1 **In deep waters, photosynthesis takes place in the upper levels. Suggest why this happens.**

Food chains

The flow of energy through an ecosystem is in one direction and is known as **energy flow**. Energy flow in an ecosystem occurs in **food chains**, in which energy from food passes from one organism to the next in a sequence, as shown in figure 3.

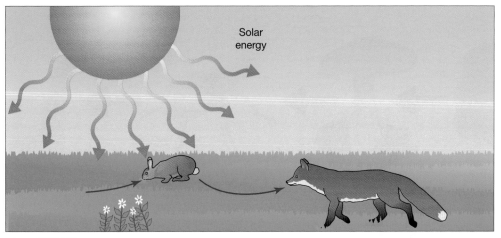

Solar energy

▲ **Figure 3**   *A simple food chain.*

The organisms in the food chain form a community and can be divided into two categories based on how they get their food: **producers** and **consumers**.

At the start of the chain are the producers, which capture the sun's energy by photosynthesis. Organisms that can do this are called **photoautotrophs**. Plants are the main producers on land (terrestrial ecosystems); in oceans, phytoplankton (microscopic plants) are the most important. Plants capture approximately 1% of light energy from the sun and convert it into chemical energy through photosynthesis; the energy is now in the form of **biomass**. Consumers, also known as **heterotrophs**, are categorised according to what they eat. The most common categories are **herbivores**, **carnivores** and **omnivores**. Herbivores eat plants to obtain chemical energy, consuming approximately 10% of the plant biomass. Herbivores are captured and consumed by carnivores which obtain about 10% of the chemical energy stored by herbivores. Carnivores also feed on other carnivores. Omnivores eat plants and animals. Some organisms have specialised feeding relationships. Parasites use the bodies of other organisms while they are still alive and saprophytes grow on the surface of dead or decaying matter.

Q

2 a) **The sun radiates 1 600 000 kilojoules per square metre per year ($kJ\,m^{-2}\,yr^{-1}$). Calculate the percentage efficiency of photosynthesis of a plant that captures 153 000 $kJ\,m^{-2}\,yr^{-1}$ of energy.**

   b) **If a rabbit consumes 9% of this plant's biomass, how many kilojoules per square metre per year does it obtain?**

   c) **Suggest why only a small amount of light energy from the sun is converted into chemical energy through photosynthesis.**

The food chain described on the previous page is an example of a **grazing food chain**, because the primary consumers feed on living matter. There is a second type of food chain called a **detritus food chain**, in which the primary consumers feed on dead or decaying matter, shown in figure 4.

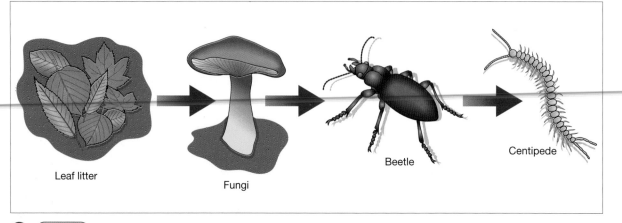

Leaf litter

Fungi

Beetle

Centipede

▲ (Figure 4) *A detritus food chain. Dead plant material forms a litter on the ground known as **detritus**. This provides a source of food for detritivores (e.g. earthworms) and decomposers (e.g. soil fungi and bacteria).*

These organisms can be split into two types: **detritivores** and **decomposers**. Detritivores feed on dead organic matter, which passes through their digestive system. Decomposers can then decompose the waste matter that is produced. Decomposers secrete digestive enzymes onto the dead or decaying material and then absorb any soluble molecules such as amino acids. The combined activities of the decomposers and detritivores lead to the breakdown of materials (decomposition) and recycling of nutrients.

Transfer of energy

When organic molecules are broken down in cellular respiration, the energy becomes available to the cells to use for synthesising new molecules, active transport, cell division and muscle contraction. As energy is used in cells, some of it is released as heat which is unsuitable for use in organisms. Heat energy escapes into the environment and radiates into space. Birds and mammals have adapted to make use of the waste heat to regulate their body temperatures. Other organisms use heat from the environment to keep warm.

Each level in a food chain is called a **trophic level**. Producers form the first trophic level, **primary consumers** (herbivores) the second, **secondary consumers** (carnivores) the third, **tertiary consumers** the fourth, and so on. Decomposers are not normally shown in a food chain.

Simple food chains rarely exist; there are very few organisms that eat just one other kind of organism. In nature, each organism will have a number of different organisms from which to choose. Therefore in an ecosystem the flow of energy can follow several food chains. The combination of all the food chains in an ecosystem is a **food web**.

Food webs

A food web describes how energy passes from one organism to another in a given ecosystem, i.e. it shows how the members of the community interact. Look at the terrestrial and aquatic food web in figure 5. You can see that it is made up of many food chains.

Figure 5 A food web.

3 a) **Identify the following using the food web shown in figure 5: i) producer, ii) primary consumer, iii) secondary consumer, iv) tertiary consumer, v) herbivore, vi) carnivore.**
   b) **Name an organism at each of the following trophic levels: i) first; ii) second; iii) third; iv) fourth.**
   c) **Draw three food chains from the food web above.**

As energy is transferred from trophic level to trophic level, the majority is lost through heat and metabolic use. The loss is about 80% to 95% depending on the food chain. This loss of energy explains why food chains are usually short. A third level of carnivores is very rare because there is not enough energy available for their survival.

Energy budget of a plant

Figure 6 shows the energy budget of a plant.

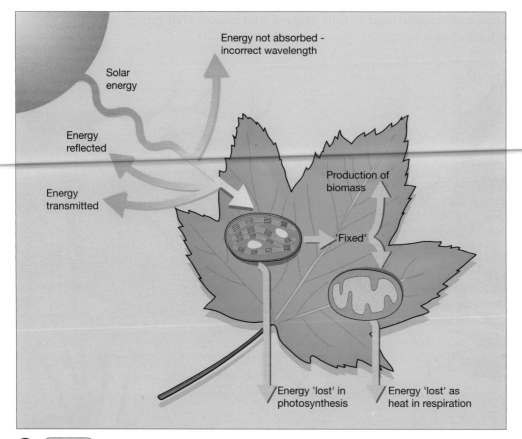

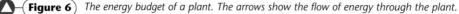

Figure 6   The energy budget of a plant. The arrows show the flow of energy through the plant.

Not all the solar energy that is available at the leaf surface is captured. The solar energy that is not captured is 'lost' in a number of ways: by reflection from the leaf, by transmission through the leaf, or because it is not of the correct wavelength. Of the energy absorbed by the chlorophyll, only about 20% is converted to chemical energy in photosynthesis and the rest is 'lost' as heat. The rate at which this chemical energy is stored by plants is known as **gross primary productivity** (**GPP**). Up to 50% of the GPP is 'used' by a plant in respiration. The remaining energy is known as **net primary productivity** (**NPP**). The relationship between GPP and NPP is given as:

NPP = GPP − Respiration 'losses'

Q 4 a) The total solar energy falling on a plant is $1 \times 10^6 \, \text{kJ m}^{-2} \text{yr}^{-1}$. Calculate the gross primary productivity (GPP) if only 2% of the total solar energy is converted to chemical energy by photosynthesis.

b) Calculate the net primary productivity if 30% of the GPP is 'used' by the plant in respiration.

Energy budget of an animal

Figure 7 shows the energy budget of a consumer.

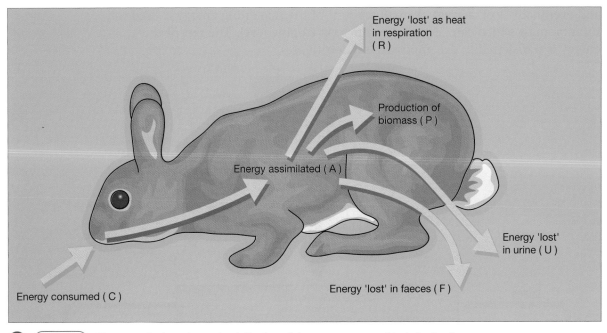

Energy 'lost' as heat in respiration (R)

Production of biomass (P)

Energy assimilated (A)

Energy 'lost' in urine (U)

Energy 'lost' in faeces (F)

Energy consumed (C)

Figure 7 *The energy budget of an animal. The fate of the energy consumed is similar in all consumers. Mammals are less efficient at converting assimilated energy into the production of biomass because they use a large amount of energy maintaining body temperature.*

The energy consumed does not equal the NPP of the plants eaten by the rabbit because feeding is inefficient. Of the food eaten, about 60% is 'lost' in faeces without being digested. Even though about 40% of the energy consumed is assimilated (digested and absorbed), only about 4% is used in the production of biomass. Almost 90% of energy assimilated is 'consumed' by respiration and eventually 'lost' as heat. Energy is also 'lost' in urine.

The energy budget of an animal can be given as:

$$C = P + R + U + F$$

> **Q** 5 a) Using the letters given in figure 7, write an equation to show the total energy loss, E.
>
> b) i) For every 150 kJ of energy consumed by the rabbit, 56.25 kJ of energy is assimilated. Calculate the percentage of consumed energy assimilated.
>
> ii) Only 4% of the energy assimilated is used in the production of biomass. Calculate the amount of energy that will be available for a secondary consumer.
>
> iii) What happens to the energy assimilated that is not used in the production of biomass?

Energy flow through an ecosystem

Energy flow diagrams can be used to show what happens to the energy that passes into each trophic level. Most of the energy is consumed by respiration and eventually 'lost' as heat. A small amount of the remaining energy is used to form biomass which can be passed to the next trophic level. The rest of the energy is transferred to decomposers and detritivores.

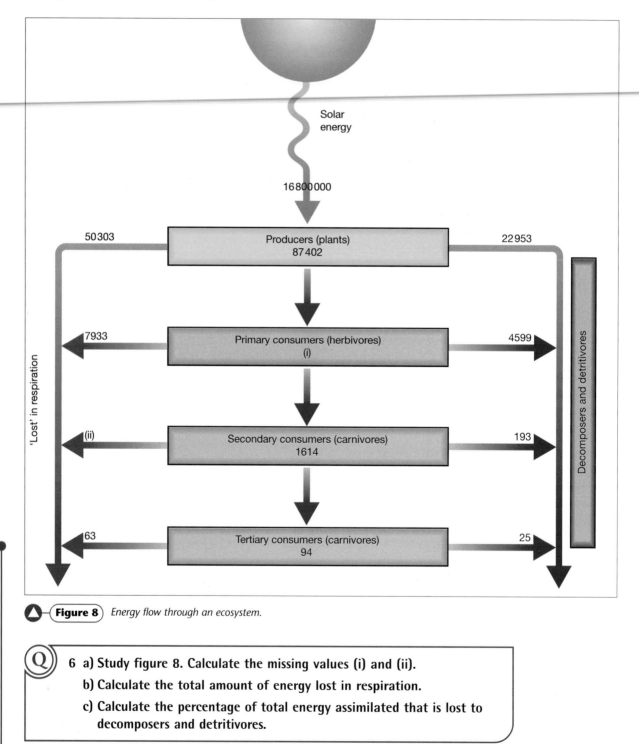

Figure 8　*Energy flow through an ecosystem.*

Q　**6 a)** Study figure 8. Calculate the missing values (i) and (ii).

　　b) Calculate the total amount of energy lost in respiration.

　　c) Calculate the percentage of total energy assimilated that is lost to decomposers and detritivores.

Key ideas 195–202

- Photosynthesis is the major route by which energy enters an ecosystem.

- Energy is transferred through the trophic levels in food chains and food webs and is dissipated.

- Gross primary productivity is the total energy converted to chemical energy in photosynthesis and represents about 1% of the solar energy available.

- Net primary productivity is the energy available for consumption by primary consumers.

- In a producer, energy is 'lost' by reflection from leaves, by transmission through leaves, in the reactions of photosynthesis and respiration, and because it is not the correct wavelength.

- Consumers 'lose' energy as heat from respiration, in urine and in faeces.

- Energy may be lost from individuals at any trophic level when they die. Energy in urine, faeces and dead bodies is available to decomposers and detritivores.

- The total producer biomass and the efficiency of energy transfer between trophic levels limit the number of trophic levels.

Pyramids

The trophic levels of any ecosystem can be arranged in a pyramid shape, with the first trophic level being placed at the bottom and subsequent levels being placed on top of each other. Ecological pyramids can be drawn to show changes in number, biomass or energy content of the organisms at each trophic level. The type of pyramid used depends on the type of data that have been collected and what features of the ecosystem you are interested in.

Memory joggers

- The number of organisms at each stage of a food chain can be shown as a pyramid of numbers.
- The mass of living material (biomass) at each stage in a food chain is less than it was at the previous stage.
- The biomass at each stage can be drawn to scale and shown as a pyramid of biomass.

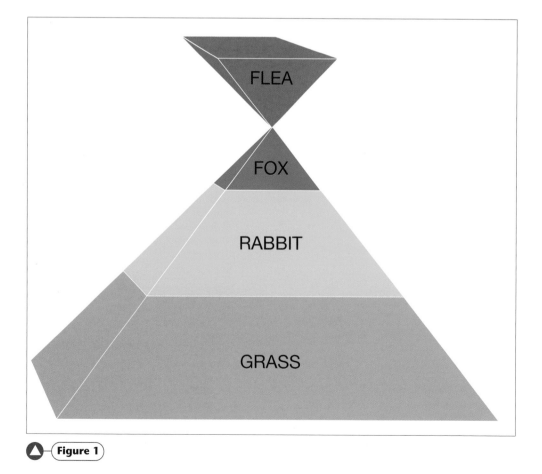

Figure 1

Pyramids of number

A **pyramid of numbers** shows the number of organisms at each trophic level in an ecosystem or food chain. The greater the number of organisms at a trophic level, the wider the section of the pyramid, therefore the width of each block is proportional to the numbers of organisms present at each trophic level. In most pyramids of numbers, each successive trophic level is occupied by fewer organisms, as shown in figure 2.

One disadvantage of showing a food chain in this way is that the range of numbers can be enormous; for example four billion phytoplankton (microscopic plants) support eleven fish which in turn support only one bird. A second disadvantage is that the pyramid may be inverted; for example one oak tree can provide food for hundreds of leaf-eating insects, a few blue tits and only one sparrowhawk, as shown in figure 3. A similar effect occurs with parasites, which are smaller and more numerous than their hosts.

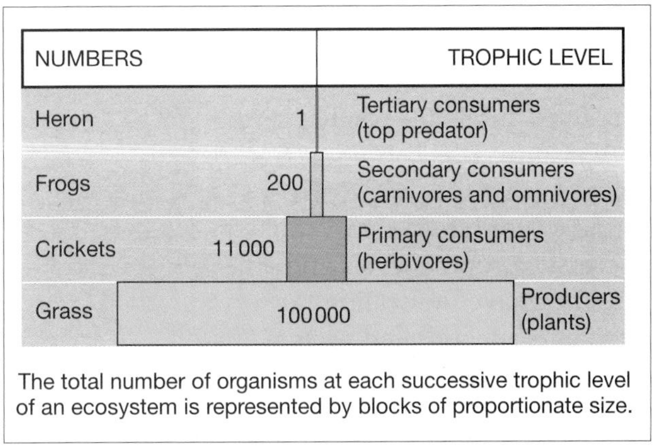

NUMBERS		TROPHIC LEVEL
Heron	1	Tertiary consumers (top predator)
Frogs	200	Secondary consumers (carnivores and omnivores)
Crickets	11 000	Primary consumers (herbivores)
Grass	100 000	Producers (plants)

The total number of organisms at each successive trophic level of an ecosystem is represented by blocks of proportionate size.

 Figure 2 *A pyramid of numbers is based on the number of organisms at each trophic level.*

ORGANISM	TROPHIC LEVEL
Sparrowhawk	Tertiary consumers
Blue tits	Secondary consumers
Insects	Primary consumers
Oak tree	Producers

For some ecosystems the pyramid of numbers can be inverted. For example, a woodland has a small number of large producers that support a much larger number of small primary consumers.

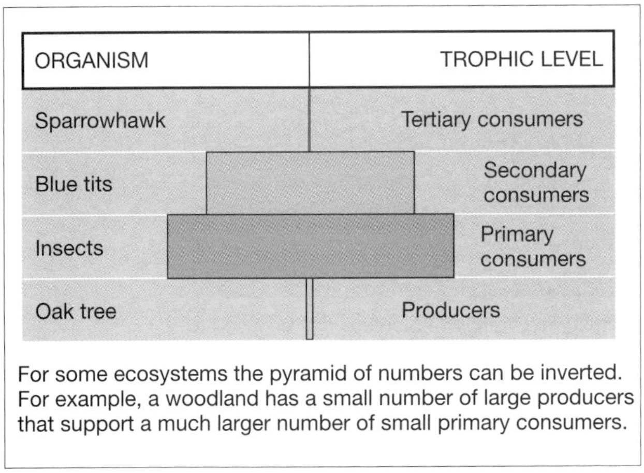

Figure 3 *An inverted pyramid of numbers can occur when the producer is very large.*

Q 1 a) **One billion producers support 400 000 primary consumers, which support 24 000 secondary consumers, which in turn support one tertiary consumer. Construct a pyramid of numbers to represent this food chain.**

b) **What process allows the producers to provide food for the primary consumers?**

c) **Explain why there are fewer secondary consumers than primary consumers.**

Pyramids of biomass

A pyramid of numbers does not take into account the size of an organism whereas a **pyramid of biomass** shows the total biomass at each successive trophic level. **Biomass** is a quantitative estimate of the total mass and is calculated for each trophic level as follows:

Biomass = Number of individuals × Mass of each individual

Biomass may be represented as total volume or as dry mass. Live mass can be used but gives unreliable results. A typical pyramid of biomass, figure 4, shows a progressive reduction of biomass in successive trophic levels and does not have the scaling problems encountered with a pyramid of numbers.

However, there are still situations where inverted pyramids of biomass can occur, as shown in figure 5. A pyramid of biomass shows the biomass at one particular time and does not take into account the fact that biomass can vary at each trophic level over time. This variation can occur if the producer level includes organisms that can rapidly reproduce leading to a high productivity (productivity is a measure of the energy content of each trophic level) over a period of time.

For example, in a marine ecosystem **zooplankton** (microscopic animals) quickly eat phytoplankton. Since the **phytoplankton** do not have time to achieve a high biomass, they reproduce very quickly (have a high turnover rate).

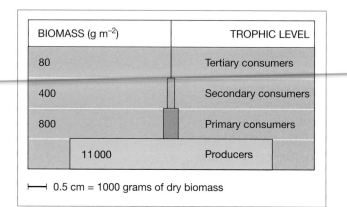

BIOMASS (g m^{-2})	TROPHIC LEVEL
80	Tertiary consumers
400	Secondary consumers
800	Primary consumers
11 000	Producers

├─────┤ 0.5 cm = 1000 grams of dry biomass

▲ **Figure 4**   *A pyramid of biomass eliminates the effect of body mass by comparing total population biomass (in grams per square metre).*

BIOMASS (g $^{-2}$)	TROPHIC LEVEL
Human	Tertiary consumers
Perch	Secondary consumers
Zooplankton	Primary consumers
Phytoplankton	Producers

In aquatic ecosystems, the pyramid of biomass can be inverted because phytoplankton grow and reproduce rapidly.

▲ **Figure 5**   *An inverted pyramid of biomass can occur when the producer has a high turnover rate.*

(Q) 2 a) **In January, 4 g m^{-2} of phytoplankton support 21 g m^{-2} of zooplankton. Draw a pyramid of biomass to represent this food chain.**

b) **Over the whole year, the total biomass of zooplankton exceeds the biomass of phytoplankton. Suggest a reason why this occurs.**

Pyramids of energy

A **pyramid of energy**, figure 6, shows the flow of energy through each trophic level of an ecosystem or food chain during a fixed period of time, therefore it compares productivity.

Productivity is measured in kilojoules per square metre per year ($kJ\,m^{-2}\,yr^{-1}$) and is obtained by converting the mass of new organic material produced per unit area per year into an equivalent energy value. A pyramid of energy is never inverted. It illustrates the fact that there is a dramatic reduction in energy content at each trophic level.

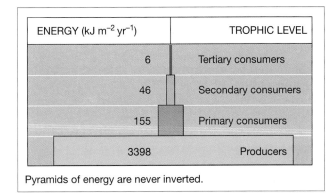

ENERGY ($kJ\,m^{-2}\,yr^{-1}$)	TROPHIC LEVEL
6	Tertiary consumers
46	Secondary consumers
155	Primary consumers
3398	Producers

Pyramids of energy are never inverted.

 Figure 6 *A pyramid of energy shows the flow of energy through each trophic level of an ecosystem.*

Variations in productivity

A pyramid of energy can be used to show gross primary productivity and net primary productivity, as in figure 7.

Ecosystems differ in their productivity. Terrestrial communities are generally more productive than aquatic ones. This is partly because of the greater availability of light for photosynthesis and partly because of higher concentrations of available nutrients.

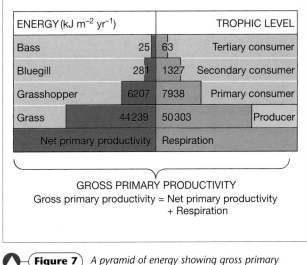

ENERGY ($kJ\,m^{-2}\,yr^{-1}$)			TROPHIC LEVEL
Bass	25	63	Tertiary consumer
Bluegill	281	1327	Secondary consumer
Grasshopper	6207	7938	Primary consumer
Grass	44239	50303	Producer
	Net primary productivity	Respiration	

GROSS PRIMARY PRODUCTIVITY
Gross primary productivity = Net primary productivity + Respiration

Figure 7 *A pyramid of energy showing gross primary productivity and net primary productivity.*

Q 3 **Using the information given in figure 7:**

   a) calculate the gross primary productivity

   b) name the factors that determine the gross primary productivity

   c) calculate the percentage energy consumed by the grasshopper that is available to the bluegill.

Key ideas 204–207

- Ecological pyramids provide information about each trophic level in an ecosystem.

- A pyramid of numbers represents the numbers of different organisms at each trophic level in an ecosystem at any one time.

- A pyramid of biomass represents the biomass at each trophic level at any one time.

- Biomass is calculated by multiplying the number of individuals by the mass of each individual.

- The units of biomass are mass per unit area ($kg\,m^{-2}$).

- A pyramid of energy represents the flow of energy through each trophic level of an ecosystem during a fixed time period.

- The units of energy are energy per unit area per year ($kJ\,m^{-2}yr^{-1}$).

Recycling

A food chain with decomposers included is called a **nutrient cycle**.
When trees shed their leaves in autumn the leaves decay; the chemical energy
that was stored during photosynthesis is released and escapes from the
ecosystem in the form of heat energy. However, the chemicals, such as
organic compounds, obtained form the water, air and minerals in the soil are
constantly recycled. Before they can be reused, the chemicals must be
converted from complex organic compounds to simple inorganic forms by
decomposers. If the leaves are removed before decomposition has occurred,
the nutrients and energy locked in them are also removed. The nutrient cycle
has been broken and the ecosystem is put at risk. Two elements that are
extremely important to living organisms are carbon and nitrogen.

Memory joggers

- Living things remove materials from the environment for growth and other
  processes.
- These materials are returned to the environment either in waste materials
  or when living things die and decay.
- Materials decay because they are broken down (digested) by micro-organisms.
- Organisms that feed on dead or decaying organisms are called saprophytes.
- Saprophytic fungi obtain nutrients by extracellular digestion.
- Micro-organisms digest materials faster in warm, moist conditions. Many
  micro-organisms are also more active when there is plenty of oxygen.
- The decay process releases substances that plants need to grow.
- In a stable community, processes that return materials balance the
  processes that remove materials. The materials are constantly recycled.
- The constant cycling of carbon is called the carbon cycle.

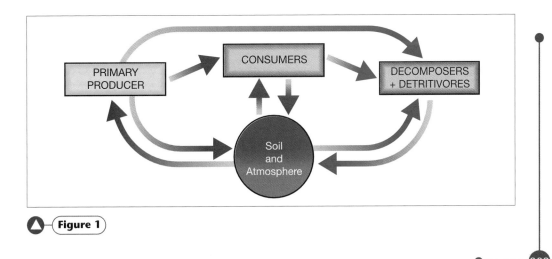

Figure 1

The carbon cycle

All life is based on carbon. Proteins, carbohydrates and other molecules essential to life contain carbon, so living organisms must have carbon available to them. Carbon cycles between the abiotic and the biotic components of the environment. It is stored as:

- organic molecules in living and dead organisms
- carbon dioxide in the atmosphere
- organic matter in soils
- fossil fuels and sedimentary rock, e.g. limestone
- dissolved carbon dioxide and calcium carbonate in the oceans.

Ecosystems gain most of their carbon in the form of carbon dioxide from the atmosphere. The carbon cycle is shown in figure 2.

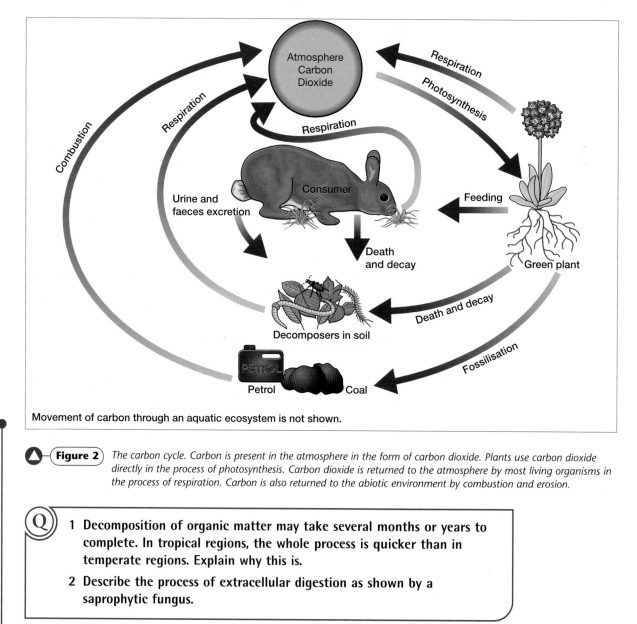

Movement of carbon through an aquatic ecosystem is not shown.

Figure 2 *The carbon cycle. Carbon is present in the atmosphere in the form of carbon dioxide. Plants use carbon dioxide directly in the process of photosynthesis. Carbon dioxide is returned to the atmosphere by most living organisms in the process of respiration. Carbon is also returned to the abiotic environment by combustion and erosion.*

Q
1 **Decomposition of organic matter may take several months or years to complete. In tropical regions, the whole process is quicker than in temperate regions. Explain why this is.**

2 **Describe the process of extracellular digestion as shown by a saprophytic fungus.**

Cycling carbon

During photosynthesis, plants remove carbon dioxide from the atmosphere and **fix** (incorporate) it into complex organic compounds. Some of these compounds are then passed along food chains through feeding. Carbon is released from ecosystems as carbon dioxide by the process of respiration. Decomposition is the main process that recycles nutrients back into the soil. This recycling of carbon is known as the **carbon cycle**.

A number of organisms have a role in the decomposition of organic matter, such as those shown in figure 3. Decomposers, such as fungi and bacteria, secrete digestive enzymes onto the organic matter and absorb the digestion products. This type of feeding is called **saprophytic nutrition**.

Fragments of decomposing material are called detritus. Many small animals, known as **detritivores**, feed on detritus and so contribute to the decomposition process. Detritivores include soil organisms such as earthworms, arthropods (ants, beetles and woodlice) and gastropods (slugs and snails). These organisms break down the organic matter into smaller pieces which can be decomposed by smaller organisms such as fungi and bacteria.

Figure 3 (a) Fungi play an important role in the decomposition process, converting organic matter back into inorganic molecules.
(b) Earthworms are one of the most important detritivores. They consume large amounts of organic matter and soil. As the organic matter passes through the digestive system, it is subjected to digestive enzymes and the grinding action of soil particles.

Q 3 The rate of decomposition varies according to the environmental conditions.

i) Make a list of the factors that you think affect the rate of decomposition.

ii) Describe and explain the effect of the factors you have listed on the rate of decomposition.

The nitrogen cycle

Living organisms use nitrogen to produce a number of complex organic molecules, such as proteins and nucleic acids. The largest store of nitrogen is found in the atmosphere where it exists as a gas. Other major stores include organic matter found in soils and oceans. Despite its abundance in the atmosphere, nitrogen is often the most limiting nutrient for plant growth. This problem occurs because most plants take up nitrogen in two forms: **ammonium (NH_4^+)** and **nitrate (NO_3^-)**. Most plants obtain the nitrogen they need as inorganic nitrate from the soil solution. Animals receive nitrogen by feeding. The nitrogen cycle is shown in figure 4.

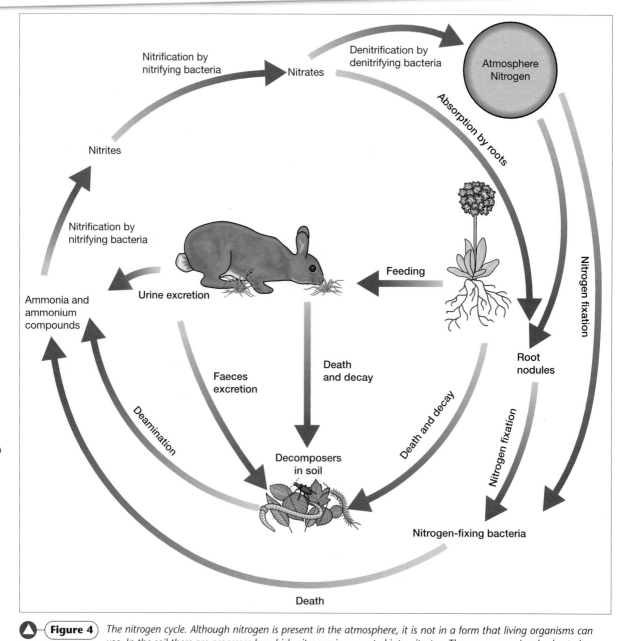

Figure 4   *The nitrogen cycle. Although nitrogen is present in the atmosphere, it is not in a form that living organisms can use. In the soil there are processes by which nitrogen is converted into nitrates. These processes involve bacteria.*

Cycling nitrogen

Living organisms use nitrogen to produce organic molecules, such as proteins. Saprophytic fungi and bacteria decompose proteins via amino acids to ammonia when an organism dies. This process is called **deamination** and is shown in figure 5. Deamination involves the removal of an amino group ($-NH_2$) and a hydrogen atom; these combine to form ammonia (NH_3).

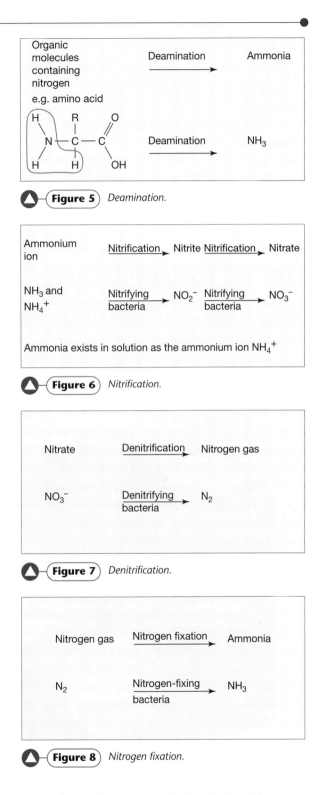

Figure 5 Deamination.

A specific group of bacteria, **nitrifying bacteria**, chemically alter most of the ammonia to nitrite. Further modification by another type of nitrifying bacteria converts the nitrite to nitrate ions. Both of these processes are known as **nitrification** and are shown in figure 6.

Figure 6 Nitrification.

Nitrate is very soluble and can be absorbed by roots. Some of the nitrate ions are converted back into nitrogen by **denitrifying bacteria** in the process of **denitrification**, shown in figure 7.

Figure 7 Denitrification.

Almost all the nitrogen found in a terrestrial ecosystem originally came from the atmosphere. Small proportions enter the soil in rainfall or through the effects of lightning. The majority is biochemically fixed within the soil by specialised micro-organisms, **nitrogen-fixing bacteria**. The process is known as **nitrogen fixation** and is shown in figure 8.

Figure 8 Nitrogen fixation.

Legumes (members of the bean family) and some other plants form mutualistic relationships with nitrogen-fixing bacteria. The bacteria convert nitrogen into ammonia. In exchange for the nitrogen source, the bacteria receive from the plant carbohydrates and special structures (nodules) in roots where they can exist in a moist environment.

Composting

Decomposition occurs graduallly and involves both chemical and biological processes. This breakdown of organic materials has been taking place in nature since life started appearing on Earth. More recently, gardeners and horticulturists have controlled the process. Organic materials such as vegetable matter and animal manure can be converted to a form suitable for use as a soil improver. The process used is called **composting** and the final product of composting is called **compost**.

In the early stages of composting **chemical decomposers**, such as bacteria, fungi, protozoa, actinomycetes and other saprophytic organisms, feed upon decaying organic matter. In the later stages **physical decomposers**, such as mites, millipedes, centipedes, springtails, beetles and earthworms, further break down the composting material.

Life in a compost heap

Some of the organisms involved in composting are shown in figure 9.

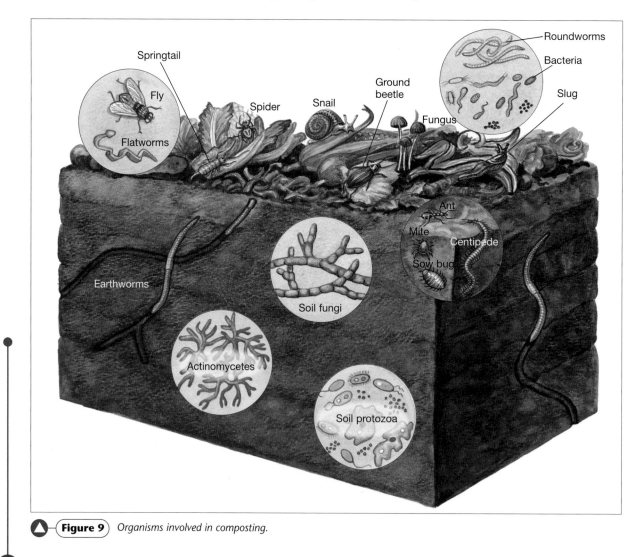

Figure 9 *Organisms involved in composting.*

Bacteria are the most important organisms in composting because they are the most nutritionally diverse of all organisms (i.e. as a group they can eat nearly anything). Most compost bacteria are **heterotrophic**, obtaining nutrition from living or dead organic compounds.

Fungi obtain energy by breaking down organic matter in dead plants and animals. They are involved in the later stages of chemical decomposition. Protozoa are the simplest form of animal organism. Although they are single-celled and microscopic in size, they are larger and more complex in their activities than most bacteria. They are present in fewer numbers than bacteria and so they have a smaller role to play.

Actinomycetes are a group of higher bacteria similar to fungi and moulds, and are important in the formation of humus, the organic component of soil.

Physical decomposers are larger than chemical decomposers. They chew and grind their way through the compost heap and are higher up in the food chain.

4 To which kingdoms do i) bacteria and ii) protozoa belong?

Key ideas 209–215

- Decomposers break down complex organic molecules into simple inorganic molecules that can be recycled.
- Carbon dioxide is made available for reuse in the carbon cycle.
- Nitrogen is made available for reuse in the nitrogen cycle.
- Detritivores feed on detritus, so contributing to the decomposition process.
- Decomposers break down proteins via amino acids to ammonia when an organism dies. Deamination involves the removal of an amino group and a hydrogen atom; these combine to form ammonia.
- Nitrifying bacteria recycle ammonium to nitrate via nitrite.
- Atmospheric nitrogen is made available by nitrogen-fixing bacteria.
- Nitrate may be converted to nitrogen by denitrifying bacteria.

Dynamics of ecosystems

In the natural world, many of the interactions between organisms are to do with eating or being eaten. However, there are just as many relationships in which organisms work together, often to the advantage of those involved.

An ecosystem supports a certain size of population of any one species. All living organisms tend to reproduce in greater numbers than can survive. The size of a population may be limited by the total amount of food or nutrients available, competition for food or nutrients, living space and light, predation or grazing, and disease.

Memory joggers

- Plants often compete with each other for space, and for water and nutrients from the soil.
- Animals often compete with each other for space, food, water and mates.
- Animals that kill and eat other animals are called predators; the animals they kill and eat are called prey.
- In a community, the number of animals of a particular species is usually limited by the amount of food available.
- If the population of prey increases, more food is available for its predators and their population may also increase.
- If the population of predators increases, more food is needed and the population of prey will decrease.

Figure 1

Living together

The term 'community' is used to describe all the populations of different organisms living in a particular area at a given time. They vary in size, lack precise boundaries and are rarely completely isolated. Every organism has its own role within the structure and functions of an ecosystem; this is its **ecological niche**.

There are two aspects to an organism's niche: the role the organism *could* play in the community and the role it actually fulfils. The potential niche of an organism is its **fundamental niche**; however, factors such as competition with other species may exclude it from part of this niche. Therefore, the lifestyle that an organism actually pursues and the resources it actually uses make up its **realised niche**.

Look at the example in figure 2. The fundamental niches of two different species overlap. Species A is able to out-compete species B. This results in a restricted niche for species B.

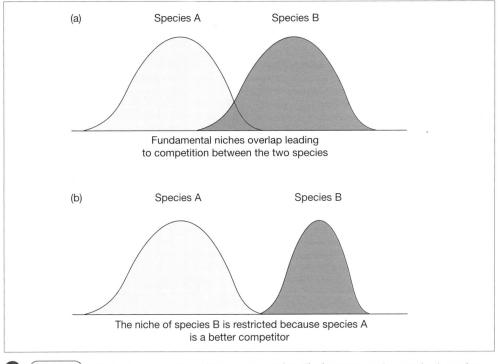

(a) Species A   Species B

Fundamental niches overlap leading
to competition between the two species

(b) Species A   Species B

The niche of species B is restricted because species A
is a better competitor

Figure 2 *The fundamental niches of two species overlap. The better competitor, species A, restricts the fundamental niche of species B.*

All natural communities consist of numerous species, many of which compete to some extent, and the complex interactions among them produce the realised niche of each.

If two species occupy the same ecological niche, the interactions between them will lead to the extinction of one of the species. This is known as **competitive exclusion**. In this process, one species is excluded from a niche as a result of competition between the two species (interspecific competition). Interspecific competition determines a species' realised niche.

Biotic interactions

Biotic factors regulate the size of populations more intensely than abiotic factors. Interacting species have an enormous influence on the size of each other's populations. This influence can occur at two different levels: **interspecific** interactions occur between different species; **intraspecific** interactions occur between members of the same species.

Competition

When two of more organisms in the same community compete for a resource that is in limited supply, such as food, water or nesting space, a competition occurs. If the competition is among individuals of the same species it is called intraspecific competition. Competition among individuals of different species is interspecific competition.

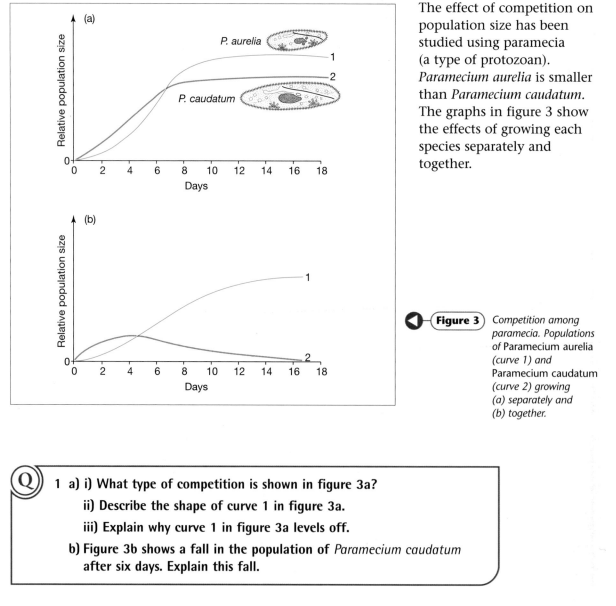

The effect of competition on population size has been studied using paramecia (a type of protozoan). *Paramecium aurelia* is smaller than *Paramecium caudatum*. The graphs in figure 3 show the effects of growing each species separately and together.

Figure 3 *Competition among paramecia. Populations of* Paramecium aurelia *(curve 1) and* Paramecium caudatum *(curve 2) growing (a) separately and (b) together.*

Q

1 a) i) What type of competition is shown in figure 3a?

　ii) Describe the shape of curve 1 in figure 3a.

　iii) Explain why curve 1 in figure 3a levels off.

b) Figure 3b shows a fall in the population of *Paramecium caudatum* after six days. Explain this fall.

Exploitation or interference

Competition may be the result of two different processes: **exploitation** and **interference**. Competition by exploitation occurs between individuals when the indirect effects of two or more species or individuals reduce the supply of the limited resource or resources needed for survival. The exclusion of one organism by another can only occur when the dominant organism requires less of the resource to survive. Also, the dominant organism must be able to reduce the quantity of the resource to a critical level with respect to the other organism. Exploitation does not always cause the exclusion of a species from a community. It may just cause a reduction in potential growth of the species.

Competition by interference occurs when an individual directly prevents the physical establishment of another individual in a portion of a habitat. This is shown in figure 4. Established plants can pre-empt the invasion and colonisation of other individuals by means of dense root mats, peat and litter accumulation, or mechanical abrasion.

 Figure 4 Established plants prevent the invasion and colonisation of other individuals by means of dense root mats.

Amensalism

Amensalism is an interaction where one species suffers and the other interacting species experiences no effect. For example, some plants produce and release chemical substances that inhibit the growth of another species.

An example of amensalism is shown by the black walnut tree (*Juglans nigra*), figure 5. Black walnut trees secrete a secondary substance called juglone, which inhibits the growth of any trees, shrubs, grasses and herbaceous plants found growing nearby.

Figure 5 Black walnut trees secrete juglone, a secondary substance that inhibits the growth of trees, shrubs, grasses and herbaceous plants growing nearby.

Symbiosis

Symbiosis is any intimate relationship or association between members of two or more different species. The partners of the relationship are called **symbionts**. They may benefit from, be unaffected by or be harmed by the relationship.

Mutual benefit

Mutualism is the name given to associations between pairs of species that bring mutual benefit. The individuals in the populations of each species tend to grow, reproduce and survive at a higher rate when in the presence of individuals of the other species.

One example of mutualism is lichen, shown in figure 6. Lichen is not a single organism but consists of a fungus and an alga in symbiosis. Both organisms benefit by living together. The algal cells contain chlorophyll and can make carbohydrate and other food products needed for the survival of both organisms. The fungus provides water and minerals for the alga. The fungus is made up of tiny, thread-like structures that are able to retain water and provide a shelter for the alga.

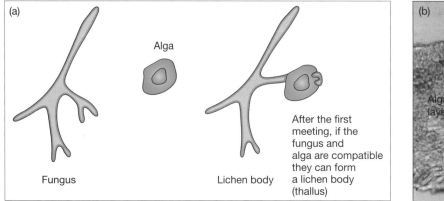
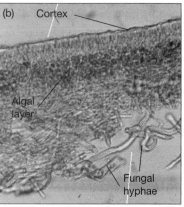

Figure 6　*(a) The formation of a lichen body. (b) A cross-section through a lichen. The top of the lichen has a hard surface called the cortex. The algal layer is located below the upper fungal layer.*

More common in nature is non-symbiotic mutualism. In this interaction, the mutualists live independent lives yet cannot survive without each other.

A common example of this type of interaction is the relationship between plants and their pollinators, as shown in figure 7.

Figure 7　*Many flowering plants rely on bees to pollinate them. The reward to the pollinator is nectar (a sugary solution) and pollen. The nectar of flowers pollinated by bees contains the concentration of sugar needed to make honey. Bees use pollen to make beebread, which is eaten by their larvae.*

Taking without harming

Commensalism is a type of symbiosis in which one organism benefits and the other one is neither harmed nor helped. In most cases, the organism gains by taking advantage of the feeding habits of the other.

An example of commensalism is the relationship between a tropical tree and its **epiphytes**. Epiphytes are smaller plants that live attached to the bark of the tree's branches, as shown in figure 8. The epiphyte is not rooted in the soil and anchors itself to the tree for support, but does not obtain nutrients or water directly from the tree. Its position on the tree enables it to obtain adequate light, water and minerals.

Figure 8 *A climbing vine growing on a stilt palm. The vine is an example of an epiphyte.*

Taking with harming

Not all close relationships are beneficial. Predation is an interspecific interaction. A **predator** obtains its food at the expense of its **prey**, the animal on which it feeds. **Parasites** obtain food at the expense of their **hosts**. Although it may weaken the host, it rarely kills it. Some parasites live within the host, for example a tapeworm. Others, such as ticks, live outside the host's body.

Some parasites cause disease and sometimes the death of the host; these are known as **pathogens**. Female mosquitoes belonging to the genus *Anopheles* spread malaria. The mosquito acts as a primary host to a protozoan parasite from the genus *Plasmodium*, and humans act as a secondary host.

Insect larvae can be parasitic. Plant galls are home to various insect larvae, including those of the gall wasp. The adults lay their eggs inside a leaf which reacts by forming a growth (gall) around them. The eggs turn into larvae within the gall, later emerging as adult insects.

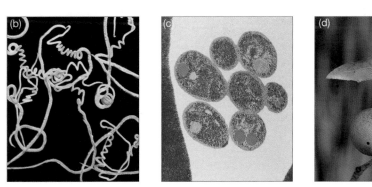

Figure 9 *Parasitic organisms. (a) A tick on a dog. (b) Tapeworms from the gut of a sheep. (c) Plasmodium – a protozoan parasite that causes malaria. (d) Wasp gall on a tree.*

Associations and the nitrogen cycle

Nitrogen in the atmosphere is fairly unreactive so it needs to be converted into more reactive forms, such as nitrate, nitrite or ammonia. This conversion, known as **nitrogen fixation**, is part of the nitrogen cycle. You will remember that this fixation is performed mainly by **nitrogen-fixing bacteria**. Nitrogen-fixing bacteria possess enzymes for converting the nitrogen atom to ammonia (inorganic nitrogen). Once in this form, the roots of the plant absorb the nitrogen which is then converted into organic nitrogen-containing compounds.

The bacterial associations that may occur in nitrogen fixation are summarised below:

- symbiosis – two organisms live together (bacteria are inside the root)
- association – two organisms are loosely associated (bacteria are not in the root, but in the area around the root)
- free-living – bacteria fix nitrogen on their own.

Seventy per cent of all the nitrogen fixed is through symbiosis.

> (Q) 2 Draw a fully labelled diagram of the nitrogen cycle.

Legume symbiosis

There are 15 000 species of legume that can undergo a mutually beneficial relationship with bacteria of the genus *Rhizobia*. The association is specific because each species of *Rhizobia* can form a relationship only with a very limited range of plants. The bacteria convert nitrogen into ammonia. In exchange for the nitrogen source, the bacteria receive carbohydrates from the plant and special structures (nodules) in roots where they can exist in a moist environment. The formation of a root nodule is shown in figure 10.

How a root nodule forms

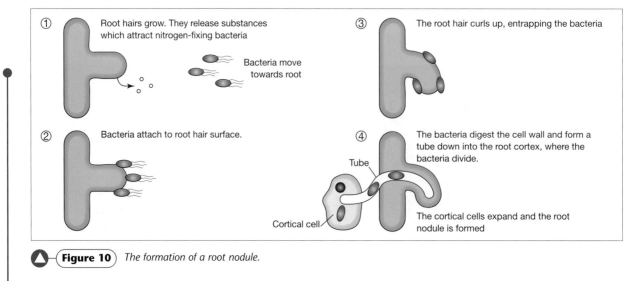

① Root hairs grow. They release substances which attract nitrogen-fixing bacteria

Bacteria move towards root

② Bacteria attach to root hair surface.

③ The root hair curls up, entrapping the bacteria

④ The bacteria digest the cell wall and form a tube down into the root cortex, where the bacteria divide.

Tube

Cortical cell

The cortical cells expand and the root nodule is formed

Figure 10 *The formation of a root nodule.*

Predation

Predation is an interspecific interaction. A predator obtains its food at the expense of its prey (the animal on which it feeds). Predator–prey relationships are important in determining the distribution of organisms in an ecosystem.

The size of the population of a predator depends on the availability of its food source. The larger the prey population, the larger the predator population it can support. However, if there are more predators they will eat more prey so the prey population will decrease. This process is shown in figure 11.

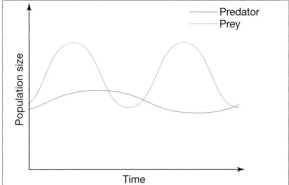

◀ **Figure 11** *Predator–prey numbers fluctuate and the numbers of each seem to be dependent on each other. The prey need to reproduce more rapidly than the predators if their population is to survive. The graph shows this theoretical cyclical predator–prey relationship.*

Predators do not usually control prey populations. Factors such as food availability and abiotic factors regulate prey populations. Most predators have more than one prey species. When one prey species becomes scarce, a predator will prey on another prey species that is available. In ecosystems where one species of prey is the main food item and there are no other prey species available, the prey population may regulate the predator cycle.

Invertebrate predators and parasites can be effective in controlling the numbers of their prey. Some farmers and gardeners use such predators as an alternative to chemical methods of controlling the size of prey populations.

Stability of populations

A global population of organisms changes over time as shown in figure 12.

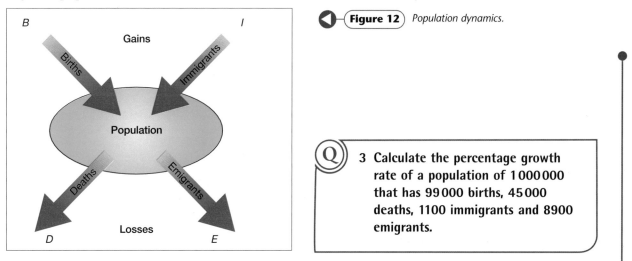

◀ **Figure 12** *Population dynamics.*

Q **3 Calculate the percentage growth rate of a population of 1 000 000 that has 99 000 births, 45 000 deaths, 1100 immigrants and 8900 emigrants.**

Maximum population growth

The maximum rate at which a population could increase under ideal conditions is known as its **biotic potential**. Different species have different biotic potentials. Biotic potential is influenced by several factors: the age at which reproduction begins, the proportion of the life span during which the organism is capable of reproducing, and the number of offspring produced during each period of reproduction.

Generally, larger organisms have lower biotic potentials. Bacteria have the greatest biotic potentials. Under ideal conditions, some bacteria can reproduce every 20 to 30 minutes. If bacteria reproduce every 30 minutes, the population will increase from one to over 1000 in five hours and to more than 1 000 000 in ten hours.

A growth curve can be plotted to show the increase in the number of bacteria versus time under ideal conditions, as in figure 13. This produces a J-shaped curve which is characteristic of exponential growth. The shape of the curve is always the same for any organism; the only variable is time. The population growth rate is slow at first due to the limited number of individuals; this is called the **lag phase**. This is followed by a sharp rise in growth rate called the **exponential phase**.

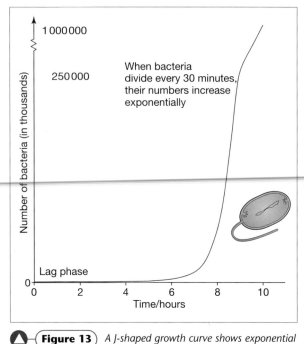

Figure 13 *A J-shaped growth curve shows exponential growth. If an organism has a low biotic potential it will take longer for the population to reach a certain size. Under ideal conditions a population will always grow exponentially.*

Q **4 A certain species of bacterium reproduces by splitting in half every 20 minutes. Starting with a single bacterium, calculate the size of the population after a) one hour, b) five hours, c) ten hours.**

Limiting population growth

Organisms cannot reproduce indefinitely at their biotic potentials because the environmental conditions are not always ideal. When conditions exist that reduce the growth rate of a population it is known as **environmental resistance**. Such conditions are known as **limiting factors** and include competition, disease, predation and the accumulation of toxic waste. The number of organisms in a population is controlled by the ability of the environment to support them. Look at figure 14.

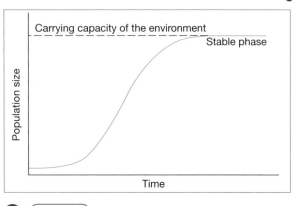

Figure 14 *Exponential growth slows as the carrying capacity is approached, producing a characteristic S-shaped curve.*

Over long periods of time, the rate of population growth for most organisms decreases to around zero. This occurs at or near the limit of the environment's ability to support the population. The highest population that can be maintained for an indefinite period of time by a particular environment is called the **carrying capacity**.

If the number of bacteria is plotted over a longer period of time, an S-shaped curve is produced. You can still see the population's initial exponential increase. This is followed by a levelling off (a plateau) as the carrying capacity is reached; this is the **stable phase**.

Decreasing population growth

Once capacity has been reached, the population size remains stable because the death rate equals the birth rate. Over a period of time, limiting factors such as food, space, water and light may cause the carrying capacity to fall. Once the death rate exceeds the birth rate the population numbers decline. This is known as the **death phase**, shown in figure 15.

In most natural populations, once the population number has reached a maximum, the population levels off and remains fairly constant; this is known as S-shaped or **sigmoid growth**. Not all populations grow in a sigmoid manner. Sometimes, when a population exceeds the carrying capacity a population crash can occur. This happens when a population has the capacity to grow faster than its food can regenerate. This is common when herbivores are introduced into an area where there are no predators.

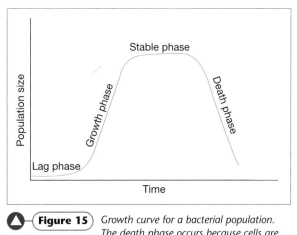

Figure 15 Growth curve for a bacterial population. The death phase occurs because cells are beginning to die so the population growth rate declines.

Key ideas 216–225

- Within a habitat a species occupies a niche which is governed by its adaptation to food and/or abiotic factors.

- An ecosystem supports a certain size of population of any one species.

- A population size may vary as a result of the effect of abiotic factors, interactions between organisms, interspecific competition, intraspecific competition and predation.

- Competition among individuals of the same species is called intraspecific competition. Competition among individuals of different species is interspecific competition.

- Symbiosis is any intimate relationship or association between members of two or more different species.

- Mutualism is an association between pairs of species that brings mutual benefit.

- Commensalism is a type of symbiosis in which one organism benefits and the other one is neither harmed nor helped.

Changing communities

Communities develop gradually through a series of stages called **seres**. The process of community development over time, which involves species in one stage being replaced by different species, is called **succession**. An area is initially colonised by certain organisms that are replaced over time by other organisms. This process continues until a relatively stable community develops, which is in equilibrium with the existing environment. This community is called a **climax community**.

Memory joggers

- The types of organism in a community vary from place to place and from time to time.
- Organisms have features that enable them to survive in the conditions in which they normally live.

| Bare soil | Grasses | Shrubs | Trees e.g. birch | Large trees e.g. oak |

Figure 1

Changing communities

The type of plant community found in an area depends mainly on the abiotic factors present, particularly climate. The most stable community in an area is called the **climax community**. Climax communities represent the dominant vegetation of an area. They are not permanent, but change as environmental conditions change. In Great Britain you would expect the climax community to be temperate deciduous woodland. Although there are areas of deciduous woodland, there are also a large number of different habitats such as heathland and grassland, as shown in figure 2. These habitats reflect a range of abiotic factors and differing amounts of human and animal impact.

Figure 2 *The heathland shown in the foreground is very different from the grassland shown in the background.*

Many changes take place within a community before the climax community is reached. However, the changes that occur follow a similar pattern. This process of change is called **succession**. Succession is an orderly sequence of events in which one community paves the way for the next stage by the accumulation of biomass. Biomass decomposes, enriches the soil and provides increasing numbers of niches for plants and animals. Succession is usually described in terms of the changes in the vegetation composition of an area, although each sere also has its own characteristic animal life.

Primary succession and climax communities

Primary succession is the change in species composition over time in a habitat that has not previously been inhabited. In natural and suitable conditions land will gradually be colonised by a range of herbaceous plants (plants whose growth dies down each year), then by shrubs and finally by trees as a climax community. Look at the series of photographs in figure 3, which show the changes that take place during uninterrupted succession.

The communities change with time because of the interaction between species and their environment. At each stage, certain species can be recognised which change the environment so that it becomes more suitable for other species. The time-scale from bare ground to climax community is in the order of hundreds or thousands of years.

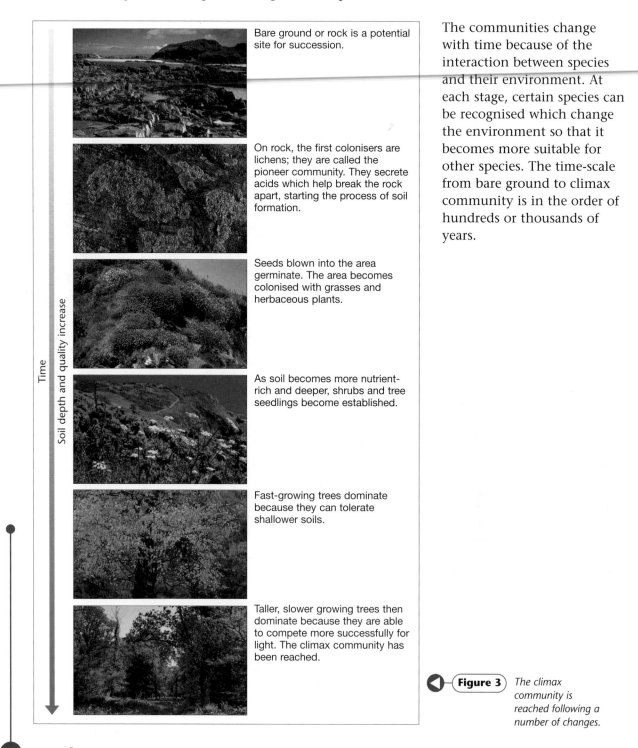

Bare ground or rock is a potential site for succession.

On rock, the first colonisers are lichens; they are called the pioneer community. They secrete acids which help break the rock apart, starting the process of soil formation.

Seeds blown into the area germinate. The area becomes colonised with grasses and herbaceous plants.

As soil becomes more nutrient-rich and deeper, shrubs and tree seedlings become established.

Fast-growing trees dominate because they can tolerate shallower soils.

Taller, slower growing trees then dominate because they are able to compete more successfully for light. The climax community has been reached.

Time — Soil depth and quality increase

Figure 3 *The climax community is reached following a number of changes.*

Primary succession on sand dunes

Sand dunes are found in coastal areas throughout the world; they are deposited by wind and water. The dunes are not permanent, but move before the wind. The sand dune environment is very severe, with high salt concentrations in the water at high tide and dehydration at low tide. The sand is deficient in certain mineral nutrients needed by plants, and only a few can tolerate the harsh conditions. As the distance from the shore increases, the sand becomes more stable and succession towards the climax community begins. You can follow the process in figure 4.

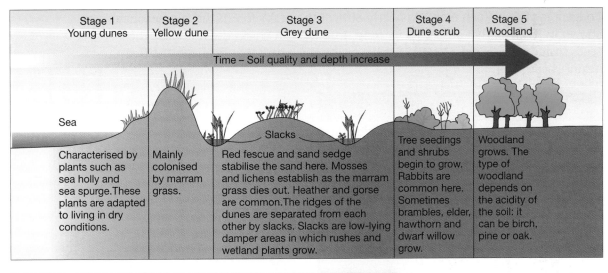

Stage 1 Young dunes	Stage 2 Yellow dune	Stage 3 Grey dune	Stage 4 Dune scrub	Stage 5 Woodland
Characterised by plants such as sea holly and sea spurge. These plants are adapted to living in dry conditions.	Mainly colonised by marram grass.	Red fescue and sand sedge stabilise the sand here. Mosses and lichens establish as the marram grass dies out. Heather and gorse are common. The ridges of the dunes are separated from each other by slacks. Slacks are low-lying damper areas in which rushes and wetland plants grow.	Tree seedings and shrubs begin to grow. Rabbits are common here. Sometimes brambles, elder, hawthorn and dwarf willow grow.	Woodland grows. The type of woodland depends on the acidity of the soil: it can be birch, pine or oak.

Time – Soil quality and depth increase

Figure 4 *Primary succession on a sand dune.*

Grasses are a common pioneer plant on a sand dune. As the grasses extend over the surface of the dune, their roots help to stabilise the dune. It is now possible for mat-forming shrubs to colonise the dunes, and the stability of the dune increases. Much later, fast-growing trees such as birch replace the shrubs, which in turn are replaced by oaks. Because the soil fertility remains low, oaks are the climax community.

Secondary succession

Secondary succession is the change in species composition over time in a habitat that has previously been inhabited. The ground becomes available because the original community has been destroyed by fire, flood or as a result of farming or industrial activities.

Fire ecology

Throughout history, landscapes such as Yellowstone National Park in the USA have been shaped by fire. Many of Yellowstone's plant species are fire-adapted. Lodgepole pines, which make up nearly 80% of the park's forests, have pinecones, shown in figure 5, that are sealed by resin. Intense heat cracks the resin and the seeds inside are released. Douglas firs have very thick bark that insulates the tree against heat.

Figure 5 *The pinecones of lodgepole pines are sealed by resin. The seeds inside are released when intense heat cracks the resin.*

In 1988 about 45% of the park was burned. In some places fires burned off all ground cover and killed all above-ground vegetation. Elsewhere some trees were left alive. This patchwork of varying burn severity allowed the forest to regenerate much faster than expected. The photographs in figure 6 show Yellowstone National Park during the 1988 fires, immediately after the fires and today. Even though the original community has been destroyed, the fires in Yellowstone have actually been beneficial to species diversity and the general 'health' of the forest.

Figure 6 *(a) A total of 50 fires started in Yellowstone National Park in 1988. (b) By September 1988 the first snows of autumn had dampened the fires. Long-term studies of the 1988 fires have been surprising. Fish and mammals survived and annual weeds covered most of the charred areas the following year. (c) Today lodgepole pines are poking through the shrubs and weeds.*

Key ideas 227–231

- In natural and suitable conditions land gradually becomes colonised. The first colonisers are herbaceous plants, then shrubs and finally trees.

- The most stable community in an area is called the climax community.

- There are many changes to a community before the climax community is reached. The changes that occur follow a similar pattern. This process of change is called succession.

- Succession is an orderly sequence of events in which one community paves the way for the next stage by the accumulation of biomass.

- There is a change in the communities with time, because of the interaction between species and their environment.

- At each stage, certain species can be recognised which change the environment so that it becomes more suitable for other species.

Ecological techniques

Ecology is the study of the interactions among organisms and between organisms and their physical environment. Within ecology, studies tend to be of two types: **autecology** is the ecology of a single species and **synecology** is the ecology of communities (organisms and their environment). Ecologists accumulate knowledge by observation, hypothesis, prediction and experiment. Making observations leads to the formulation of a hypothesis. A hypothesis is a possible answer to a question formed from your observations. From your hypothesis you can generate expected repeatable outcomes or predictions. Predictions are tested through experiments and may lead to new observations. To test a hypothesis in ecology, it is usually impractical or time-consuming to measure every individual so a small but representative part of the population is surveyed using sampling techniques. Most ecological studies also require the measurement of certain abiotic factors.

Memory joggers

- Abiotic factors that may affect organisms include temperature, amount of light, availability of water, availability of oxygen, and carbon dioxide. These factors vary according to the time of day and the time of year.
- Biotic factors (the organisms that live in an ecosystem) are also important when studying ecosystems.
- Ecologists monitor abiotic factors and sample animal populations.

Figure 1

Sampling techniques

Samples must be representative of the whole population. This can be achieved by **random sampling** or by **systematic sampling**. The sampling procedure should be repeated enough times so that a statistical test can be applied. In the study of population density, distribution and total population size, **quadrat sampling** and **transect recording** are used. Quadrat sampling is used to survey a relatively small area. To record the differences in vegetation that occur in a large area transect recording can be carried out.

Random sampling

The study area needs to be divided into a grid pattern as shown in figure 2. This is achieved by laying out two long tape measures at right angles to each other, along two sides of the study area. Random numbers are used to generate sampling co-ordinates. Each number must have an equal chance of being chosen. A quadrat is then placed at the intersection of each pair of co-ordinates and the number of individuals of each species present is recorded. This technique assumes that the area within the quadrat frame represents the whole area.

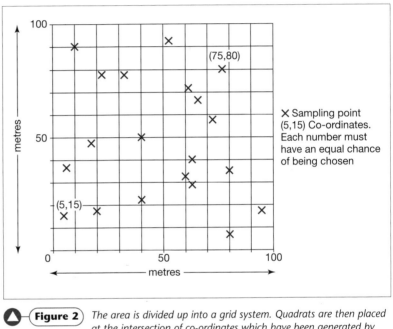

▲ **Figure 2** The area is divided up into a grid system. Quadrats are then placed at the intersection of co-ordinates which have been generated by random number tables of computers.

Systematic sampling

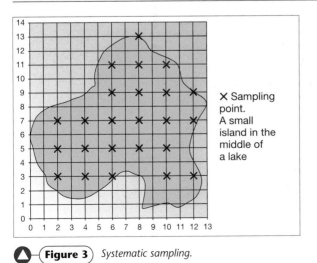

▲ **Figure 3** Systematic sampling.

For systematic sampling a grid is laid over a map of the area being studied. Sampling points are then located at regular intervals as shown in figure 3. This technique can be time-consuming but it provides more reliable data than random sampling.

Q 1 **Suggest the possible disadvantages of using random sampling.**

Quadrat sampling

A **quadrat** is a frame that outlines a known area for the purpose of sampling. There are two main types of quadrat: a **point quadrat** and a **frame quadrat**. Both types are shown in figure 4.

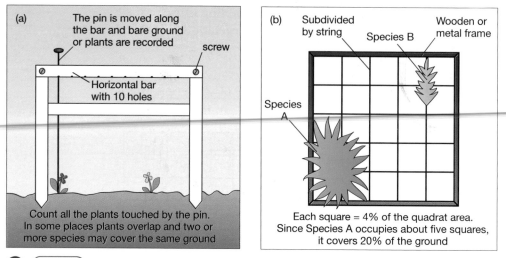

(a) The pin is moved along the bar and bare ground or plants are recorded

screw

Horizontal bar with 10 holes

Count all the plants touched by the pin. In some places plants overlap and two or more species may cover the same ground

(b) Subdivided by string　Species B　Wooden or metal frame

Species A

Each square = 4% of the quadrat area. Since Species A occupies about five squares, it covers 20% of the ground

Figure 4 *(a) A point quadrat consists of vertical legs across which is fixed a horizontal bar with ten small holes along it. Long pins are placed in each of the holes, one by one. Every time the pin touches a species, it is recorded as a 'hit'. (b) A frame quadrat is a wooden frame. It can be split into equal parts so that a grid is formed. It is placed on the ground and the species present within each part of the grid are identified and their abundance recorded.*

One problem with quadrat sampling is that some plants form clumps. This means that you may not be able to count the number of individual plants there are. To get around this problem, plant density or percentage cover can be estimated.

Quadrats are used to estimate the mean density of each species found in the study area. The procedure involves counting all the individuals in several quadrats (a quadrat must be of a known size) and using the information to work out the mean density for the whole area. To do this the following equation can be used:

$$\text{Estimated mean density} = \frac{\text{Total number of individuals counted}}{\text{Number of quadrats} \times \text{Area of each quadrat}}$$

Alternatively, the **percentage cover** may be estimated by eye. This is the proportion of the ground area, viewed from directly above, covered by the above-ground parts (stems and leaves) of the species. Regardless of which method is used, it is important that enough samples are taken to provide results that are representative of the total density.

If a point quadrat is used, each plant touched by the point of the pin is recorded and the results are converted to percentage cover. Point quadrats are more quantitative than frame quadrats because each pin touches just one plant. They are also useful where the vegetation is dense as they can sample at many different levels.

Q 2 List the advantages and disadvantages of frame quadrats.

Transect recording

Transects are a type of systematic sampling. A transect is an imaginary line along which you make systematic recordings.

Line transect sampling involves stretching a tape or rope across a habitat and sampling in a straight line at regular intervals with a quadrat, as shown in figure 5. It allows systematic sampling of an area to be carried out, although this may be time-consuming. Line transects are used where conditions and organisms change. They are particularly useful for studying different zones, for example across a sand dune system. Replication can be achieved by sampling three or more parallel transects. Point quadrats are the best method of sampling a line transect. To save time, the species touching the tape can be recorded. You can record the species all along the tape or at regular intervals.

Tape

 Figure 5 *Line transect sampling. A starting point is selected at random. A tape is stretched across the habitat and quadrats are arranged at equal intervals along it. If a point quadrat is used it is placed at right angles to the tape. The percentage cover is estimated by eye or by 'hits'.*

Belt transects can also be used. A **belt transect** is a strip across a study area, usually 0.5 m or 1 m in width. It is made by setting up two parallel line transects the chosen width apart and recording the species between them. A 0.25 m² frame quadrat is laid down at 0.5 m intervals along the transect. Species within the quadrat are counted, identified and recorded. This method is time-consuming, especially if the study area is greater than 15 m in length.

Q **3 Suggest the possible disadvantages of using a line transect.**

Monitoring abiotic factors

Most ecological studies require the measurement of abiotic factors, such as pH, light and temperature. Abiotic factors influence the abundance and distribution of animals and plants in an ecosystem.

pH

pH is a measure of the acidity or alkalinity of a solution. pH is measured on a scale of 1 to 14. A pH value of 7 is neutral; values below 7 indicate acidic conditions and above 7 alkaline conditions. Low pH affects aquatic environments. At pH values below 4.5 fish cannot survive. The low pH interferes with ion regulation, reduces the efficiency with which haemoglobin takes up oxygen, and increases mucus deposition on the gills. The pH of soil is also important. Most crop plants grow well at a pH of 6.5 and this pH will also support soil organisms. Some plants prefer acid conditions and others prefer alkaline conditions. pH meters, like the one shown in figure 6, can be used to measure the pH of water or soil samples. Alternatively, universal indicator can be used.

Figure 6 *pH meters are more accurate than universal indicator at measuring water and soil pH. Before use, the probe is washed with distilled water.*

Q 4 How does pH affect an organism's enzymes?

Light

Light is an important factor in most ecosystems, because it influences primary productivity and, therefore, the rest of the ecosystem. Light meters, like that in figure 7, are used to measure light intensity. When taking readings, it is important that the probe is always pointing in the same direction, usually towards the sun, and that readings are taken at the same height above the ground. To make comparisons, it is important that the light source remains constant while the readings are being taken. To ensure this, readings should be taken quickly.

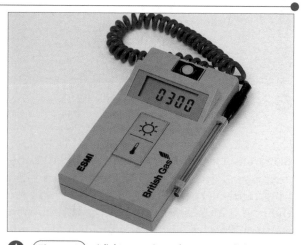

Figure 7 *A light meter is used to measure light intensity. It is not capable of measuring wavelength.*

Q 5 How does light influence primary productivity?

Temperature

Temperature is important because it can affect the metabolism of many organisms. The solubility of oxygen in water is affected by temperature: as the temperature increases, oxygen solubility decreases. An ordinary glass thermometer is too fragile for fieldwork so ecologists use electronic thermometers, like that shown in figure 8. An electronic thermometer has a metal probe which can be pushed into the soil or used to measure water at different depths.

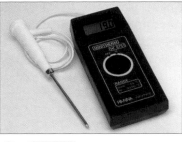

Figure 8 *Electronic thermometers with temperature probes are less fragile than glass thermometers.*

Q **6 How does temperature affect the metabolism of an organism?**

Other abiotic factors are also important, such as salinity and dissolved oxygen in aquatic environments.

Salinity is a measure of the salt content of seawater. The salts in seawater are mainly sodium and chloride, although potassium, magnesium, calcium and sulphate ions are also present. To measure salinity, a conductivity meter can be used, like the one shown in figure 9a. It measures the conductivity between two probes. The greater the salinity, the greater the conductivity.

The solubility of oxygen in water is low and is affected by temperature. Without oxygen, organisms that respire aerobically will die. An instrument called a dissolved oxygen meter, shown in figure 9b, can be used to give a measurement of the oxygen concentration in a water sample.

(a)

(b)
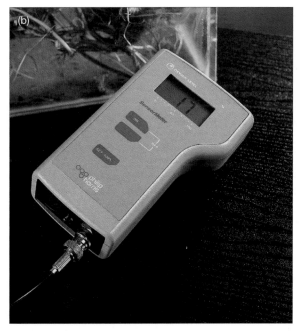

Figure 9 *(a) A conductivity meter is used to measure the salinity of seawater. (b) A dissolved oxygen meter can be used to measure the oxygen concentration in a water sample.*

Representing data

Once all the data have been collected they must be represented in a suitable form. Tables, graphs and diagrams are commonly used. Line graphs, scatter graphs, histograms, bar charts, pie graphs and pyramids are all suitable ways of representing ecological data. Three ways of representing data are shown in figure 10.

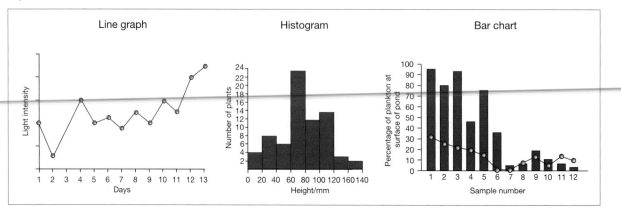

Figure 10 *Representing data.*

Another graphical method that can be used is a **kite diagram**. Look at figure 11. You can see that a kite diagram is a special type of bar graph.

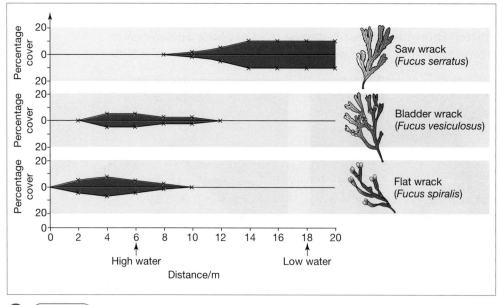

Figure 11 *Kite diagrams are used to show changes in abundance.*

The kite diagram provides a visual display of the changes in population numbers over distance or time. The data for each species are plotted on separate kite diagrams. They are often used to display transect data. The width of each band represents the relative abundance of each organism.

Statistical analysis

Statistical analysis is a tool by which results can be analysed. Standard deviation and chi-squared are two statistical tests that are used in reporting the results of ecological studies.

Standard deviation

When frequency distribution is plotted against some continuously variable data such as height, a bell-shaped curve may be obtained. This is called a normal distribution, and is shown in figure 12. Data that are normally distributed show that certain sizes contain more data points than others, and that the frequencies become progressively less as the classes are further from the **mean**. The mean is calculated by adding together all the values of the observations and dividing by the total number of observations.

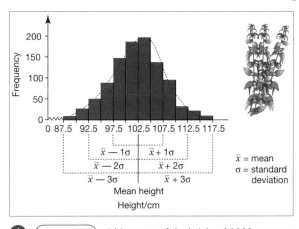

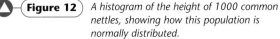

$\bar{x}$ = mean
σ = standard deviation

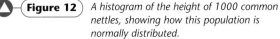

Figure 12 *A histogram of the height of 1000 common nettles, showing how this population is normally distributed.*

To show how spread out a number of observations are, you can calculate the **standard deviation**. The standard deviation is a measure of the spread of data around their mean. Once the mean is known, the standard deviation is calculated. The wider the spread in the data, the larger the standard deviation.

For a normal distribution, 68% of the data would be distributed within the range of one standard deviation above and one standard deviation below the mean, that is ±1 standard deviation of the mean; 95% would be distributed in the range ±2 standard deviations of the mean.

> **Q** 7 The heights of 50 bee orchids were measured. The mean height was calculated as 28.50 cm and the standard deviation was calculated as 5.94. In this example 68% of the bee orchid population is expected to have a height in the range 28.50 ± 5.94 cm. Using these data, what height range would you expect 95% of the bee orchid population to have?

Statistical tests can be used to compare data. They can help you decide the **significance** of the results observed. Significance is a measure of whether a difference has occurred by chance. To help you decide the significance of a result, statisticians have developed statistics tables that contain critical values. For a result to be significant there must be less than a 5% probability ($P < 0.05$) that the result was due to chance.

Chi-squared test

The **chi-squared test** (χ^2) is used to compare **observed frequencies** with **expected frequencies**, which helps you decide the significance of the results. To do this, statisticians have developed a table of critical values of chi-squared shown in table 1. For a result to be significant there must be less than a 5% probability ($P < 0.05$) that the result was due to chance. By comparing the calculated chi-squared value with the critical value, the significance can be determined. To use the table, the number of degrees of freedom needs to be calculated using the equation:

Degrees of freedom = Number of categories − 1

The number of categories refers to the number of different groups that have been studied.

Degrees of freedom	Number of categories	χ^2									
1	2	0.016	0.064	0.15	0.46	1.07	1.64	2.71	3.84	5.41	6.64
2	3	0.21	0.45	0.71	1.39	2.41	3.22	4.61	5.99	7.82	9.21
3	4	0.58	1.01	1.42	2.37	3.67	4.64	6.25	7.82	9.84	11.34
4	5	1.61	2.34	3.00	4.35	6.06	7.29	9.24	11.07	13.39	15.09
Probability (P) that chance alone could produce the variation		0.90 (90%)	0.80 (80%)	0.70 (70%)	0.50 (50%)	0.30 (30%)	0.20 (20%)	0.10 (10%)	0.05 (5%)	0.02 (2%)	0.01 (1%)

▲ **Table 1** Table of chi-squared values.

Q **8 Determine the significance of the results for a calculated chi–squared value of 6.89 with three degrees of freedom.**

The chi-squared test can only be used if there are at least two sets of frequency data, the total number of observations is more than 20 and the expected frequency in any category is five or more. The comparison between the observed and expected frequency is based on a prediction. The prediction can take the form of either a hypothesis or a **null hypothesis**. A null hypothesis assumes that there will be no *significant* difference between the observed and the expected frequencies. The formula for chi-squared is shown in figure 13.

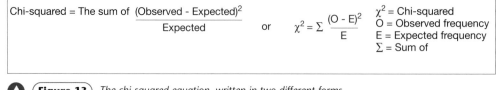

Chi-squared = The sum of $\dfrac{(\text{Observed} - \text{Expected})^2}{\text{Expected}}$ or $\chi^2 = \Sigma \dfrac{(O - E)^2}{E}$

χ^2 = Chi-squared
O = Observed frequency
E = Expected frequency
Σ = Sum of

▲ **Figure 13** The chi-squared equation, written in two different forms.

A worked example of a chi-squared test is shown in figure 14.

Example

The numbers of climbing mice observed in three different habitats were as follows:

Burnt bushland   34

Grassland   2

Bushland   15

The null hypothesis being tested is that there should be no difference between the numbers of mice found in each area.

For there to be a significant difference the calculated chi-squared value must be greater than the table chi-squared value at P = 0.05.

Categories

Observed frequency

Expected frequency

	Burnt bushland	Grassland	Bushland	Total
O	34	2	15	51
E	17	17	17	51
(O-E)	17	-15	-2	
$(O-E)^2$	289	225	4	
$\dfrac{(O-E)^2}{E}$	17	13.2	0.2	$\Sigma = 30.4$

Sum of

As there are three categories, the number of degrees of freedom is three minus one, which equals two.

Using the table of chi-squared values (table 1 on page 240) at P = 0.05 and two degrees of freedom, the table value of chi-squared is 5.99.

Probability = 5%

Critical value

Since the calculated value of chi-squared is 30.4, there is a significant difference between the observed and expected values, and the null hypothesis has been rejected.

The conclusion is that there is a significant difference between the numbers of climbing mice observed in the three different habitats.

Figure 14 *A worked example of a chi-squared test.*

Key ideas 232–241

- Samples must be representative of the whole population. This is usually achieved by using random numbers from tables or computers.

- Sampling procedures should be repeated enough times so that a statistical test can be applied.

- Quadrat sampling is used to study population density, distribution and total population size.

- Line transect sampling allows systematic sampling of an area to be carried out. It is used where conditions and organisms change.

- pH meters can be used to measure the pH of water or soil samples.

- Light meters are used to measure light intensity.

- Temperature can be measured using an electronic thermometer with a metal probe.

- The standard deviation is a measure of the spread of data around their mean. The wider the spread in the data, the larger the standard deviation.

- The chi-squared test is used to compare observed frequencies with expected frequencies.

Human impact

8

Human activities can impose far-reaching effects on the environment. When Earth's human population was much smaller, the effects of human activity were usually small and local. With the rapid growth in the human population over the last 400 to 500 years these effects have become less localised.

Change has been occurring gradually since humans first began to clear the woodland and scrub with axe and fire. Wildlife species have had to adapt or move elsewhere. Since the 1950s modern farming methods have been responsible for a number of ecological problems, for example soil degradation and water pollution.

Memory joggers

- For healthy growth, plants need mineral ions including nitrate (for protein synthesis), potassium (for enzyme activity) and phosphate (for ATP production).
- The uptake of mineral ions is from the soil into the root.
- Humans reduce the amount of land available for other organisms by farming.

 Figure 1

Importance of farming

Farming is essential: it produces the food we eat. For over 10 000 years humans have been growing **crops** (plants grown for food). If the human population continues to rise as predicted there might come a time when the world food supplies will not be adequate. Look at figure 2. In some countries, such as those in Africa and South America, food production often falls short of feeding the entire population, leading to famine. In other countries, such as those in Western Europe and North America, there is more than sufficient food for everyone. These food reserves are often described as 'lakes' and 'mountains'. This surplus is a result of the application of scientific methods to the problems of growing crops.

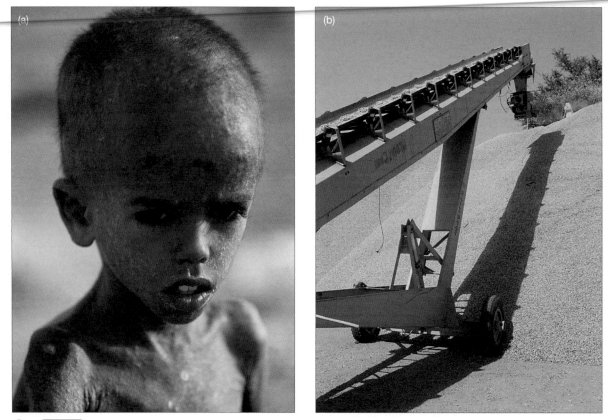

Figure 2 (a) A starving child in Somalia. (b) A groundnut mountain in Senegal.

Traditional farming methods

Traditional farming makes use of mixed farming methods and was widespread in Great Britain until the 1950s. The methods used include:

- growing a variety of crops
- keeping livestock to provide meat, milk and eggs
- **crop rotation** – crops are grown in a regular sequence in each field to prevent nutrients in the soil being used up and pests from establishing themselves
- legumes are grown to build soil fertility
- farmyard manure is recycled.

Modern farming methods

Today's human population is fed by a relatively small number of crop plants. These include cereals, legumes, fruits, leaf crops and root crops. Two commonly grown crop plants are shown in figure 3.

Figure 3   *Common crop plants include potatoes and wheat.*

During the past 50 years farming has undergone rapid change. The processes that have brought about this change are **modernisation** and **industrialisation**. Modernisation has led to **intensification** (increased output per hectare), **specialisation** (removal of less profitable farm activities) and **concentration** (fewer farms). Industrialisation has led to the development of **agribusiness**, for example the vegetable farms of East Anglia. Modern farming methods aim to maximise food production by:

- **monoculture** – growing a single crop in large fields
- using high-yielding crop varieties
- **mechanisation** – using machines to plough, sow and harvest crops
- using **agrochemicals** such as fertilisers, herbicides and pesticides.

The result of all these changes has been that farming has become more intensive: higher yields per hectare are obtained by relying on greater chemical use and technological inputs. To remain competitive, farmers have been forced to become more efficient, farming ever-larger areas with larger equipment and more fertilisers and pesticides. Much larger farms, consisting of extensive fields of a single crop, have partly replaced small farms which grow a wide variety of crops. As a result, the number of farms has dropped and the mean farm size has increased.

Monoculture

The main benefit of monoculture is an economic one: more food can be grown more cheaply. The increase in mechanisation and a reduction of labour means that continuous harvesting of one crop brings a greater economic return per unit area of land.

Almost all crop plants are currently grown by monoculture. Monoculture involves growing the same crop on the same land, year after year. Compare the two photographs in figure 4.

▲ **Figure 4** *(a) Monoculture involves growing a single crop in a large field. (b) Traditional farming involves crop rotation.*

However, to maintain high yields year after year, large quantities of agrochemicals are needed. The continuous application of fertiliser means that there does not have to be a period when the monoculture crop is not sown. Fertilisers are expensive and have to be applied regularly, otherwise there is a decline in soil fertility. Large amounts of pesticides and herbicides are also required as monoculture provides large areas that can become overrun with weeds and infested with pests and diseases. Intensive farming produces large quantities of waste that must be disposed of.

Ecological impact of farming

Although modern farming methods have had positive effects and reduced many risks in farming, there has also been a significant impact on the environment.

The changes in farming practice that are most closely linked to declines in wildlife include:

- the switch from spring-sown to autumn-sown cereals
- hedgerow removal
- increased use of pesticides and fertilisers
- drainage, ploughing and reseeding of previously unimproved pasture
- the switch from hay to silage production and increased grazing levels.

Soil erosion and fertility

Erosion removes the surface topsoil. Topsoil contains most of the organic matter, plant nutrients and fine soil particles that help to retain water and nutrients in the root zones of plants. The subsoil that remains after erosion tends to be less fertile, less absorbent and less able to retain pesticides, fertilisers and other plant nutrients. On average, 1.6 times more soil erodes from agricultural fields than is replaced by natural soil formation processes. It takes up to 300 years for 2.5 cm of topsoil to form, so soil that is lost is essentially irreplaceable. The amount of erosion varies considerably from one field to another and depends on soil type, slope of the field, drainage patterns and the farming methods used. The two main causes of soil erosion are water and wind.

Water erosion

Running water washes soil down slopes. Initially this creates small channels, but these eventually deepen to form large gullies. Ploughing can cause the effects of water erosion to increase, as shown in figure 5.

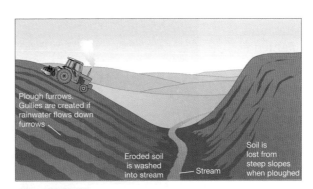

Plough furrows. Gullies are created if rainwater flows down furrows

Eroded soil is washed into stream

Stream

Soil is lost from steep slopes when ploughed

Figure 5 Ploughing increases the loss of soil due to erosion.

Wind erosion

Figure 6 A view across uncultivated peat fen with dust driven by high winds.

The effects of wind erosion are shown in figure 6. Strong winds blowing across fields can simply blow away the soil. The removal of natural vegetation increases the loss of soil. To make more land available for growing crops, farmers remove natural windbreaks such as trees and hedgerows.

Agrochemicals can also affect soil fertility. They can kill naturally occurring soil organisms that improve soil structure, such as bacteria, fungi and earthworms. Without these beneficial organisms the soil becomes hard and unproductive.

> **Q**
> 1 Describe the role of bacteria, fungi and earthworms in nutrient recycling.
> 2 Some farmers plough across a slope. Suggest why this method of ploughing decreases the loss of soil due to soil erosion.

Hedgerow removal

Hedgerows were created for a number of different reasons. As humans cleared land for growing crops, the woodland was pushed back and boundary hedgerows were created. As neighbouring fields developed, the hedgerow acted as a boundary marker. A strong, thorny hedgerow was also an effective and relatively cheap way of confining livestock before the development of other fences.

A hedgerow is a row of bushes or small trees growing closely together as shown in figure 7. They can be found along paths and roads, some mark boundaries between parishes or properties, and many have been planted for farming and gardening needs.

Well-maintained hedgerows can reduce the damage caused by wind and rain to the soil and crops by acting as natural windbreaks or drainage. They also provide a habitat for a number of different species.

Figure 7 *Hedgerows were used by farmers as field boundary markers or as a cheap and effective way of confining livestock.*

In the 1940s there were 805 000 kilometres of hedgerows in Britain, but today there is less than half that length. Britain loses an estimated 17 700 kilometres of hedgerows per year, often through neglect rather than removal. The removal of hedgerows was started to provide larger and less restricted areas for heavy farm machinery and to meet the demand for increased food production following the Second World War.

Key ideas 243–248

- Monoculture allows more food to be grown more cheaply.

- Modern farming methods have an ecological impact on the environment.

- To maintain high yields year after year, large quantities of agrochemicals are needed.

- The two main causes of soil erosion are water and wind.

- When soil is eroded, soil fertility is impaired because the natural supplies of nutrients and organic matter are lost.

- Well-maintained hedgerows can reduce damage to the soil and crops caused by wind and rain because they act as natural windbreaks.

Agrochemicals

Even when soil erosion is not excessive, modern farming methods can impair soil quality by depleting the natural supplies of nutrients and organic matter. In natural ecosystems, soil fertility is maintained by the diverse contributions and recycling of nutrients by a wide range of plant and animal species. When this diversity is replaced by a single species grown year after year, some trace elements are depleted. The organic content of the soil also decreases unless organic materials are supplied in sufficient quantities to replace those used.

Memory joggers

- Human activities may pollute water with sewage or toxic chemicals.
- Human activities may pollute land with toxic chemicals, such as pesticides and herbicides, which are washed from land into water.
- Fertilisers provide plant nutrients and are used to improve crop yields.
- Pesticides are used to kill pests.
- Herbicides are used to kill weeds.

Figure 1

Fertilisers

High-yield crops require a fertile soil for optimal growth. A fertile soil is rich in nutrients, particularly nitrogen (N), phosphorus (P) and potassium (K). Plants absorb nutrients from the soil using their roots. When a plant dies these nutrients are returned to the soil. However, the nutrients in harvested crops are removed from the farmland with the crop. If high yields are to be maintained, these nutrients need to be replaced, usually by means of inorganic and organic fertilisers.

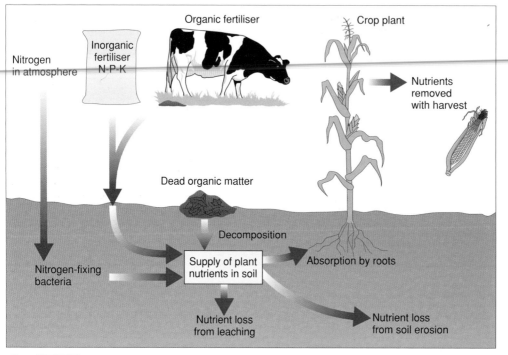

Figure 2 *Addition and loss of plant nutrients to and from the soil.*

Fertilisers can be added to soil or directly to plants. Inorganic fertilisers contain varying quantities of nitrate, phosphate and potassium hydroxide. Organic fertilisers consist of organic matter, that is material from plants and animals such as manure or sewage sludge. The processes involved in addition and loss of plant nutrients to and from the soil are shown in figure 2.

Nutrient loss

Nutrients are lost from agricultural fields through runoff, drainage or **leaching**. Leaching is the removal of soluble nutrients from the topsoil by water percolating downwards to become groundwater. Groundwater supplies water to the soil, to streams and rivers, and to plants. It is for this reason that the misuse of fertilisers has far-reaching effects.

> **Q** 1 Humans affect the nitrogen cycle by using large quantities of nitrogen fertilisers. Describe the nitrogen cycle.
>
> 2 Describe how nitrogen-based fertilisers disrupt the nitrogen cycle.

Nitrogen as a fertiliser

Of the three major nutrients in fertilisers, nitrogen is the most readily lost because of its high solubility in the nitrate form. Leaching of nitrate from agricultural fields can raise nitrate concentrations in underlying groundwater, leading to the contamination of drinking water supplies. If nitrate is leached into lakes or rivers it may cause excessive growth of aquatic plants.

Phosphorus as a fertiliser

Phosphorus does not leach as readily as nitrate because it is more tightly bound to soil particles. However, if it is carried with eroded soils into lakes or rivers, like nitrate it may cause excessive growth of aquatic plants, as shown in figure 3.

Figure 3 *Toxic cyanobacterial bloom, Darling River, Australia. The bloom is caused by high input of nutrients, high temperature and slow-moving water.*

Potassium as a fertiliser

Potassium, the third major nutrient in fertilisers, does not cause water quality problems because it is not hazardous in drinking water and is not a limiting nutrient for growth of aquatic plants. It is tightly held by soil particles and so can be removed from fields by erosion, but generally not by leaching.

Organic fertiliser

Decomposers in soil break down organic fertiliser. It is applied by spreading manure or slurry on farmland, as shown in figure 4. **Slurry** is the liquid that comes from buildings in which livestock are kept, and is a mixture of **excreta** (urine and faeces) and the water used for cleaning the buildings. It also contains large amounts of suspended solids. In addition, slurry may contain residues of heavy metals (e.g. copper) and veterinary products.

Figure 4 *Manure being spread on maize stubble.*

Severe pollution can occur if slurry is allowed to enter ponds, either directly from the farmyard or as runoff from land. The damage is caused by either the solids, which physically smother out all plant life present, or the increase in bacterial populations, which use up the dissolved oxygen in the water resulting in the disappearance of plant and animal life.

Fertilise crops, not water

Farming is one source of water contamination. Surface runoff carries manure, fertilisers and other agrochemicals into streams, lakes and reservoirs, in some cases causing unacceptable levels of bacteria, nutrients or synthetic organic compounds. Similarly, dissolved chemicals, which can include nitrate fertilisers, are leached into groundwater.

Water pollution

Water pollution is defined as the loss of any of the beneficial uses of water due to human activity. The beneficial uses of water are varied and include its use for drinking and domestic purposes, watering livestock and irrigation of crops, in fisheries, industry and food production, and for bathing, recreational and amenity use. If water is unsuitable for any of these purposes then it is polluted. The level of pollution will depend on the extent of the damage caused. A polluted river is shown in figure 5.

Figure 5 *Scummy pollutant in an Oxfordshire river.*

An enrichment problem

A lake that has low levels of nutrients is said to be unenriched, or **oligotrophic**. An oligotrophic lake has clear water and can support small populations of organisms. If a lake becomes enriched with nutrients, or **eutrophic**, the water is cloudy because of the presence of large numbers of algae and cyanobacteria. Compare the two lakes in figure 6.

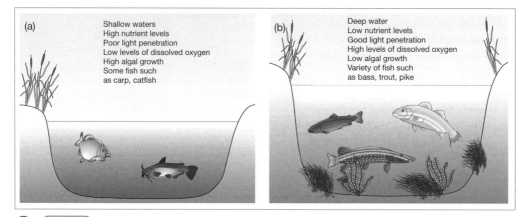

Figure 6 *Although eutrophic lakes (a) contain large populations of organisms, those that dominate are different from those found in oligotrophic lakes (b).*

The enrichment of a lake or pond by nutrients is called **eutrophication**. It is a natural process that takes place over vast periods of time. However, the rate of eutrophication is increased if fertilisers, especially nitrate and phosphate, enrich the lake or pond.

Effect on aquatic ecosystems

The flow chart in figure 7 shows the effects of fertilisers on an aquatic ecosystem. In summer, excessive growth of algae can cause **algal blooms** in lakes that are nutrient-rich. Algal blooms contain communities of suspended or floating microscopic algae which can make water cloudy, resulting in the reduced growth of rooted plants.

Q 3 Why do algal blooms lead to reduced growth of rooted plants?

A reduction in plant growth means that there is a smaller habitat for invertebrate and fish communities. The rapid growth of the algae depletes the nutrients in the water so many of the algae die and decompose.

When organisms die, they sink to the bottom of the lake and decomposition takes place.

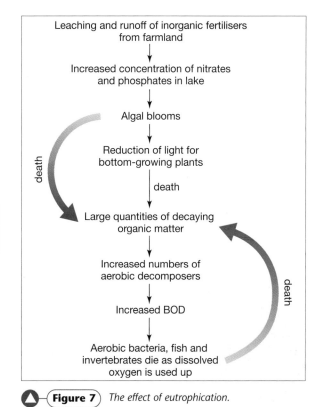

Figure 7 *The effect of eutrophication.*

In autumn, the algal bloom dies back and further decomposition takes place.

Q 4 The decay of algal blooms and other plants and animals can deoxygenate the lake water, killing invertebrates and fish. Name the process occurring during decomposition that depletes oxygen.

The increase in organic matter means that populations of decomposers grow. As they increase in number, they use up the oxygen in the water. Only organisms that can tolerate low oxygen levels will survive. The amount of oxygen needed by micro-organisms to decompose organic matter is called the **biochemical oxygen demand (BOD)**.

Q 5 Under what conditions is the BOD i) high and ii) low?

A similar effect occurs if organic effluent, such as farm slurry, runs into the lake. The main difference is at the start. There is no initial algal bloom because the suspended solids need to decompose to release the nutrients. Suspended solids make the water cloudy, killing rooted plants. Deoxygenation is the most important potential effect of organic effluent discharges.

Q 6 Draw a flow chart to show the effect of organic effluent on an aquatic ecosystem.

Pests and pesticides

A **pest** is any unwanted organism that interferes, either directly or indirectly, with human activity. Over the past 40 years, as agriculture has become more intensive and monoculture more common, farmers have been treating their crops with **pesticides**. Pesticides kill pests. Plants are the main source of food for humans, both directly and indirectly. Plants are constantly under threat from tens of thousands of diseases caused by viruses, bacteria, fungi and other organisms. Plants also have to compete with over 30000 kinds of weed and they are the food source for 10000 species of insects. It has been estimated that one-third of the world's food crop is destroyed by these pests annually. It is for this reason that farmers use pesticides. Figure 8a shows some of the effects pests have on crops, and figure 8b shows the spraying of pesticides.

Figure 8 *(a) Slug damage to a beet seedling. (b) Spraying a wheat crop with pesticide.*

The most widely used pesticides are **insecticides** (insect killers), **herbicides** (weed killers) and **fungicides** (fungus killers). However, during the past 20 years concerns have arisen as to their safety, particularly the extent to which their presence in the environment poses a threat to wildlife and humans.

The ideal pesticide

The ideal pesticide would be:

- **selective** (kill only the species for which it was intended)
- **non-toxic** to other organisms
- easily broken down (**non-persistent**) into non-toxic substances, either by micro-organisms (**biodegradable**) or by natural chemical decomposition (**non-biodegradable**)
- **non-mobile** (stay where it was applied).

Unfortunately the ideal pesticide does not exist. Most pesticides are non-selective, extremely toxic, persistent, do not degrade easily or break down into compounds that are still toxic, and are mobile in the environment. In addition, many pest species have developed resistance to pesticides.

The problem with pesticides

Pesticides are poisons and can be particularly dangerous when misused. Fish deaths, reproductive failure in birds and acute illnesses in people have all been put down to exposure to or ingestion of pesticides. Pesticide losses from areas of application, and contamination of surface water and groundwater lead to financial losses to farmers and are a threat to the environment.

Genetic resistance

Many pest species have developed a **genetic resistance** to pesticides after repeated exposure to them. Genetic resistance is any inherited characteristic that decreases the effect of a pesticide.

> Q) 7 **Using your knowledge of genetics and natural selection, explain how genetic resistance can occur.**

Non-selectivity

Most insecticides are non-selective. They can kill the pest, its natural predators and other organisms that may have been controlling the pest population size naturally. Look at figure 9. The natural populations of pest and predator fluctuate. If a pesticide is applied, both the pest and predator are affected. After a short time, the pest population increases rapidly, partly because there are no natural predators.

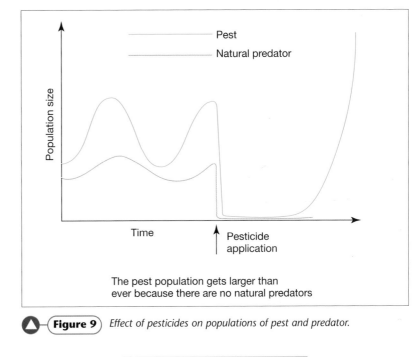

The pest population gets larger than ever because there are no natural predators

△ (Figure 9) *Effect of pesticides on populations of pest and predator.*

> Q) 8 **The effect described above can occur even if the pesticide has not killed the predator. Explain why this can happen.**

Sometimes pesticide use results in the creation of a new pest. This happens if a pesticide kills the natural predators, parasites and competitors of an organism. Without this natural population control, the organism population rises rapidly, so it becomes a pest.

Persistence and bioaccumulation

Persistence defines the 'lasting power' of a pesticide. Most pesticides break down as a result of the action of micro-organisms (biodegradation), by chemical means or by sunlight. Biodegradation can be rapid and complete breakdown can occur as long as the pesticide has not leached. Chemical degradation generally results in only partial degradation and the substances produced can still be toxic. Photodegradation is the breakdown of pesticides by sunlight and, like chemical degradation, can result in only partial degradation.

Some pesticides are extremely stable, taking many years to degrade. They accumulate in the environment and in food chains. Persistent pesticides tend to be fat-soluble and water-insoluble. This means that organisms cannot excrete them so they accumulate in their fatty tissues; this is known as **bioaccumulation**. The effect of bioaccumulation is shown in figure 10.

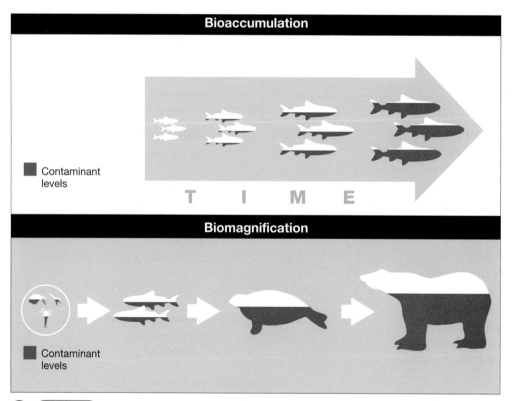

Figure 10 *Bioaccumulation and biomagnification.*

As the pesticide passes from one trophic level to another, it becomes more concentrated. This is called **biomagnification**. You can see in figure 10 that organisms higher up the food chain have the highest concentration of pesticide stored in their bodies. Because humans are at the top of many food chains and their meat consumption is fairly high, people could be carrying higher levels of pesticides than other animals.

> **Q**   **9 Suggest why bioaccumulation is common in marine mammals.**

Mobility in the environment

Some pesticides do not stay where they are applied. They can move through the soil, water and air as shown in figure 11.

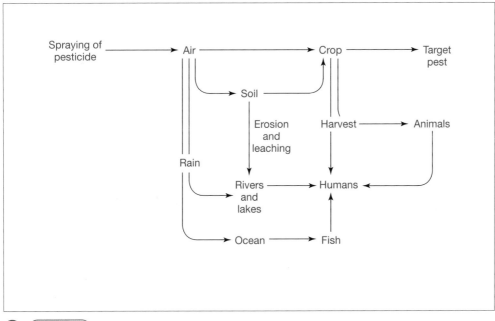

Figure 11   *The movement of pesticides in the environment.*

Pesticides can affect aquatic ecosystems. For example, the pesticides that were applied to farmland and then washed into rivers and streams when it rained can affect fish. If the pesticide level is high enough the fish may die. If the pesticide is persistent, bioaccumulation and biomagnification could occur. The biomagnification of a persistent pesticide in an aquatic ecosystem is shown in figure 12.

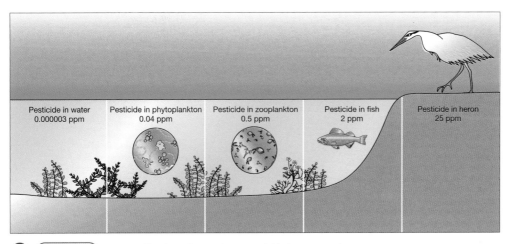

Figure 12   *Biomagnification of a persistent pesticide in an aquatic ecosystem.*

Notice how the level of pesticide concentrates in the tissues of the different organisms as you move along the food chain.

Key ideas 249–257

- Agrochemicals, such as fertilisers, herbicides and pesticides, are used to increase soil fertility.

- The enrichment of a lake or pond by nutrients is called eutrophication.

- The rate of eutrophication is increased if fertilisers enrich the lake or pond.

- Eutrophication leads to algal blooms.

- The amount of oxygen needed by micro-organisms to decompose organic matter is called the biochemical oxygen demand (BOD).

- A high BOD occurs in a eutrophic lake.

- Some pesticides are biodegradable, which means they do not persist in the environment.

- Pesticides can accumulate in the tissues of organisms; this is known as bioaccumulation.

Balancing food production

10

Agricultural productivity has increased as a result of government policy and modern farming methods, which make use of new technology, mechanisation, agrochemicals and specialisation. Although these changes have had many positive effects and reduced many of the risks in farming, there have also been significant costs to the environment such as soil erosion, soil and water contamination, and loss of wildlife and habitat.

A growing number of farmers are questioning current agricultural policy. They are looking for ways to balance food production and conservation; this is known as **sustainability**. Sustainability rests on the principle that the needs of the present must be met without compromising the ability of future generations to meet their own needs.

Memory joggers

- When Earth's human population was much smaller, the effects of human activity were usually small and local.
- Rapid growth in the human population means that raw materials are being used up and increasing amounts of waste are produced.

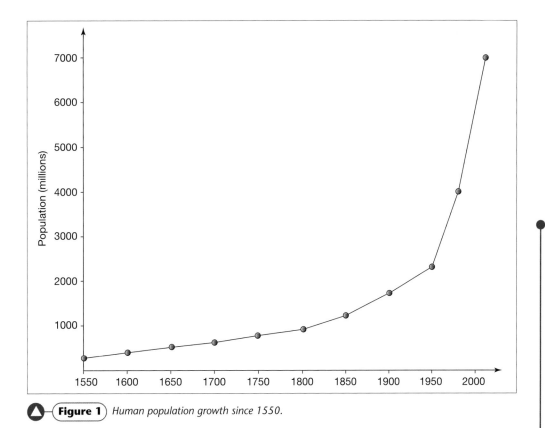

Figure 1 Human population growth since 1550.

Farm management – the future

Despite the expansion of modern farming methods, there are still millions of hectares of land being farmed using sustainable agriculture throughout Europe. Existing forms of sustainable agriculture include low-intensity traditional farming, organic farming and integrated farming.

Low-intensity traditional farming occurs in upland areas of the UK as shown in figure 2.

▲ **Figure 2** *Farmland in North Wales.*

Organic farming is of great benefit to the environment, providing a varied landscape and habitats. Integrated farming relies upon farmers cutting inputs; for example it is possible to reduce pesticide use by 20–50% without affecting profitability.

Sustainable agriculture:

- does not require large inputs of fossil fuels
- promotes polyculture instead of monoculture
- promotes perennial rather than annual crop strains
- conserves topsoil and builds new topsoil with organic fertiliser
- conserves water
- controls pests with little of no use of pesticides
- relies on beneficial biological processes and environmentally friendly chemicals (those that degrade quickly and are non-persistent).

Agricultural research has begun to focus on ways of maintaining environmental quality while producing acceptable crop yields. One example is integrated pest management, which aims to control pests through a combination of methods that minimise undesirable ecological effects.

Ecological strategies

Farms may be managed in a number of ways that help to ensure sustainability and reduce the impact on wildlife. This may be done by:

- using organic fertilisers
- preventing erosion
- controlling pesticide use
- maintaining habitat variety.

Fertiliser use

Intensive farming has become dependent on inorganic fertilisers to promote rapid growth of crops and high yields. Nitrogen fertilisers promote the growth of some plants at the expense of others, which results in reduced plant and animal diversity.

The spread of nitrogen fertilisers to grass verges, riverbanks and ditches is causing a massive reduction in the diversity of wild plants and animals on farms. Excess nettle growth has been reported in areas next to farmland, as shown in figure 3. Evidence has shown that the spread of nitrogen fertilisers to ditches has caused this excessive growth.

Figure 3 *Excessive nettle growth occurs in areas where nitrogen fertilisers have spread to ditches.*

You have already seen that the contamination of lakes and rivers with inorganic fertilisers, such as nitrates and phosphates, can cause increased growth of plants and algae.

 1 Describe the effects of nitrates and phosphates on aquatic ecosystems.

Eutrophic lakes will support a high population of wildfowl. However, algae-rich water is toxic to animals that drink the water.

The risks associated with fertiliser application can be reduced by:

- applying the recommended amount, i.e. small amounts regularly
- avoiding periods of heavy rain
- applying during periods of plant growth
- using organic fertilisers.

When nitrogen is supplied in an organic form, such as manure, leaching effects are reduced because organic nitrogen is gradually converted into inorganic nitrogen.

 2 Describe how organic nitrogen is converted into inorganic nitrogen.

Prevention of soil erosion

In England, up to 15% of the land being used to grow crops is believed to be at risk from soil erosion by water. The factors influencing this are slope, soil texture and rainfall. Soil erosion rarely occurs in areas that are well-covered by vegetation, such as wooded slopes. This is due to a number of factors which are shown in figure 4:

- the canopy (the branches of tall trees) reduces the force of rain
- leaf litter acts as a sponge, slowing down and reducing the amount of run-off
- the roots open up the soil, allowing water to percolate through and bind the soil particles together.

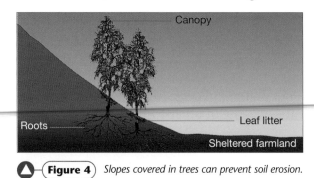

Figure 4　*Slopes covered in trees can prevent soil erosion.*

Terracing can reduce soil erosion from steeply sloping farmland. The slope is converted into a series of level terraces that are supported by stones. This reduces soil loss in rainwater running down the slope.

You have already seen that ploughing can cause soil erosion. When land is ploughed in vertical lines down a slope, rainwater runs rapidly down the plough furrows, washing the topsoil away. This effect is shown in figure 5.

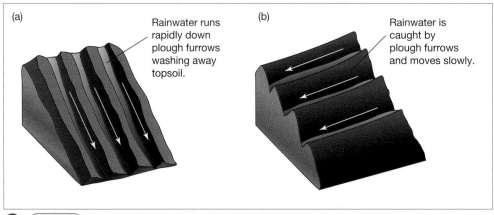

(a) Rainwater runs rapidly down plough furrows washing away topsoil.

(b) Rainwater is caught by plough furrows and moves slowly.

Figure 5　*(a) Land ploughed in vertical lines down the slope is susceptible to soil erosion. (b) Soil erosion from sloping farmland can be reduced if the land is ploughed in horizontal lines across the slope.*

To reduce the effects of ploughing on sloping farmland, farmers are encouraged to plough in horizontal lines across the slope rather than up and down it. Increasing the organic content in soil increases the capacity of the soil to retain water and maintain cohesion. Planting crops in periods of heavy rainfall should be avoided.

The trend towards fewer but larger farms has led to the removal of field boundary features, such as walls and hedgerows. These features are important in controlling soil erosion. Although hedgerows are being removed, some replanting is taking place.

Pesticide use

Since 1984 there has been an overall decrease in the use of pesticides and many of the more persistent insecticides have been banned because of their effects on wildlife. However, many farmers are reluctant to decrease the amount they use because they are worried that productivity will decline.

Pesticide use can be reduced in a number of ways including modification of cultivation procedures, artificial selection and genetic engineering, **biological control** and **integrated pest management**.

For centuries farmers have used cultivation methods to discourage or inhibit pests. Some of these are listed in table 1.

Cultivation method	Effect
Crop rotation	Population of pest cannot get established
Planting rows of hedges or trees in and around crop	Act as barrier to pest invasion, provide habitat for natural predators
Adjusting planting times	Ensures that major pests starve or are consumed by natural predators
Growing crops in areas where their major pests do not exist	Ensures no crop losses due to pests
Switching to polyculture	Plant diversity increases, pest populations cannot get established
Removing diseased or infected plants	Prevents infection of healthy plants
Using photodegradable plastic between rows of some crops	Prevents growth of weeds
Using denser planting patterns	Crowds out weeds

Table 1 *Modification of cultivation methods can be an effective method of pest control.*

Farmers can develop crop varieties that are genetically resistant to certain pests using selective breeding or genetic engineering.

Biological control involves the use of naturally occurring disease organisms, parasites or predators to control pests. It has a number of advantages. Normally it affects only the target pest species and is non-toxic to other species. Once a population of natural predators or parasites is established, control of the pest is often self-perpetuating.

An increasing number of pest-control experts believe that the best way to control crop pests is a carefully designed integrated pest management programme. In this approach, each crop and its pest are evaluated as an ecological system. Then a pest control programme is developed that uses modification of cultivation methods, biological control and chemical methods at the appropriate time.

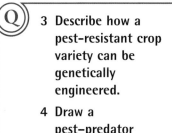

Q

3 **Describe how a pest-resistant crop variety can be genetically engineered.**

4 **Draw a pest–predator population growth curve.**

Maintenance of habitat variety

One aim of sustainable agriculture is to protect habitats. This can be achieved in a number of ways. One way is to prevent the removal of woodland areas and hedgerows. Woodland and hedgerows contain complete food chains, from wild flowers and plants via insects to mammals and birds. Although hedgerows do not contain the variety of species found in woodland, they form natural corridors along which birds, mammals and insects can travel to and from other habitats.

> **Q** **5 Why do farmers remove hedgerows?**

All farmland has some unused areas, such as headlands, verges, steep banks and fence areas, as shown in figure 6. These areas support a range of wildlife species and they also act as predator strips. Predator strips are small strips of grass left around the edges of fields specifically to encourage predators as a means of pest control.

Too often field and farm ponds are left in a derelict condition. They are often used as dumpsites and are polluted with farm wastes. Such areas are easily managed and maintained. They can be cleared with an excavator and when any overhanging trees are removed, the ponds become colonised with a variety of wildlife species.

 Figure 6 *This unused area of farmland provides a habitat for dock, ragwort and thistles.*

Ditches and streams that run alongside farmland can get clogged. To prevent flooding of the farmland these need to be dredged. A rotational system of dredging should be used so that some aquatic habitats are left undisturbed each year.

The use of herbicides has a drastic long-term effect on the environment. Their application has the direct effect of reducing plant biomass and the indirect effect of reducing the variety of food available to a range of animal species.

> **Q** **6 What is meant by the term 'biomass'?**
>
> **7 Explain why a reduction in plant biomass leads to a reduction in the number of animal species.**

Key ideas 259–264

- Sustainable agriculture is designed to balance the need for increased food production with the need to conserve the environment.

- Farms can be managed in a number of ways to ensure sustainability and reduce the impact on wildlife.

- Leaching effects can be reduced through decreased use of inorganic fertilisers and increased use of organic fertilisers.

- Soil erosion can be reduced by decreasing the number of hedgerows that are removed and by ploughing across a slope.

- Integrated pest management programmes can be used to reduce the effects of pesticides.

- Unused areas on farmland support a wide variety of species.

Unit 5 – Questions

(1) The diagram in figure 1 shows the energy flow for part of a lake (values are given in kJ m^{-2} yr^{-1}).

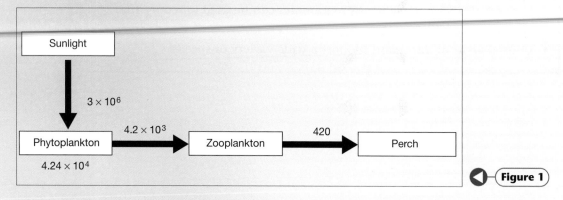

◀ Figure 1

a) i) Calculate the percentage of energy from sunlight that is fixed by phytoplankton.   **(2 marks)**

   ii) Suggest *two* reasons why not all the sunlight is used in photosynthesis.   **(2 marks)**

b) i) Calculate the percentage of energy from producers that is available to perch.   **(2 marks)**

   ii) Give *three* reasons why only a portion of the energy fixed by the producers is available to the perch.   **(3 marks)**

(Total 9 marks)

(2) The diagram in figure 2 shows three ecological pyramids of number, **A**, **B** and **C**.

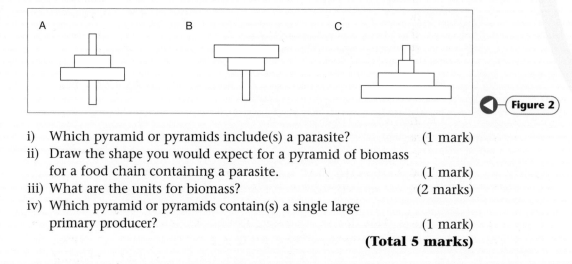

◀ Figure 2

i) Which pyramid or pyramids include(s) a parasite?   **(1 mark)**

ii) Draw the shape you would expect for a pyramid of biomass for a food chain containing a parasite.   **(1 mark)**

iii) What are the units for biomass?   **(2 marks)**

iv) Which pyramid or pyramids contain(s) a single large primary producer?   **(1 mark)**

(Total 5 marks)

3 Describe and explain the effects of organic effluents, nitrates and phosphates on aquatic ecosystems. **(Total 6 marks)**

4 The diagram in figure 3 summarises the passage of chemicals in an ecosystem.

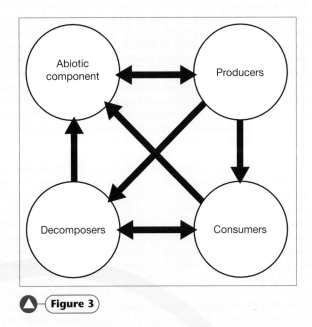

Figure 3

a) Name the compound or ion in which:
    i)   carbon passes into the producers from the abiotic component (1 mark)
    ii)   nitrogen passes between the producers and consumers.   (1 mark)
b) i)   Name *two* groups of organisms that act as decomposers.   (2 marks)
    ii)   Briefly explain the role of these organisms in the cycling
         of nutrients.   (4 marks)
                                         (Total 8 marks)

5 Quadrats are used to sample population sizes.
  a) Define the terms i) population and ii) community.   (2 marks)
  b) i)   Describe how random sampling can be carried out.   (2 marks)
       ii)   Give *one* limitation of random sampling.   (1 mark)
  c) During succession there is a change in species composition of a community.
      i)   Describe the process of succession.   (6 marks)
      ii)   Describe the techniques that you would use to study succession.
                                            (4 marks)
                                     (Total 15 marks)

6 Two species may interact in a number of ways.
  a) Name an interaction which i) is beneficial to, ii) is harmful to,
      iii) has no effect on the individuals involved.   (3 marks)
  b) The size of a population may vary as a result of competition.
      Define the terms i) interspecific competition and ii) intraspecific competition.
                                           (2 marks)
  c) Population size is also affected by abiotic factors. Name *two*
      abiotic factors and describe how they can be measured.   (4 marks)
                                        (Total 9 marks)

Module 5 – Test yourself

1. Table 1 shows the energy flow through a food chain.

Trophic level	Total energy flow through each trophic level/kJ m^{-2}yr^{-1}	Total energy available to produce biomass at each trophic level/kJ m^{-2} yr^{-1}
First	88 221	37 694
Second	15 169	7010
Third	1623	293
Fourth	94	28

△ Table 1

a) Draw a pyramid of energy for the food chain in table 1.   (1 mark)
b) Give two reasons for the energy losses that occur at each trophic level.
                                                                     (2 marks)
c) Calculate the percentage efficiency of the secondary consumers in this food chain.   (2 marks)
d) What effect does the loss of energy between trophic levels have on biomass in higher trophic levels?   (1 mark)
                                                            (Total 6 marks)

2. The diagram in figure 1 shows a food web for a woodland ecosystem.

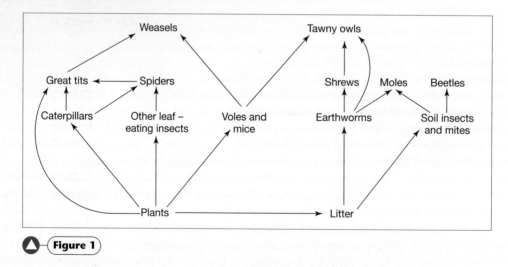

△ Figure 1

a) From the information in figure 1, name i) a primary consumer and ii) a tertiary consumer.   (2 marks)
b) i)   Which animals are eaten by moles?   (1 mark)
   ii) Suggest how this community might change if the population of moles died.   (3 marks)
                                                            (Total 6 marks)

(3) Most cereal fields in Britain are sprayed with selective herbicides. In order to conserve wildlife, farmers are recommended to leave unsprayed a 6 metre strip, called a headland, around each cereal field.

a) Explain how spraying selective herbicide on a headland might affect the number of insects living there. (2 marks)

Table 2 shows the results of an investigation to find the effect of leaving headlands unsprayed on populations of butterflies living there.

Butterfly species	Number of each species recorded on headland sprayed with selective herbicide	Number of each species recorded on headland not sprayed with selective herbicide	χ^2	Significance (NS = not significant
Small skipper	2	41	35.4	P<0.001
Large skipper	1	17	14.2	P<0.001
Large white	38	56	3.4	NS
Holly blue	13	29	6.1	P<0.05
Hedge brown	59	93	7.6	P<0.05
Small heath	0	11	11.0	P<0.01
Ringlet	23	52	11.2	P<0.01

▲ Table 2

b) Why was a χ^2 (chi-squared) test applied to the results? (1 mark)
c) What conclusions can be drawn from the results of the χ^2 test? (3 marks)

(Total 6 marks)

AQA (NEAB) Ecology BY05, 26 Feb 1996

(S) (4) Crops can be improved by selective breeding, which means that the phenotypes are selected by humans, rather than the natural environment.

a) i) Explain why selective breeding tends to decrease the size of the gene pool. (2 marks)

ii) Once a desirable crop has been produced by selective breeding it may be cloned. What is the advantage to a farmer of cloned plants? (1 mark)

b) i) Many commercial varieties of wheat are hybrids produced by crossing two pure breeding parents. Explain why these varieties have the same genotype. (1 mark)

ii) If a farmer plants the seeds from the hybrid wheat the yield is not as high in the following year. Explain why. (2 marks)

c) Genetic modification of crops is used to make the crop resistant to herbicides. Suggest advantages and disadvantages of this type of genetically modified crop. (4 marks)

(Total 10 marks)

⑤ In an investigation into the roles of different organisms in the breakdown of leaves, leaf discs of standard size were placed in bags with varying mesh sizes and buried in newly cultivated soil. After nine months the bags were dug up and the area of leaf that had disappeared was measured. Table 3 shows the organisms able to enter through each mesh and the amount of decomposition after nine months.

Mesh size/mm	Organisms which can enter the bag	Percentage decomposition after 9 months
7	Micro-organisms and invertebrates	95
1	Micro-organisms and invertebrates except earthworms, slugs and snails	60
0.5	Micro-organisms and small invertebrates such as mites and springtails	30
0.003	Micro-organisms	5

 Table 3

a) Describe the pattern shown by the decomposition in relation to the size of the mesh and the type of organism.   (1 mark)
b) Suggest how the invertebrates may aid the breakdown of the leaves by micro-organisms.   (2 marks)
c) Describe how micro-organisms break down the leaves.   (3 marks)

(Total 6 marks)

Ⓢ ⑥ Figure 2 shows part of the carbon cycle.

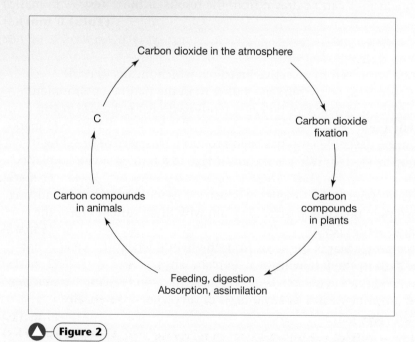

 Figure 2

a) Describe how carbon dioxide in the air is fixed into carbon compounds in plants.   (4 marks)

b) Explain how each of the processes occurring between plants and animals allows animals to synthesise carbon compounds. (4 marks)

c) i) During which stage of the process occurring at **C** is carbon dioxide released?

ii) Describe the metabolic pathway that releases carbon dioxide during process **C**. (4 marks)

(Total 12 marks)

(7) A community in a hostile environment has fewer populations than a community in a less hostile environment.

a) Define the terms i) habitat and ii) niche. (2 marks)

b) Explain how selection leads to the adaptation of a species to a particular environment. (4 marks)

c) Suggest why a community in a hostile environment has fewer populations than a community in a less hostile environment. (3 marks)

(Total 9 marks)

(8) The wastes of animals contain substances that can be recycled.

a) Figure 3 shows part of the ornithine cycle in which mammals produce a nitrogen-containing waste.

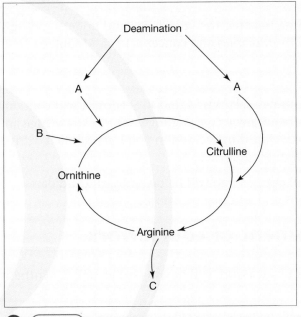

⚠ Figure 3

i) Name the substances **A**, **B** and **C**.

ii) Describe how deamination produces substance **A**.

iii) What is the role of the ornithine cycle? (6 marks)

b) Explain why nitrogen-containing substances may also be present in the faeces of mammals. (2 marks)

c) Describe the role of micro-organisms in recycling nitrogen-containing wastes to nitrogen-containing inorganic molecules that can be used by plants. (4 marks)

(Total 12 marks)

Synoptic assessment

As an A level student you should be able to:

- bring together principles and concepts from different areas of biology and apply them in a particular context, expressing ideas logically and using appropriate specialist vocabulary
- use biological skills in contexts which bring together different areas of the subject.

This is known as synthesis of knowledge, understanding and skills, or **synoptic assessment**. Synoptic assessment accounts for 20% of the total A level mark. Six per cent has been assigned to Module 5 Environment as follows: 3.5% to the written paper and 2.5% to the experiment and investigation coursework. The remaining 14% will be tested in the optional module.

Synoptic assessment of written papers

Module 5

You will be required to bring together the knowledge and understanding you developed in Module 5 with principles and concepts from Modules 1 to 4.

Option module

Each option test is split into two sections, A and B. Section A will contain synoptic questions which require you to bring together the knowledge and understanding you have developed in the option you have studied, with principles and concepts from Modules 1 to 5.

Section B is common to all options and will be taken by all candidates. It consists of data questions and an essay question.

Synoptic assessment of coursework

The synoptic assessment of coursework will be assessed as skill E 'synthesis of principles and concepts'.

The assessment of skill E will be based on skill A 'planning' and skill C 'analysing evidence and drawing conclusions'. When planning an investigation you will need to use your biological knowledge and understanding to identify, describe, explain and justify the range of factors you have taken into account. In the analysis you will have to use your biological knowledge and understanding to explain the outcomes of the investigation.

One way in which you can be tested synoptically is shown in the example below. In this example you are expected to apply something you know to a situation with which you are unfamiliar.

'Two types of seed were grown separately and together on damp filter paper in a petri dish. The percentage of seeds germinated is shown in figure 1.'

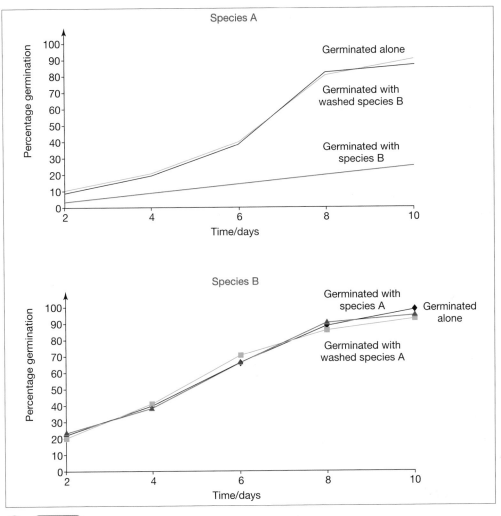

▲ (Figure 1)

A question you may be asked is:

'Suggest an explanation for the results in figure 1.'

In this example you are being asked to synthesise ideas. In other words, what does the pattern of data show and how can the results obtained be explained?

The pattern appears to be that germination of the seeds from species A is inhibited by species B. Germination of seeds from species B is not inhibited by species A. Washing the seeds of species B stops the inhibition.

This suggests that the seeds from species B produce a substance that inhibits germination in A. This substance must be soluble in water otherwise it would not be able to diffuse from species B to species A.

Data questions

Data questions require you to apply the principles and skills you have developed during the study of Modules 1 to 5. You will be given some data which you will be expected to analyse. Analysis means looking for patterns in data and drawing conclusions. Data can be presented in a number of ways. Favourites with examiners are tables, graphs and diagrams. The usual context is an investigation. Sometimes these are similar to investigations you may have carried out, but often they are unfamiliar to you.

What am I being asked about?

The first step in analysing is to decide:

- What area of biology is this investigation about?
- What aspect of the stated topic is this investigation about?
- What other links are there?

For example, an introduction to a question reads:

'In an investigation into mineral uptake by plants, the roots of two sets of fifty seedlings were placed in solutions containing the same concentration of radioactive phosphate. For the experimental set of plants, nitrogen gas was bubbled through the solution. The control plants had air bubbled through the solution. At regular intervals the quantity of radioactive phosphate was measured in the solutions surrounding the roots.'

In this example it is not immediately clear what the question is about, although there are some clues. In figure 2 you can see some of the connections you could make.

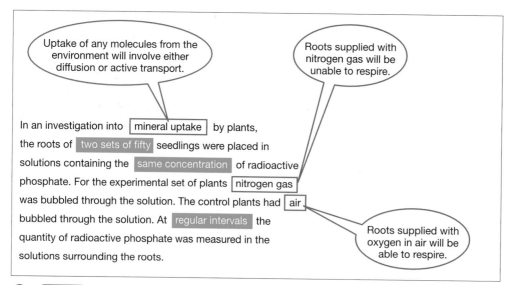

Figure 2 *Making connections.*

As questions about <u>experimental variables</u> or <u>controls</u> are often asked it is also worth noting these as you read through.

What do results mean?

Results of investigations like this mineral uptake example are given either as tables or graphs. Table 1 shows the results of this investigation.

As you read a question, try to develop an idea of what the results ought to be, and why. In this case you should be thinking about mineral uptake by diffusion and active transport, active transport and respiration, oxygen supply and respiration.

Time from placing roots in solution / minutes	Concentration of radioactive phosphate in the solution surrounding the roots/ arbitrary units	
	Experimental plants	Control plants
0	5.0	5.0
10	4.5	2.5
20	4.2	1.5
40	4.0	0.9
60	4.0	0.5

▲ Table 1

Q 1 a) What pattern do these results show?

S b) Explain the pattern in terms of diffusion, active transport and respiration.

You might be asked to carry out some further processing of the data and then explain what this shows. Figure 3 shows an example.

'Calculate the rate of mineral salt uptake by the control plants in the first 20 minutes and in the last 20 minutes.'

'Suggest an explanation for the difference in the rate of mineral salt uptake.'

As you do the rate calculations you should again be making connections. You already know the question is about active transport and diffusion, so what else affects these processes? The main connections you could make are shown in figure 3.

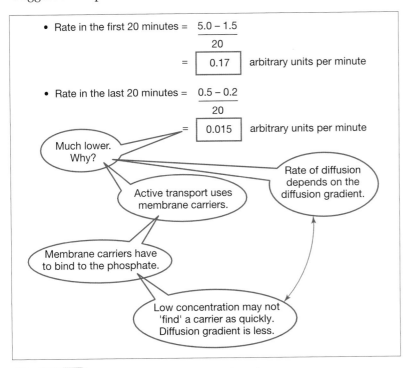

- Rate in the first 20 minutes = $\dfrac{5.0 - 1.5}{20}$

  = 0.17 arbitrary units per minute

- Rate in the last 20 minutes = $\dfrac{0.5 - 0.2}{20}$

  = 0.015 arbitrary units per minute

Much lower. Why?

Active transport uses membrane carriers.

Rate of diffusion depends on the diffusion gradient.

Membrane carriers have to bind to the phosphate.

Low concentration may not 'find' a carrier as quickly. Diffusion gradient is less.

▲ Figure 3 Calculations and conclusions from data.

Testing a hypothesis

Another way of testing understanding of experimental design is to ask about the hypothesis of the experiment. This can be done in two ways:

- stating a hypothesis and asking whether a design tests the hypothesis
- giving results and asking for a hypothesis which can then be tested.

Designing an investigation

Many plants grow poorly in areas affected by acid rain. A hypothesis put forward to explain this is: 'Acid rain slows down the rate of germination'.

The design of a group of students to test this hypothesis is shown in figure 4.

The statement at the beginning of the experimental design means that the hypothesis is not being tested. As the seeds used were already germinated before testing the acid concentrations, the investigation is measuring the effect of acid on the growth of seedlings.

The students have thought about standardising variables, as shown in figure 4.

- Cress seeds were germinated by growing them on the filter paper dampened with water until the root was just visible.

- Groups of five seeds were transferred onto filter paper dampened with a different concentration of sulphuric acid and left for three days to continue germination.

- The quantity of acid used to dampen the filter paper was the same in each case.

- The seeds were left in the same temperature and light conditions.

- The mean length of the roots in each acid concentration was calculated.

- A statistical test was carried out to see if the differences in root growth were significant.

Figure 4 Plan to test a hypothesis that acid rain inhibits germination.

Q 2 a) Suggest how the design should be modified to test the original hypothesis.
  (S)
  b) Give two other improvements that should be made to the design.

Another question may ask for evidence from data to support either a hypothesis or an expected result. An example is given on the next page.

Testing a hypothesis – is the test valid?

In an investigation into the effect of salivary amylase on starch for two groups of people – smokers and non-smokers – saliva was mixed with starch solution. The mixture was tested for the presence of starch and sugar at five minute intervals. Table 2 shows the results.

Time/min	Non-smoker		Smoker (20 cigarettes a day)		KEY:
	Starch	Sugar	Starch	Sugar	+ Starch or sugar present
0	+++	–	+++	–	
5	+++	–	+++	–	– Starch or sugar absent
10	–	+	+++	–	
15	–	+	+++	–	
20	–	++	+++	–	The number of + signs indicates the concentration
25	–	+++	++	–	
30	–	+++	++	+	
35	–	+++	–	++	

 Table 2

A group of students gave two hypotheses to account for the results for smokers and non-smokers.

1 The saliva of a non-smoker contains more amylase than the saliva of a smoker.

2 The amylase in the saliva of a smoker is inhibited by substances in cigarette smoke.

You are likely to be asked to modify the experimental set-up to test these hypotheses, including an explanation for your changes. Figure 5 shows how hypothesis 1 could be tested.

- Make a set of solutions of known amylase concentrations.
- Mix separately with a known concentration of starch solution.
- Use quantitative Benedict's test to measure the amount of sugar produced in 30 minutes by each concentration of amylase.
- Plot a calibration curve as shown below.

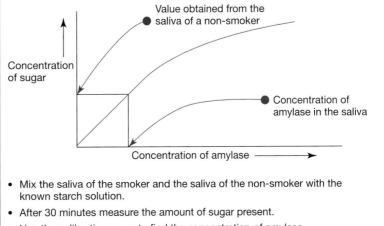

- Mix the saliva of the smoker and the saliva of the non-smoker with the known starch solution.
- After 30 minutes measure the amount of sugar present.
- Use the calibration curve to find the concentration of amylase.

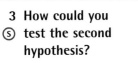 **3 How could you test the second hypothesis?**

▶ **Figure 5** *Testing hypothesis 1.*

Essay question

The essay question requires you to use knowledge and understanding from Modules 1 to 5. You will also have to show an understanding of the broad principles of experimental investigation.

What the examiners will be testing in this part of the examination is your ability to bring together principles and concepts from different areas of biology and combine them in the particular context of the essay, clearly and logically, using appropriate biological vocabulary.

Before starting to talk about writing an essay, it would be useful to look at the way in which examiners mark them. For an essay with 25 marks, a typical marking scheme might be as follows:

Knowledge and understanding	16 marks
Breadth of knowledge	3 marks
Ability to select relevant and suitable examples	3 marks
Quality of written English	3 marks

The plan

The best way to approach an essay is to spend a few minutes making a plan. This should be set out so that you can see the ideas and examples that you intend to put in your essay. The example shown in figure 6 is an essay plan for the essay 'How ATP is produced and used in living organisms'.

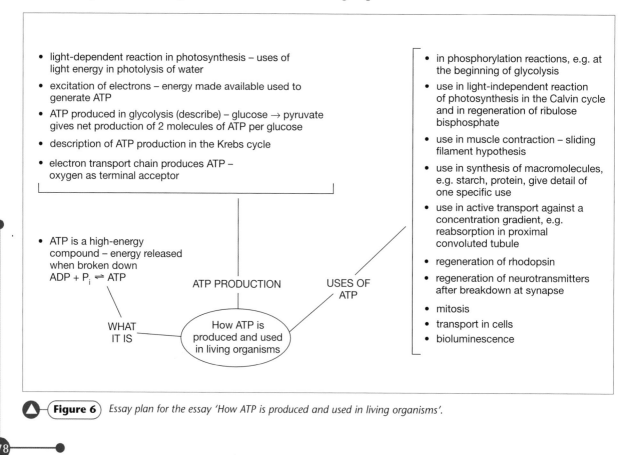

- light-dependent reaction in photosynthesis – uses of light energy in photolysis of water
- excitation of electrons – energy made available used to generate ATP
- ATP produced in glycolysis (describe) – glucose → pyruvate gives net production of 2 molecules of ATP per glucose
- description of ATP production in the Krebs cycle
- electron transport chain produces ATP – oxygen as terminal acceptor

- ATP is a high-energy compound – energy released when broken down
  ADP + P$_i$ ⇌ ATP

WHAT IT IS

ATP PRODUCTION

USES OF ATP

How ATP is produced and used in living organisms

- in phosphorylation reactions, e.g. at the beginning of glycolysis
- use in light-independent reaction of photosynthesis in the Calvin cycle and in regeneration of ribulose bisphosphate
- use in muscle contraction – sliding filament hypothesis
- use in synthesis of macromolecules, e.g. starch, protein, give detail of one specific use
- use in active transport against a concentration gradient, e.g. reabsorption in proximal convoluted tubule
- regeneration of rhodopsin
- regeneration of neurotransmitters after breakdown at synapse
- mitosis
- transport in cells
- bioluminescence

Figure 6 *Essay plan for the essay 'How ATP is produced and used in living organisms'.*

The essay

As you can see, there are many ways in which ATP can be used in living organisms. Writing a biology essay isn't the same as writing an English essay. You don't need to have a dramatic opening, and there's no need to repeat information in the essay to make a neat ending. The items in the plan need to be described and explained clearly and in sufficient detail if they are to gain marks. For example, in this essay:

- You would need to describe ATP production in both respiration and photosynthesis to gain full marks.

  Describing only respiration would lose marks in both knowledge and understanding and breadth of knowledge.

- The range of examples you give for the uses of ATP should be drawn from all the biology you have learned over the whole A level course.

  Giving only one or two examples would lose marks in both breadth and ability to select relevant examples.

- You should also use diagrams where these help, but do make sure they are clearly labelled and annotated. Diagrams could be very useful, for example, in explaining active transport or the sliding filament theory of muscle contraction.

  Including irrelevant diagrams just to fill up space may lose you marks in ability to select relevant examples.

- The 'quality of written English' marks will be awarded if you have organised the work clearly, your spelling and punctuation are good, and you have used biological terms correctly.

  You will certainly lose marks if you write about enzymes being killed rather than denatured, or if you mention messages passing along nerves, rather than impulses.

Sample essay titles

Look at figure 7 which shows an essay plan for the essay 'The properties of enzymes and their importance in living organisms'.

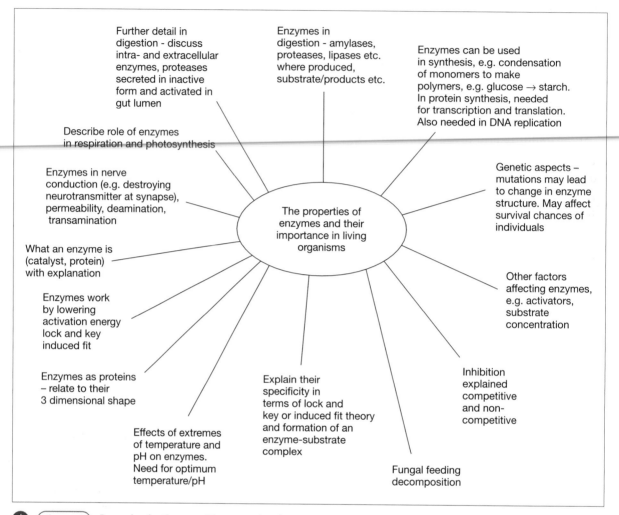

Further detail in digestion - discuss intra- and extracellular enzymes, proteases secreted in inactive form and activated in gut lumen

Enzymes in digestion - amylases, proteases, lipases etc. where produced, substrate/products etc.

Enzymes can be used in synthesis, e.g. condensation of monomers to make polymers, e.g. glucose → starch. In protein synthesis, needed for transcription and translation. Also needed in DNA replication

Describe role of enzymes in respiration and photosynthesis

Enzymes in nerve conduction (e.g. destroying neurotransmitter at synapse), permeability, deamination, transamination

The properties of enzymes and their importance in living organisms

Genetic aspects – mutations may lead to change in enzyme structure. May affect survival chances of individuals

What an enzyme is (catalyst, protein) with explanation

Enzymes work by lowering activation energy lock and key induced fit

Other factors affecting enzymes, e.g. activators, substrate concentration

Enzymes as proteins – relate to their 3 dimensional shape

Explain their specificity in terms of lock and key or induced fit theory and formation of an enzyme-substrate complex

Inhibition explained competitive and non-competitive

Effects of extremes of temperature and pH on enzymes. Need for optimum temperature/pH

Fungal feeding decomposition

Figure 7 *Essay plan for the essay 'The properties of enzymes and their importance in living organisms'.*

Q ⓢ **4 Use the plan in figure 7 to prepare a draft essay.**

Here are some more essay titles you might like to plan.

- The importance of carbohydrates in living organisms.
- The roles of membranes in living organisms.
- Ways in which cells are adapted to their functions.
- The importance of proteins in living organisms.
- Light and life.
- The role of carbon-containing compounds in living organisms.
- The role of nitrogen-containing compounds in living organisms.
- Diffusion and its importance in living organisms.
- Transport mechanisms in living organisms.

Synoptically tested content

There are many ideas that are spread throughout biology. This means that examiners have ample opportunity to test you synoptically. Examples of subject content that can be tested synoptically include:

- biological molecules
- membrane structure
- cell transport
- exchange of materials
- enzymes
- the genetic code
- energy supply

- photosynthesis
- respiration
- survival and co-ordination
- homeostasis
- analysis and integration
- selection and evolution
- human impact

You can use diagrams similar to the ones for the essay plans to show how subject content can be used synoptically. Look at figure 8. You can see that a knowledge and understanding of biological molecules is needed for many of the areas you study in biology.

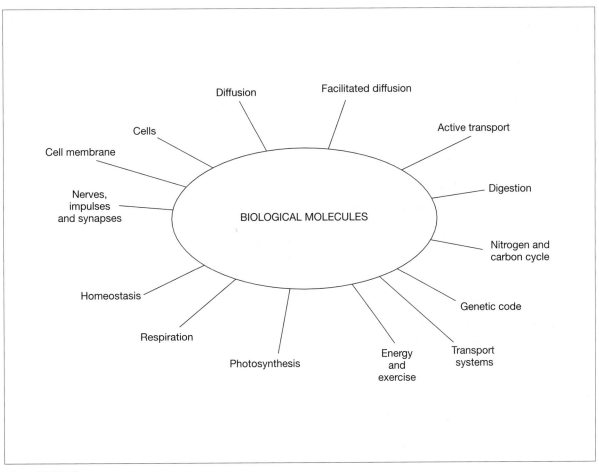

Figure 8 *Biological molecules are linked to many parts of the AQA B specification.*

Try drawing diagrams to show how the subject content listed above links to the different parts of the AQA B specification.

Module 4
Energy, Control and Continuity

Unit 1   Inheritance

1   Inheritance (pages 6–13)

1   Nose shape and leg length

2   a)   bbLl and bbLL or $I^bI^bI^lI^l$ and $I^bI^bI^lI^l$

    b)   Bbll and BBll or $I^BI^bI^lI^l$ and $I^BI^BI^lI^l$

3

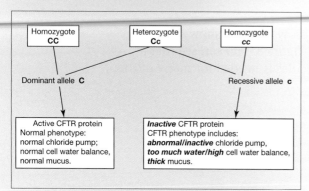

| Homozygote **CC** | Heterozygote **Cc** | Homozygote **cc** |

Dominant allele **C**   Recessive allele **c**

Active CFTR protein
Normal phenotype:
normal chloride pump;
normal cell water balance,
normal mucus.

Inactive CFTR protein
CFTR phenotype includes:
abnormal/inactive chloride pump,
too much water/high cell water balance,
thick mucus.

4

Genotype	Proteins produced	Phenotype
I^AI^A	Protein A only	Group A
I^AI^O	Protein A and Protein O	**Group A**
I^BI^B	**Protein B only**	**Group B**
I^BI^O	Protein B and Protein O	Group B
I^AI^B	**Protein A and Protein B**	Group AB
I^OI^O	**Protein O only**	Group O

5   a)   Blood group AM

    b) I^AI^AMN or I^AI^OMN

6   AaBb is able to synthesise both active enzymes and therefore complete both steps in the pathway, forming dark blue pigment.

    AAbb is able to synthesise active enzyme A and produce pale blue pigment, but inactive enzyme B cannot complete the pathway.

    aaBB has inactive enzyme A so the white/colourless substrate is not metabolised. Active enzyme B has no substrate, so the flower remains white/colourless.

2   Passing on genes (pages 14–19)

1    $2^{10} = 1024$

2

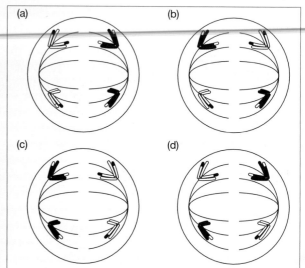

(a)   (b)

(c)   (d)

3   Crossing over, independent assortment of non-homologous pairs, independent assortment of sister chromatids.

4   Fertilisation is random, so any gamete from one parent can fuse with any gamete from the other parent.

3   Following inheritance (pages 20–29)

1   a)   1Yy : 1yy

    b)   The genotype ratio occurs because there are two types of gamete from the yellow parent (Y or y), but only one type of gamete (y) from the green parent. Either gamete from the yellow parent has an equal chance of being fertilised by a gamete from the other parent, so there are two possible combinations (yy or Yy).

        The phenotype ratio occurs because the dominant Y allele hides the effects of the recessive y allele in heterozygotes.

2   Genotype ratio 1Yy : 1YY

    The phenotype of all the offspring is yellow, because all the gametes of the homozygous yellow parent contain a dominant allele, so all the offspring will inherit this allele.

3 a)

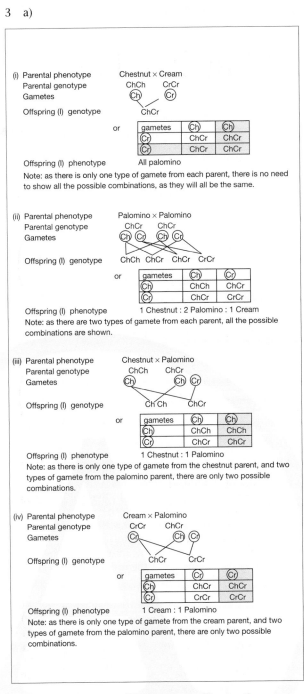

(i) Parental phenotype   Chestnut × Cream
Parental genotype   ChCh   CrCr
Gametes   (Ch)   (Cr)

Offspring (l) genotype   ChCr

or

gametes	(Ch)	(Ch)
(Cr)	ChCr	ChCr
(Cr)	ChCr	ChCr

Offspring (l) phenotype   All palomino

Note: as there is only one type of gamete from each parent, there is no need to show all the possible combinations, as they will all be the same.

(ii) Parental phenotype   Palomino × Palomino
Parental genotype   ChCr   ChCr
Gametes   (Ch)(Cr)   (Ch)(Cr)

Offspring (l) genotype   ChCh ChCr ChCr CrCr

or

gametes	(Ch)	(Cr)
(Ch)	ChCh	ChCr
(Cr)	ChCr	CrCr

Offspring (l) phenotype   1 Chestnut : 2 Palomino : 1 Cream

Note: as there are two types of gamete from each parent, all the possible combinations are shown.

(iii) Parental phenotype   Chestnut × Palomino
Parental genotype   ChCh   ChCr
Gametes   (Ch)   (Ch)(Cr)

Offspring (l) genotype   ChCh   ChCr

or

gametes	(Ch)	(Ch)
(Ch)	ChCh	ChCh
(Cr)	ChCr	ChCr

Offspring (l) phenotype   1 Chestnut : 1 Palomino

Note: as there is only one type of gamete from the chestnut parent, and two types of gamete from the palomino parent, there are only two possible combinations.

(iv) Parental phenotype   Cream × Palomino
Parental genotype   CrCr   ChCr
Gametes   (Cr)   (Ch)(Cr)

Offspring (l) genotype   ChCr   CrCr

or

gametes	(Cr)	(Cr)
(Ch)	ChCr	ChCr
(Cr)	CrCr	CrCr

Offspring (l) phenotype   1 Cream : 1 Palomino

Note: as there is only one type of gamete from the cream parent, and two types of gamete from the palomino parent, there are only two possible combinations.

b) i) 1 homozygous dominant (chestnut) :
     2 heterozygous codominant (palomino) :
     1 homozygous dominant (cream)
ii) 1 homozygous dominant parental colour
     (chestnut or cream) : 1 heterozygous
     codominant (palomino)

4   C > H > Ch > a

5 a)

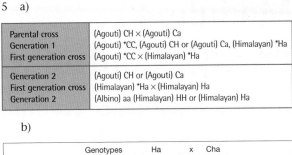

Parental cross	(Agouti) CH × (Agouti) Ca
Generation 1	(Agouti) *CC, (Agouti) CH or (Agouti) Ca, (Himalayan) *Ha
First generation cross	(Agouti) *CC × (Himalayan) *Ha
Generation 2	(Agouti) CH or (Agouti) Ca
First generation cross	(Himalayan) *Ha × (Himalayan) Ha
Generation 2	(Albino) aa (Himalayan) HH or (Himalayan) Ha

b)

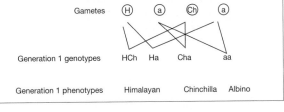

Genotypes   Ha   x   Cha
Gametes   (H)   (a)   (Ch)   (a)

Generation 1 genotypes   HCh   Ha   Cha   aa

Generation 1 phenotypes   Himalayan   Chinchilla   Albino

6

Parent phenotype	Yellow wrinkled seeds	Green smooth seeds
Parent genotype	YyWw	yyww
Parent gametes	(YW)(Yw)(yW)(yw)	(yw)
Offspring genotypes	YyWw, Yyww yyWw yyww	
Offspring phenotypes	yellow yellow green green wrinkled smooth wrinkled smooth	
Phenotype ratio	1 : 1 : 1 : 1	

7 a) All yellow wrinkled
b) 3 yellow : 1 green, all the surfaces the same
    (there are two possible colour alleles, but only
    one surface alleles, so all the offspring inherit
    the same surface genes)
c) 3 wrinkled : 1 smooth, all the same colour
    (there are two possible surface alleles, but only
    one colour allele, so all the offspring inherit the
    same colour genes)
d) 1 yellow wrinkled: 1 yellow smooth : 1 green
    wrinkled : 1 green smooth (the unknown parent
    has four possible gametes, so there are four
    possible combinations)

8   Epistasis reduces the number of possible phenotypes.

9

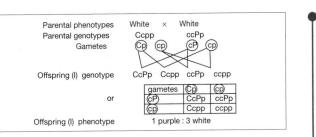

Parental phenotypes   White   ×   White
Parental genotypes   Ccpp   ccPp
Gametes   (Cp) (cp)   (cP) (cp)

Offspring (l) genotype   CcPp   Ccpp   ccPp   ccpp

or

gametes	(Cp)	(cp)
(cP)	CcPp	ccPp
(cp)	Ccpp	ccpp

Offspring (l) phenotype   1 purple : 3 white

Module 4
Energy, Control and Continuity

Unit 1   Inheritance (continued)

4   Sex inheritance (pages 30–35)

1   The Y chromosome has no homologous part of the X chromosome to carry a dominant allele which would hide the effects of the recessive allele.

2

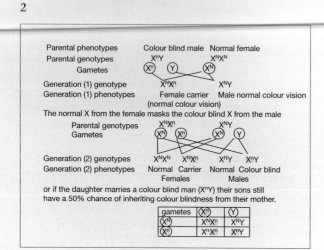

3   As tortoiseshell colour is due to codominance, there must be two X chromosomes, one carrying a black allele and the other a ginger allele. As males have only one X chromosome, they cannot be tortoiseshell.

4

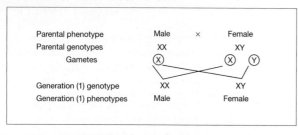

5   Unit 1 – Questions (pages 36–37)

1   a) i)   Inherited by offspring when only one parent is affected

   ii)   Inherited by a female offspring of an affected male and unaffected mother

b)   i)   Either 0.25 or 25% or 1:3

   ii)   Three of:
   - each parent must have a recessive 'normal' finger allele
   - each parent has two types of gamete
   - either gamete of one parent has an equal chance of fertilising either gamete of the other parent
   - 1 in 4 chance of these two alleles coming together at fertilisation.

2   a)   Single gene with two alleles; short is dominant to long.

b)

Rabbit phenotype	Genotype
Short haired parent	Ss
Long haired offspring	ss
Short haired offspring	Ss or SS

Symbols:
S = short, s = long
(any other letter acceptable if correctly labelled)

3   a) i)   The alleles of a gene an individual inherits are the same as each other.

   ii)   The alleles of a gene an individual inherits are different from each other.

b)   Cross the unknown animal with an animal showing the recessive phenotype; the offspring will include animals with the recessive phenotype if the unknown is heterozygous.

c)

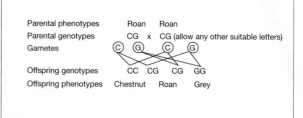

4 a) A gene for a specific characteristic is carried on a sex chromosome; expression of the gene in the phenotype is associated with particular sex/gender.
   b) i) X^OY orange; X^BY black
      ii)

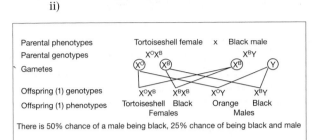

Parental phenotypes — Tortoiseshell female × Black male
Parental genotypes — X^OX^B X^BY
Gametes — X^O X^B X^B Y
Offspring (1) genotypes — X^OX^B X^BX^B X^OY X^BY
Offspring (1) phenotypes — Tortoiseshell Black Females / Orange Black Males
There is 50% chance of a male being black, 25% chance of being black and male

5 a) PpBb
   b)

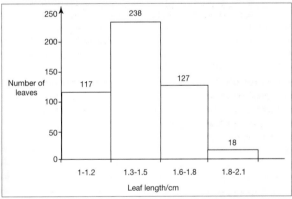

Gametes	PB	pB	Pb	pb
PB	PPBB blue	PpBB blue	PPBb blue	PpBb blue
pB	PpBB blue	ppBB white	PpBb blue	ppBb white
Pb	PPBb blue	PpBb blue	PPbb purple	Ppbb purple
pb	PpBb blue	ppBb white	Ppbb purple	ppbb white

Genotypes
Offspring 2

Unit 2   Variation

1   Variation (pages 38–45)

1 The female gamete (ovum) is fertilised by a sperm cell to give a zygote. After fertilisation the cell divides by mitosis into two separate zygotes, but these will have exactly the same genes as each other.

2 Clones all have the same genotype, so any difference must be due to environment.

3 Body mass has a large genetic component, but is influenced more by environment than height is. The mean difference in mass between identical twins reared apart is different from those reared together, and closer to that of non-identical twins reared together.

4 Homozygous pattern baldness shows in both men and women, but in heterozygotes it is only shown by men. Men produce different hormones from women, so the internal environment (hormones) is modifying the expression of the genes.

5 a)

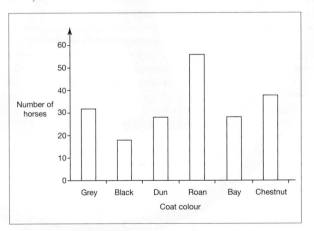

   b) Controlled by a gene with many alleles, which show a dominance series (similar to rabbit coat colour on page 25). Discontinuous variation.

6

Leaf length/cm	1–1.2	1.3–1.5	1.6–1.8	1.9
Number of leaves	117	238	127	18

2   Natural selection (pages 46–57)

1 Lower level of nutrient allows the other, slower growing plants to compete more effectively.

2 • Surface area:volume ratio is increased so may lose heat too fast
  • Body organs may be too small to function correctly or not fully developed.

3 In non-polluted areas speckled type better camouflaged and less likely to be eaten, so these more likely to breed and pass on their alleles for speckled markings. Frequency of this allele increases. Dark/melanic type visible and so likely to be eaten. In industrial polluted areas, dark type better camouflaged and so less likely to be eaten, so these more likely to breed and pass on their dark alleles. Frequency of dark allele increases.

4 Mutation in the bacteria gives rise to an allele that gives resistance to antibiotic. These bacteria survive and breed when in presence of antibiotic. Resistance allele increases in frequency.

Module 4
Energy, Control and Continuity

Unit 2   Variation (continued)

5 a) Mutation introduces new versions of alleles into the gene pool; immigrating organisms bring a different set of alleles into gene pool.

   b) Emigrating organisms take some alleles from the gene pool which may not be present in remaining organisms; directional selection operates against certain phenotypes which are related to particular alleles, so these decrease in frequency.

6 a) Stabilising selection tends to maintain the gene pool with relatively little change in allele frequency.

   b) Disruptive selection would eventually result in two separate gene pools with different frequencies of specific alleles which have been selected. For instance, if the alleles are concerned with mass, the frequency of high mass alleles would increase in one pool, and the frequency of low mass alleles would increase in the other pool. Alleles favouring medium mass would decrease in frequency.

7 Humans have invaded places where other organisms lived and have changed the environment to suit their own needs. Other organisms are unable to compete and many are killed by humans or have no other environment in which they can survive. The rate of change is very fast, so even if there were sufficient space for other organisms, they could not evolve fast enough to be able to survive in the changed environment.

3   Putting into groups (pages 58–71)
1

Taxonomic rank	Common oak	Human
Kingdom	Plant	Animal
Phylum	Angiosperm	Chlordate
Class	Dicotyledon	Mammal
Order	Fagales	Primate
Family	Fagaceae	Hominid
Genus	Quercus	Homo
Species	robur	sapiens (sapiens)

2 Prokaryotic cells do not have organelles; DNA is circular and the single chromosome does not have any protein associated; walls are of a carbohydrate and amino acid polymer called murein.

3 Mosses have two stages in their life cycle: a diploid sporophyte that produces haploid spores by meiosis, and a haploid gametophyte that produces gametes by mitosis.

4 Monocotyledons have a single specialised leaf in their seed; dicotyledons have two specialised storage leaves in their seeds.

5 Plant cells have cellulose walls to the outside of the cell membrane and a large central vacuole. Some have chloroplasts.

4 Unit 2 – Questions (pages 72–73)

1 a) Table 1 shows continuous variation; table 2 shows discontinuous variation. Table 1 has a range of phenotypes which merge into each other; in table 2 the categories are discrete.

   b) i) Height in maize is more likely to be controlled by several genes (indicated by the overlapping categories).

      ii) Bristle number is more likely to be controlled by a small number of genes (indicated by more distinct categories).

   c) Clones all have the same genotype so any differences must be due to environment.

2 a) Five of:
   • all originate from one population
   • original gene pool has mutations
   • different phenotypes were occurring all the time (variation existed)
   • some ancestor type may have become separated/environment changed/became isolated
   • selection favoured different phenotypes in a new environment – survival to reproductive age
   • over long periods differences prevent interbreeding.

   b) Three of:
   • eukaryotic cell structure
   • cells without cell walls
   • multicellular
   • heterotrophic nutrition
   • highly organised organs and tissues including nervous co-ordination
   • the only haploid cells they have form gametes.

3 a) gene mutation   meiosis   random fertilisation

   b) i) Three of:
   • natural selection acts on phenotypes
   • individuals with best adaptations/features suited to a specific environment survive
   • best adapted most likely to breed and pass on their genes
   • over time, the population changes towards the best adapted phenotype.

      ii) Isolation separates part of a population from the original population; different environments result in different selection; if separated long enough, differences between the two populations are so great they can no longer breed.

4 a) i) Height and hand span are mainly genetic.
Differences between identical twins reared
apart in different environments and identical
twins reared together in similar environments
are approximately the same.

   ii) Mass has greater environmental influence.
Differences between identical twins reared
apart in different environments are much
greater than between identical twins reared
together in similar environments and almost
the same as non-identical twins reared together.

   b) Identical twins have the same genotype so
any differences between them must be due
to environment.

5 a) hierarchy; *Ranunculus;* species; fertile offspring

   b)

Kingdom	Plant
Phylum	Angiosperm
Class	Dicotyledon
Order	Ranales
Family	Ranunculaceae
Genus	*Anemone*
Species	*nemorosa*

Unit 3   Survival and co-ordination

1   Stimulus and response (pages 74–78)

1   It informs the brain of the stimulus received,
ensuring awareness of the environment, otherwise
you could touch the hot ring again and burn
yourself badly.

2   The cells have receptor proteins on their surface
membranes which are specifically shaped to enable
insulin to fit in and bind.

3

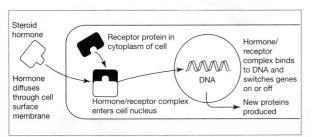

2   Homeostasis (pages 79–91)

1

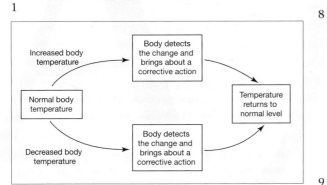

2   Water has a high specific heat capacity so it removes
a great deal of heat energy from the skin when heat
from body is used to vaporise water in clothing.
Wind causes faster vaporisation, so more heat is lost.

3 a) Large ears, trunk, long legs, loose skin

   b) Short neck, short legs, small ears, short tail.

4 a) Thermoreceptors in hypothalamus and skin

   b) Hypothalamus

c) Muscles in arterioles and sweat glands, erector
pili muscles (skeletal muscle and adrenal glands)

d) Vasoconstriction (leads to reduced blood flow
through skin and thus less heat loss); less sweat
released (leads to less evaporation and less heat
loss); piloerection (leads to a thicker layer of air
being trapped next to the skin). Shivering
generates heat, adrenaline increases metabolic
rate.

5   Water has a high specific heat capacity and
so removes a lot of heat from the skin when it
vaporises.

6   Body temperature rise causes an increase in enzyme
activity. Increase in enzyme activity increases
metabolic rate, releasing more energy so temperature
rises further. Enzyme activity increases, leading to
a rise in metabolic rate and more heat produced.

7   Lowering hair reduces the layer of insulation
between the skin and the air, allowing evaporation
and radiation to occur more readily. Shivering
generates heat, so heat losses are not replaced.

8   • move further apart – more surface area is
exposed to the air so more heat can escape

   • take off clothes – the layers of insulation
between skin and air are reduced so heat can
escape more easily

   • stretch out as far as possible – more surface area
and extremities of the body are exposed so more
heat can escape

   • sit still – making as little muscle movement
as possible means less heat is generated

   • keep in the shade – avoids absorbing heat from
the environment.

9 a) Water potential falls *or* becomes more negative
or becomes lower

   b) If water potential rises cells may gain too much
water and burst. If water potential falls cells lose
too much water and shrink. They may become
too concentrated for metabolic processes to
occur. Also, if blood water potential changes, this
will affect blood volume and blood pressure.

Module 4
Energy, Control and Continuity

Unit 3   Survival and co-ordination (continued)

10

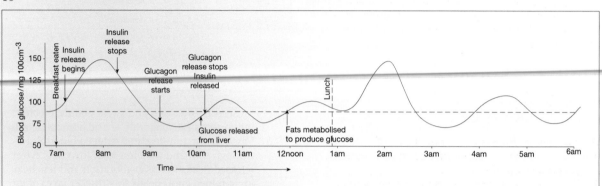

11 After a meal containing carbohydrate (usually about 1 hour afterwards). Digestion and absorption of glucose occur in the small intestine and into the hepatic portal vein.

12 Insulin binds to the receptors on the cell membrane. This makes more facilitated channels available for glucose uptake. Inside the cell, the change in the membrane as insulin binds activates enzymes that cause the conversion of glucose to glycogen.

13 a) β-cells in the islets of Langerhans in the pancreas
   b) β-cells in the islets of Langerhans in the pancreas
   c) Liver, muscle (all respiring cells)
   d) Glycogenesis, as more enzymes convert glucose to glycogen.

14

```
Decreased ──▶ Detected ──▶ ∝-cells ──▶ Glucagon ──▶ Glycogenolysis
blood          by islets of   secrete       binds to      and
glucose        Langerhans    glucagon      receptor      gluconeogenesis
level                                        proteins
                                             on cell
                                             surface
                                             membranes
                                                          Increased blood
                                                          glucose level

                                      Inhibition
```

15 Diet: eat regular, small meals; avoid eating high levels of sugar which cause glucose levels to increase rapidly; eat starch instead which releases glucose more slowly as it is digested. Exercise: uses up glucose so reduces blood glucose levels.

3   The role of the kidney (pages 92–100)

1 Peristalsis is a wave of muscular contraction which passes along the ureter. It is brought about by the co-ordinated activity of longitudinal muscles and circular muscles. The circular muscles constrict the ureter and the longitudinal muscles cause a wave of constriction to pass along the ureter. The same activity is seen in the digestive system.

2 The basement membrane normally prevents large proteins passing through. If it is damaged, they are able to pass into the filtrate, because the gaps between the podocytes and the gaps in the capillary endothelium are too large to keep them out.

3 a) large surface area provided by microvilli mitochondria to provide ATP for active transport
   b) Water moves from an area of high water potential to an area of low water potential. Reabsorption of glucose, salts and amino acids causes the water potential of the filtrate inside the proximal convoluted tubule to increase above that of the epithelial cell, so water enters the cell along a water potential gradient. As the water potential in the blood is lower than the water potential in the cell, the water enters the blood by osmosis.

4 A solution has the same water potential as another solution.

5 The high salt concentration causes the tissues to have a more negative (lower) water potential than the fluid in the descending tubule. Water leaves the descending tubule by osmosis.

6 Sodium has a positive charge (is a cation), chloride has a negative charge (is an anion), so the sodium balances charges of the ions.

7 a) Osmoreceptors in the hypothalamus
   b) Pituitary gland
   c) Cells of the distal convoluted tubule and collecting duct
   d) Increased permeability of the distal convoluted tubule and collecting duct to water.

8

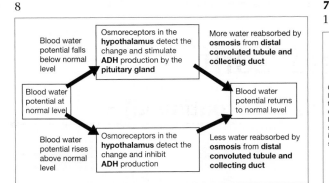

4 The nervous system (pages 101–105)

1 Slow it down: in myelinated nerves sodium ions are exchanged only at nodes, so sodium ions can 'jump' from one node to the next, reducing the number of sodium ions exchanged.

5 The nerve impulse (pages 106–112)

1 The resting potential would be lost, as insufficient potassium would leak back.
2 The inside of the neurone is more negatively charged than the outside.
3 Sodium channels open, allowing sodium ions in. After this, potassium channels open, allowing potassium ions out.
4 The membrane has to repolarise before another action potential can occur.
5 Ion exchange cannot occur where the membrane is surrounded by a myelin sheath.

6 Synapses (pages 113–117)

1 Transmitter substance binds to receptor proteins in the postsynaptic membrane. As the transmitter binds, the protein changes shape and opens the gated channel.
2 Receptor sites have a complementary shape to the substance that binds to them.
3 Acetylcholine remains bound to the receptors so the sodium channels remain open.
4 Activate GABA channels causing synapse inhibition; prevent the release of acetylcholine; compete with acetylcholine and prevent the opening of sodium channels; inhibit acetylcholinesterase so acetylcholine remains in the synapse; block the receptor proteins for the transmitters.

7 The mammalian eye (pages 118–130)

1

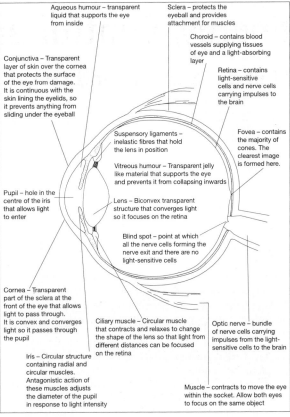

2 a) A
  b) B
3 Light would be reflected from the back of the eye and create an after-image.
4 A decrease in the permeability of the receptor membrane to sodium, so less neurotransmitter is released.
5 Bipolar neurones become hyperpolarised so less neurotransmitter is released to the ganglion cells. The ganglion cells then produce an action potential as gated channels open and allow sodium to enter.
6 In the brightly lit room most of the rhodopsin in the cones is bleached. It takes a few minutes for it to reform. However, once the rhodopsin has reformed, you can see much more clearly in dim light.
7 White is perceived when all three types of cone cell are stimulated evenly. Black is perceived when none of the cone cell types is stimulated at all.
8 Any colour that has a red component will be perceived as a different colour, e.g. orange is now perceived as green.
9 If a female has an X chromosome carrying the allele that codes for a faulty red-absorbing iodopsin she may pass it to male offspring.

Module 4
Energy, Control and Continuity

Unit 3   Survival and co-ordination (continued)

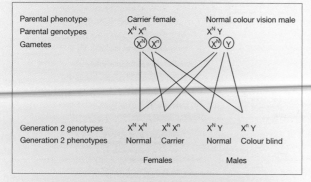

Parental phenotype — Carrier female — Normal colour vision male
Parental genotypes $X^N X^n$ — $X^N Y$
Gametes

Generation 2 genotypes — $X^N X^N$ — $X^N X^n$ — $X^N Y$ — $X^n Y$
Generation 2 phenotypes — Normal — Carrier — Normal — Colour blind
Females — Males

10 Stimuli from several receptors are directed into one bipolar neurone, so these stimuli are interpreted as a single stimulus. The image has less input so it is less clearly defined.

8 Analysis and integration (pages 131–143)

1 Medulla contains receptors that detect carbon dioxide level. It also co-ordinates input from carbon dioxide receptors in the carotid body and aortic body. When carbon dioxide level rises in the blood, the medulla causes an increase in the heart rate and breathing rate through the sympathetic nervous system. When carbon dioxide levels fall the medulla causes a decrease in heart rate and breathing rate.

2 Contains receptors for blood temperature and co-ordinates the (sympathetic) nerve supply to the skin arterioles. Causes vasoconstriction when blood temperature falls and vasodilation when blood temperature rises.

3 Lips, tongue, hand, hip

4 Lips, hand, tongue, hip

5 Mathematical and logical ability would be impaired, as would voluntary movement of the right side of the body.

6 Area 5 is the visual sensory area and area 6 is the visual association area, where visual processing takes place.

7 Sympathetic has an inhibitory effect on some systems: it inhibits gut peristalsis and secretion of digestive juices, and decreases urine output. Parasympathetic has a stimulatory effect on some systems. As it is antagonistic to the sympathetic it will stimulate the systems inhibited by the sympathetic.

8

		Sympathetic	Parasympathetic
1	Where do preganglionic neurones leave the CNS?	Along the length of the spinal cord	At the base of the brain and the end of the spinal cord
2	Are preganglionic neurones short or long?	Short	Long
3	Are ganglia interconnected or discrete?	Discrete	Interconnected
4	Are postganglionic neurones short or long?	Long	Short

9 Sympathetic nervous system
10 Sympathetic nervous system
11 Area when fully dilated = $3.14 \times 4^2 = 50.24\,mm^2$
Area when fully constricted
$= 3.14 \times 0.75^2 = 1.77\,mm^2$
Therefore change in area = $50.24 - 1.77 = 48.47\,mm^2$
Percentage decrease in area
$= (48.47 \div 50.24) \times 100 = 96.48\%$
12 These are controlled by sympathetic nerves which increase the secretion of sweat.
13 A reduction in production of tears
14

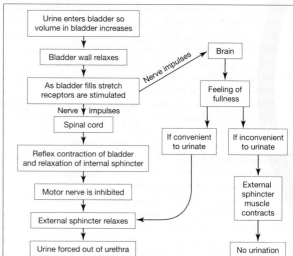

9 Muscles (pages 144–153)

1 The arm would stay locked in one position and it would not be possible to bend or straighten it.
2 a) Gets shorter
    b) Gets narrower
    c) Stays the same
    d) Stays the same
    e) Stays the same.

10 Unit 3 – Questions (pages 154–155)

1 a) i) The liver is still deaminating excess amino acids, producing urea which passes into the blood; but there are no kidneys to filter the blood so level of urea rises.

ii) Urea level rises during first 8 hours because the liver is still producing urea via the ornithine cycle. Curve levels off and starts to fall after 8 hours because once the liver has been removed no more urea can be produced.

b) i) Urea is not being produced by the liver and not being removed by the kidneys.

ii) Liver is not producing urea and the kidneys remove any urea that had previously been formed.

2 a) Total of six from i) and ii):

i) • the arrangement of rods in blocks which connect to the same bipolar cell increases sensitivity
   • the response of a single rod to a low level of stimulus is insufficient to generate a nerve impulse
   • the additive effect of a number of rods is sufficient for an impulse to be generated allowing low intensity light to be detected
   • the blocked arrangement of rods means that individual stimuli falling in rods close to one another are merged to a single stimulus

ii) • the one-to-one arrangement of cones to a bipolar cell increases acuity
   • the sensitivity is less because a lot of light is needed before the cone responds
   • individual stimuli falling on cones very close together can be detected as separate stimuli.

b) In the brightly lit room, most of the rhodopsin in the cones is bleached; it takes 10 minutes for all the rhodopsin to reform. Once the rhodopsin has reformed, it can respond to light so vision becomes clearer in dim light.

c) Sensory area receives input from the optic nerve/retina.
Association area interprets the visual input so objects are recognised.

3 a) Sodium gated channels open so sodium ions move into the neurone. The inside of the axon become positively charged and sodium gated channels close. Potassium gated channels open so potassium ions can now diffuse out. The membrane repolarises and returns to its original resting potential.

b) i) A stimulus has to be above a certain threshold value if it is to cause an action potential and, once generated, all action potentials are the same size.

ii) By the frequency of action potentials: the greater the stimulus the more frequent the action potentials.

4 a)

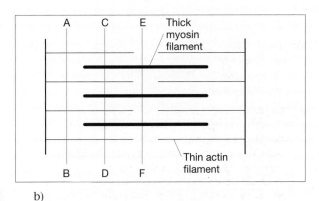

b)

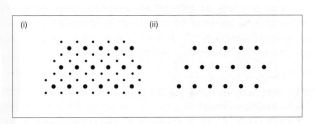

Unit 4   Energy supply

1 Energy supply (pages 156–161)

1 It has three phosphate groups attached to carbon 5 instead of one phosphate group.

2

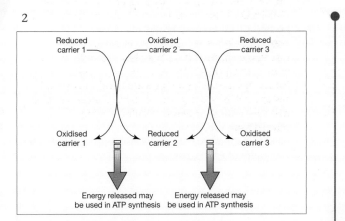

Module 4
Energy, Control and Continuity

Unit 4   Energy supply (continued)

3

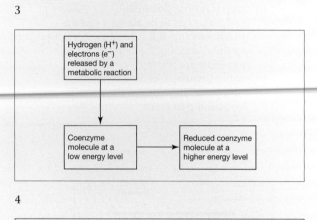

4

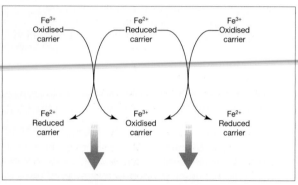

$$\text{Photosynthesis } 6CO_2 + 6H_2O \xrightarrow{\text{Light energy}} C_6H_{12}O_6 + 6O_2$$
$$\text{Respiration: } C_6H_{12}O_6 + 6O_2 \longrightarrow 6CO_2 + 6H_2O + \text{ATP and heat energy}$$

2   Respiration (pages 162–171)

1   The Krebs cycle in the matrix; electron transport in the cristae.

2   Although four molecules of ATP are made, two molecules of ATP are used at the beginning to start the reactions.

3   It would stop: all the carriers would be full, so there would be nowhere for the enzymes to transfer the hydrogen.

4   It releases the carriers so they can be used in glycolysis.

5   One

6   Pyruvate + NAD → two-carbon compound
    oxidised   reduced
                    + reduced NAD + carbon dioxide

7   Starting from the left and going clockwise: 6, 5, 4

8   It diffuses out of the cell and is carried to gas exchange surface for removal. The exact method of transfer depends on the organism (refer to AS book for fish, mammals and plants).

9   Four: one between 6C and 5C molecules; one between 5C and 4C molecules; two in regeneration of 4C carrier.

10 Four molecules reduced NAD produced for every pyruvate. This gives a total of eight molecules reduced NAD per glucose as two molecules of pyruvate are formed from every glucose. One molecule reduced FAD produced for every pyruvate. This gives a total of two molecules of $FADH_2$ per glucose.

11

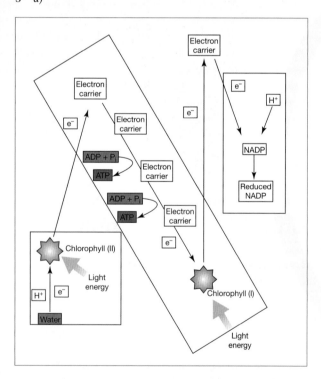

3   Photosynthesis (pages 172–181)

1   It loses electrons, which is an oxidation reaction

2   $NADP + H^+ + e^-$ (reduced electron carrier) →
    reduced NADP + oxidised electron carrier

3   a)

b) Excitation of chlorophyll (II) and the transfer of electrons to an electron carrier.

c) Replacement of an electron in chlorophyll (II) to replace the electron lost during the excitation of chlorophyll (I) and transfer of the electron to NADP.

4 The splitting of water provides the electrons and the protons to be transferred to NADP.

5 Light energy excites chlorophyll (I) and chlorophyll (II) molecules so electrons are emitted and taken up by electron carriers. Excited chlorophyll (II) causes the photolysis of water to obtain electrons to replace those lost. Electron carriers transfer electrons from chlorophyll (I) to chlorophyll (II) to replace those lost. As these electrons are transferred, energy is released and used to move protons from the photolysis of water through the thylakoid membrane. Energy from the movement of electrons and protons is used to synthesise ATP from ADP and inorganic phosphate. Protons and electrons from chlorophyll (I) are used to reduce NADP.

6 Glycerate-3-phosphate (GP)

7 Reduced NADP reduces GP to sugar and ATP is hydrolysed to provide the energy to drive the reaction. ATP is also used to recycle ribulose bisphosphate. ATP and reduced NADP are both produced in the light-dependent reaction.

8 Carbon dioxide fixed into GP is converted to sugars, which can then be used to synthesise glucose, which can be converted to starch and stored in a starch grain.

4 Unit 4 – Questions (pages 182–183)

1 energy; cytoplasm; pyruvate; the Krebs; matrix; NAD/FAD

2 a) A = water, B = reduced NADP, C = carbon dioxide.
  b) i) Photophosphorylation; electrons are excited by light in chlorophyll; passed through a chain of electron carriers to another chlorophyll molecule; energy from the movement of electrons is used to combine ADP and P_i to form ATP.
    ii) It provides the energy; to reduce GALP; to recycle RuBP.

3 a) outer membrane/two membranes; folded inner membrane/large internal surface area; electron carriers in membranes; central fluid-filled space containing enzymes.

  b) i) Three of:
    • electron carriers/electron acceptors/coenzymes
    • energy released during electron transfer
    • ADP is phosphorylated/reacts with inorganic phosphate
    • redox reactions involved.
    ii) Four of:
    • photosynthesis uses light energy
    • respiration uses organic molecules/sugar
    • photosynthesis forms reduced NADP
    • respiration uses reduced NAD/FAD
    • respiration produces some ATP directly in reactions/substrate level
    • photosynthesis involves photolysis/release of oxygen from water
    • respiration uses oxygen to produce water.
  c) Two of:
    • during glycolysis ATP hydrolysed/broken down to ADT + P_i + energy
    • phosphate group added to glucose
    • activates the sugar/provides energy to start reactions.

4 a) i) Thylakoid/grana
    ii) Stroma
  b) i) GP cannot be used/converted to sugar; needs reduced NADP/ATP from light reactions; RuBP used to react with carbon dioxide to form GP; level out when all RuBP used/no RuBP being recycled.
    ii) To form other molecules/named molecule; in respiration.

5 a) X = carbon dioxide, Y = reduced NAD (accept X and Y in reverse), Z = acetylcoenzyme A.
  b) Added to a 4C carrier molecule; dehydrogenated/oxidised; reduced NAD formed; carbon dioxide released/decarboxylated.
  c) NAD is in limited supply; electron transport chain/oxidative phosphorylation recycles NAD; electron transport chain passes hydrogen/electrons to oxygen.

Module 5   Environment

Unit 5   Ecosystems

2 Energy and the environment (pages 195–203)

1 Light can only travel to a certain depth through water. Photosynthesis can only happen where there is light.

2 a) $(153\,000 \div 1\,600\,000) \times 100 = 9.56\%$
   b) $(9 \div 100) \times 153\,000 = 13\,770\,\mathrm{kJ\,m^{-2}yr^{-1}}$.
   c) Of the light energy leaving the sun, some is lost in the atmosphere, some is the wrong wavelength for photosynthesis, some is reflected, some is not absorbed, some falls on non-photosynthetic parts of the plant, some passes through the plant, some does not fall on the plant.

3 a) i)   Grass/phytoplankton/algae
      ii) Pond snail/water flea/grasshopper/water hog louse
      iii) Dragonfly nymph/diving beetle larva/stickleback/small fish/blackbird/frog
      iv) Stickleback/small fish/frog/blackbird/heron
      v)   Pond snail/water flea/grasshopper
      vi) Heron/small fish/large fish/stickleback/diving beetle larva/dragonfly nymph/frog/snake/bird of prey/blackbird
   b) i)   Phytoplankton/grass/algae
      ii) Pond snail/water flea/grasshopper/water hog louse
      iii) Dragonfly nymph/diving beetle larva/stickleback/small fish/blackbird/frog
      iv) Frog/heron/small fish/blackbird/snake.
   c)

Alga →Pond snail → Small fish → Heron
Decaying plant and animal matter →hog louse →Diving beetle larva →Frog → Snake → Bird of prey
Decaying plant and animal matter →hog louse →Stickleback →Small fish →Large fish
Decaying plant and animal matter →hog louse →Stickleback →Small fish →Heron
Phytoplankton→ Water flea →Dragonfly (larva) →Blackbird
Grass →Grasshopper →Frog → Snake →Bird of prey
Grass →Grasshopper →Blackbird

4 a) $(2 \div 100) \times 10^6 = 2 \times 10^4\,\mathrm{kJ\,m^{-2}yr^{-1}}$.
   b) 70% of the total is NPP:
      $(70 \div 100) \times (2 \times 10^4) = 1.4 \times 10^4\ \mathrm{kJ\,m^{-2}yr^{-1}}$.

5 a) $E = F + U + R$
   b) i) $(56.25 \div 150) \times 100 = 37.5\%$
      ii) $(4 \div 100) \times 56.25 = 2.25\,\mathrm{kJ}$
      iii) 90% is used for respiration and lost as heat. Some is lost in urine.

6 a) i) $87\,402 - (50\,303 + 22\,953) = 14\,146\,\mathrm{kJ\,m^{-2}yr^{-1}}$
      ii) $1614 - (193 + 94) = 1327\,\mathrm{kJ\,m^{-2}yr^{-1}}$
   b) $63 + 1327 + 7933 + 50\,303 = 59\,626\,\mathrm{kJ\,m^{-2}yr^{-1}}$
   c) $22\,953 + 4599 + 193 + 25 = 27\,770\,\mathrm{kJ\,m^{-2}yr^{-1}} = 32\%$ of $87\,402\,\mathrm{kJ\,m^{-2}yr^{-1}}$

3 Pyramids (pages 204–208)

1 a)

   The blocks should be drawn to scale on graph paper. The depth of the bars should be the same.
   b) Photosynthesis
   c) The total primary biomass and the efficiency of energy transfer between primary and secondary consumers limit the numbers of secondary consumers.

2 a)

   The blocks should be drawn to scale on graph paper. The depth of the bars should be the same.
   b) Zooplankton quickly eat phytoplankton. The phytoplankton do not have time to achieve a high biomass. The phytoplankton reproduce very quickly, so at another time period, the phytoplankton may have a higher biomass than the zooplankton.

3 a) $44\,239 + 50\,303 = 94\,542\,\mathrm{kJ\,m^{-2}yr^{-1}}$.
   b) Availability of light: the more light available the greater the gross primary productivity. Availability of nutrients: the more nutrients available the greater the gross primary productivity
   c) $6207 + 7938 = 14\,145\,\mathrm{kJ\,m^{-2}yr^{-1}}$ (energy consumed)
      $281 + 1327 = 1608\,\mathrm{kJ\,m^{-2}yr^{-1}}$ (energy passed on)
      $(1608 \div 14\,145) \times 100 = 11.37\%$

4 Recycling (pages 209–215)

1 In tropical regions the temperature is higher than in temperate regions. Enzymes can function more rapidly and the rate of reproduction of micro-organisms is faster.

2 The fungus secretes enzymes onto the food source outside the organism. The fungus absorbs the products of digestion.

3 i) and ii) Temperature: the higher the temperature the faster the rate of decomposition up to the temperature at which enzymes are denatured.
pH: extreme conditions of pH limit the range of organisms that can live there, so decomposition is slower. In very acid conditions it may not occur at all.
Water availability: very dry or very wet conditions limit the range of organisms that can live there, so decomposition is slower. Aquatic environments have their own range of decomposers.
Exposure: may cause erosion or sudden changes in temperature which limits the rate of decomposition. As a general principle, the more extreme an environment, the slower the rate of decomposition.

4 i) Prokaryotes
ii) Protoctists

5 Dynamics of ecosystems (pages 216–225)

1 a) i) Intraspecific
   ii) From day 0 to 8 there is a gradual rise in the population size. From day 8 the curve levels off.
   iii) The paramecium has reached equilibrium with the environment. There are insufficient resources for the population size to increase any further. At this point the death rate and reproduction rate are equal.

   b) *Paramecium caudatum* does not compete as effectively as *Paramecium aurelia*.
   Possibly *Paramecium aurelia* grows faster than *Paramecium caudatum* and uses the resources more effectively.

2

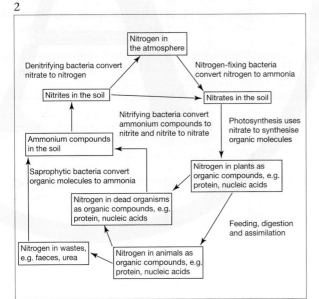

3 $(1\,000\,000 + 99\,000 + 1100) - (45\,000 + 8900)$
$= 1\,046\,200$. Increase $= 46\,200 = 4.62\%$.

4 a) 8
   b) 32 768
   c) 1 073 741 824

7 Ecological techniques (pages 232–242)

1 Rare species or species limited to one small part of the whole environment may be missed.

2 Advantages: can record over a larger area; can record a greater number in each sample.
Disadvantages: do not record at different depths; some plants form clumps so are difficult to count.

3 Species that form clumps may not fall on the line; intervals between points may bypass some rare or clustered species; line may not be representative of the whole area.

4 Enzymes have an optimum pH. pH values on either side of the mean cause changes in the shape of the enzyme active site so it is unable to function. Extreme pH may cause denaturing of enzymes.

5 As light increases, photosynthesis increases, thus primary productivity increases. At very high light intensities, chlorophyll may be damaged, reducing photosynthesis and primary productivity.

6 At low temperature, metabolism decreases as enzymes function more efficiently. As temperature increases, metabolism increases until enzymes are working at their optimum.

7 28.50 cm ± 11.88 cm

8 A χ^2 value of 6.89 is less than the critical value of 7.82 at three degrees of freedom so the result is not significant.

8 Human impact (pages 243–248)

1 Larger invertebrates like earthworms feed on organic matter. As it passes through the gut, enzymes break down some of the organic molecules. Faeces consists of undigested material that has been broken down to smaller particles, so it becomes easier for micro-organisms to digest.
Fungi are saprophytes and secrete extracellular enzymes that digest the organic molecules to small molecules which are then absorbed. This releases some minerals which can be recycled.
Bacteria are also saprophytes and, like fungi, can release minerals during digestion of large organic molecules. Some bacteria are nitrogen-fixing so they convert nitrogen in the air into ammonia, which can then be used by plants. Some bacteria are nitrifying and can convert ammonia released by the breakdown of amino acids and urine into nitrites and nitrates which can be used by plants.
Denitrifying bacteria break down nitrates in the soil to nitrogen and so reduce that available to plants. The respiration of all the organisms recycles carbon dioxide.

2 As water runs downhill it is caught in the furrows. Vertical furrows allow water to run all the way downhill and it is more likely to carry soil with it, leading to erosion.

Module 5   Environment

Unit 5   Ecosystems (continued)

9 Agrochemicals (pages 249–258)

1 Nitrogen in the air is fixed by nitrogen-fixing bacteria. These convert nitrogen to ammonia. Plants can make use of this to synthesise proteins and nucleic acid. Animals feed on plants and digest them to obtain nitrogen-containing compounds which they convert into their own proteins and nucleic acid. Decomposers digest the dead bodies of both plants and animals. During decomposition, ammonia is released which reacts in the environment to form ammonium compounds. Nitrifying bacteria convert ammonium compounds to nitrite, and nitrite to nitrate. Nitrates can be absorbed by plants and recycled. Denitrifying bacteria may break down nitrate to nitrogen gas, returning nitrogen to the air.

2 The increase in the nitrate level may increase the activities of denitrifying bacteria.

3 The excess algal growth covers the surface of the water and blocks the light to the rooted plants. These plants are unable to photosynthesise and so they die.

4 Respiration

5 i) When there is a large quantity of organic matter in the environment.
   ii) When there is a low quantity of organic matter in the environment or the conditions inhibit microbial action.

6

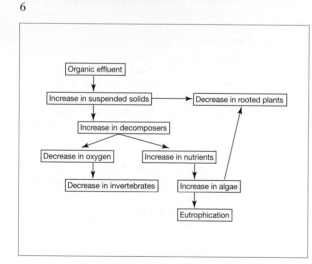

7 Mutations in the population give some individuals resistance to pesticide. These resistant individuals survive, while non-resistant individuals die. The resistant individuals breed and pass on resistance to their offspring. This process is repeated over many generations, so the frequency of the resistance allele increases in the population and the non-resistant allele decreases. Eventually all the population is resistant.

8 The pesticide killed many of the pest organisms. Thus the predator food supply was reduced, leading to the death or migration of predators. The pest population recovers as the pesticide wears off and there are no longer sufficient predators to feed on the pest.

9 Marine mammals have very thick fat layers for insulation in cold water and for buoyancy. Pesticides accumulate in fat, and so more accumulate in marine mammals.

10 Balancing food production (pages 259–265)

1 Both cause excessive growth of algae and rooted plants. Excessive growth of algae blocks light from rooted plants so they die. The rapid growth of algae causes 'blooms' that cover the whole water surface: with very high nitrate levels these are mainly green algae; with very high phosphate levels these are mainly cyanobacteria. The excess growth depletes the nutrient supply so the algae die. Microbial decomposition of the dead organisms uses up oxygen causing the death of invertebrates and fish.

2 Organic nitrogen is in the form of proteins or urea. Saprophytic decomposers digest proteins to amino acids. Excess amino acids are deaminated and ammonia released. Urea is decomposed by bacteria to release ammonia. In the soil, ammonia reacts with mineral salts to form ammonium compounds. Ammonia is inorganic nitrogen. Other forms of inorganic nitrogen are formed from ammonia by nitrifying bacteria. Ammonium compounds are converted by some types of nitrifying bacteria to nitrite. Other types of nitrifying bacteria convert nitrite to nitrate.

3 Restriction endonucleases are used to cut resistance genes from a donor organism. The Ti plasmid from *Agrobacterium* is cut with the same endonuclease. The resistance gene and the plasmid are mixed with ligase enzyme. Recombinant plasmids are used to transform plant cells. New plants are grown from calluses of plant cells containing the resistance gene.

4

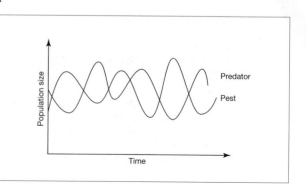

5 To increase the amount of land for crop growing and to allow large machinery to be used efficiently.

6 The mass of all living tissue. Usually the dry mass is used as it is more reliable.

7 Plant biomass is the basis of food chains. Each animal feeding on plants needs a certain amount of biomass to support it. So the lower the biomass of plants, the fewer animals can be supported.

11 Unit 5 – Questions (pages 266–267)

1 a) i) $[(4.24 \times 10^4) \div (3 \times 10^6)] \times 100 = 1.4\%$
    ii) Two of:
      - some is reflected
      - some is not absorbed
      - some is the wrong wavelength
      - some misses the plant.
   b) i) $[420 \div (4.2 \times 10^3)] \times 100 = 10\%$
    ii) Three of:
      - some is not digested
      - some is used by the producers for respiration
      - some is used by the plant for metabolic processes such as active transport
      - some is lost as heat from the metabolism of the producers
      - some is not eaten.

2 i) A and B
   ii)

   iii) general: unit mass/unit area, examples in kg m^{-2}
   iv) A and B

3 Organic effluents contain suspended solids; these block light to rooted plants, preventing photosynthesis; bacteria feed on the organic material and dead plants, releasing nitrates, phosphates and other minerals; respiration of bacteria uses up oxygen, causing death of invertebrates and fish; phosphates and nitrates cause excessive growth of floating algae; algal blooms block light to rooted plants causing same effects as suspended solids; rapid growth of algae depletes nitrates/phosphates causing eutrophication.

4 a) i) Carbon dioxide
     ii) Proteins/amino acids
   b) i) Fungi, bacteria
     ii) Any four:
      - they are saprophytes/saprophytic nutrition
      - enzymes secreted on dead organic matter
      - break down large organic molecules to small organic molecules
      - cause the release of ammonia that can be recycled
      - respiration releases carbon dioxide.

5 a) i) A population is a group of organisms of the same species that live together in the same area at the same time.
     ii) A community is all the populations of different species that live and interact together in the same area at the same time.
   b) i) The study area is divided into a grid pattern by laying out two long tape measures at right angles to each other, along two sides of the study area. Random numbers are used to generate sampling co-ordinates. Each number must have an equal chance of being chosen. A quadrat is then placed at the intersection of each pair of co-ordinates and the species recorded.
     ii) May miss rare or clustered species
   c) i) Primary succession is the change in species composition over time in a habitat that has not previously been inhabited. In natural and suitable conditions land will gradually be colonised by a range of herbaceous plants (whose growth dies down each year), then by shrubs and finally by trees as a climax community. Secondary succession is the change in species composition over time in a habitat that has previously been inhabited.
     ii) Four of:
      - line or belt transects
      - several transect lines laid across the distance of the succession
      - sampling stations at fixed distances along the transect
      - for a belt transect two lines are laid 0.5/1 metre apart and quadrats used
      - for a line transect a point quadrat is used to record species.

6 a) i) Symbiosis
     ii) Parasitism
     iii) Commensalism.
   b) i) Interspecific competition occurs when different species compete for the same resources.
     ii) Intraspecific competition occurs when members of the same species compete for the same resources.
   c) Temperature: an electronic thermometer has a metal probe which allows water to be measured at different depths or the probe can be pushed into soil.
   pH: pH meters are used to measure the pH of water or soil samples or universal indicator can be used.
   Light: light meters measure light intensity. Readings are taken with the probe always pointing in the same direction and readings taken at the same height above the ground.

Synoptic assessment

Pages 272-281

1 a) Experimental results show some uptake in the first 20 minutes then appear to stop. Control shows uptake throughout the investigation. Rate is gradually decreasing over time.

   b) Experimental plants can only take up phosphate by diffusion. Without oxygen respiration cannot occur so no active uptake can take place. In the control, both active transport and diffusion can take place. The results indicate that active transport is responsible for more uptake than diffusion.

2 a) Put the ungerminated seeds onto filter paper dampened with the different acid concentrations.

   b) Use more than five seeds per batch (minimum of ten).
   Use more than one petri dish at each concentration (minimum of three).
   Test a range of acid concentrations beforehand, or research the pH of acid rain and make up solutions within that range.

3 Make up a solution of amylase of known concentration. Test its activity by mixing with starch for 30 minutes and measuring the amount of sugar present. Use a pump system to draw cigarette smoke through a fresh amylase solution of the same concentration. A different number of cigarettes could be used to obtain a range of enzyme solutions. Test the activity of these amylase solutions in the same way. If cigarette smoke affects the activity of amylase, less sugar would be expected.

4 **Essay question**
   This is not intended as a model answer.
   The points from the plan have been put together in a logical sequence and examples you might quote have been included.

'The properties of enzymes and their importance in living organisms'

All enzymes are proteins that are produced by living organisms and act as biological catalysts. They speed up the rate of reactions in cells by lowering the activation energy necessary for the reaction to take place. Many reactions in living organisms would not take place without enzymes. There are a wide variety of intracellular enzymes in living organisms as every reaction in the body depends on an enzyme. In addition, heterotrophs have extracellular enzymes, which are important in obtaining food.

The digestive enzymes of heterotrophs fall into three categories, one for each of the classes of polymers that are hydrolysed in digestion. These are: proteases, which digest proteins to amino acids; carbohydrases (amylases), which digest polysaccharides to disaccharides and monosaccharides; and lipases, which digest lipids to fatty acids and glycerol. Different organisms have different types of these enzymes, but they all function in the same way by hydrolysing the bonds between the monomers from which the polymers are formed. These enzymes are extracellular, as the polymers are too large to be absorbed. Saprophytic bacteria and fungi secrete the enzymes directly onto the food source. As the polymers are digested, inorganic molecules are released for recycling. Multicellular animals with a digestive system secrete the enzymes into the cavity of the intestine. Mammals also produce some intracellular digestive enzymes which complete the hydrolysis of disaccharides and dipeptides in the small intestine.

The majority of intracellular enzymes are involved in the control of metabolic processes. Protein synthesis in all living organisms involves RNA polymerase to transcribe the DNA for the protein and enzymes in the ribosomes which condense the amino acids to form a polypeptide. Similarly, an enzyme controls every reaction in respiration and photosynthesis. For example, the synthesis of ATP in both these processes uses ATPase enzyme to condense inorganic phosphate and ADP. Enzymes in respiration also result in the release of carbon dioxide so it can be recycled in photosynthesis. Photosynthesis enzymes enable carbon dioxide to be converted into forms that heterotrophs can use. For example, the sugars formed in the Calvin cycle can be used in metabolic pathways that synthesise lipids, polysaccharides and proteins. Other important processes that involve enzymes are nerve transmission, in which the enzyme acetylcholinesterase hydrolyses the transmitter acetylcholine to prevent unnecessary stimulation of the postsynaptic neurone, and muscle contraction in which ATP is hydrolysed to provide the energy for contraction. Deamination in the liver of humans and by bacteria in the soil involves enzymes and is important in the recycling of nitrogen.

Many of the properties of enzymes are influenced by their protein nature. Enzymes function by binding to their substrate, so they have a specific shape on the surface of the molecule, called the active site, which is complementary to the substrate. The shape of the active site is due to the folding of the protein molecule into a tertiary structure. The shape of the active site makes enzymes specific, so they are unable to bind to any other substrate. According to the lock and key theory, the substrate matches to an active site on the surface of the enzyme. The induced fit theory is a modification of the lock and key theory. According to this theory the binding of the substrate and enzyme causes the active site to take up its fully complementary shape. In both theories, however, the shape of the enzyme active site is critical to its function.

To function efficiently enzymes require carefully balanced conditions. All enzymes have an optimum pH and temperature at which they function at maximum efficiency. If the pH changes too much, the enzyme loses its shape as bonds holding the tertiary structure and secondary structure break. At low temperatures, enzymes have less kinetic energy and so the rate of reaction is lower. At high temperatures, the enzyme denatures. Most organisms have mechanisms to ensure that their cells are kept close to the optimum for their enzymes. Some enzymes also have additional requirements in order to function effectively, for example cofactors like metal ions and coenzymes like CoA and NAD in respiration and NADP in photosynthesis. Certain molecules that may be present in the environment can interfere with enzyme function. For example, heavy metals like lead and mercury cause the tertiary structure to be lost. In sufficient quantities these may kill organisms, so they are an environmental hazard. Other molecules are sufficiently like the substrate to compete for the active site. Organisms can use this to control metabolic pathways, as the build-up of the product of a reaction blocks the active site of the enzyme responsible for its production. Alternatively the enzyme has an alternative site where a product molecule can fit and change the shape of the active site.

The precise shape of the tertiary structure is determined by the primary structure, which in turn is determined by a DNA sequence. The order of the amino acids in the primary structure is critical to the correct folding of the protein. Once the secondary coiling has occurred, interactions between specific amino acids form cross-links which hold the shape. If these amino acids are changed by mutations in the DNA coding for an enzyme, then the tertiary structure may be incorrect, preventing the enzyme from binding correctly to the active site.

Some mutations may result in non-functional enzymes, which have effects on the metabolism. Examples are: lactose intolerance, in which lactase is not synthesised so lactose is not digested; galactosemia, in which galactose cannot be metabolised; and phenylketoneuria, in which phenylalanine cannot be metabolised. Gene therapy can now be used to treat some human conditions that are due to faulty enzymes. Virus restriction endonuclease and ligase enzymes are used to cut and splice genes from human chromosomes to bacterial chromosomes. Cloning using bacterial enzymes allows many copies of human genes to be used for treatments. Other techniques in genetic engineering make use of enzymes extracted from bacteria, for example DNA polymerase from bacteria, used in PCR.

Other mutations may result in an enzyme better able to carry out its function and thus increase the chances of survival of an organism. For example, bacteria which live in hot springs have enzymes that are not denatured by high temperatures. These bacteria have a selective advantage which allows them to survive in an environment not available to other organisms. Some fungi produce enzymes able to digest rock to obtain minerals. Other organisms improve their chances of survival by forming symbiotic relationships with these bacteria or fungi, for example lichens.

Enzymes are critical to the survival of living organisms. Their primary role is to catalyse chemical reactions that are part of the metabolic activities of an organism. As metabolism is very complex and involves both anabolic and catabolic reactions, there is a huge diversity in the type of reactions that occur in different organisms.

Glossary

α-cells   Cells in the islets of Langerhans that secrete glucagon.

Abiotic   Refers to the non-living component of the environment.

Acetylcholine   A type of neurotransmitter.

Acetylcholinesterase   The enzyme in the synaptic cleft that breaks down acetylcholine after it has diffused across the synaptic cleft.

Actin   A protein forming thin filaments in muscle fibres, involved in muscle contraction.

Actinomycete   A non-motile filamentous anaerobic bacterium.

Action potential   The changes that take place in a nerve cell membrane as the result of sodium ions moving into the neurone and potassium ions moving out.

Adaptation   Changes that occur over time in living organisms which enable them to survive better in a particular environment.

Adenosine triphosphate (ATP)   A free nucleotide used as an energy carrier by living organisms. Hydrolysis of the phosphate bonds releases energy that can be used to drive reactions in living organisms.

Adrenergic nerves   Nerves that release noradrenaline.

Afferent arteriole   An arteriole that carries blood towards a structure.

Agrochemicals   Chemicals used in agriculture.

Algal bloom   Population explosion of algae in lakes and ponds due to an increase in plant nutrients, such as nitrates and phosphates.

Alleles   Alternative forms of a gene; a single allele at each gene locus is inherited separately from each parent (e.g. at a locus for eye colour the allele might result in blue or brown eyes).

All-or-nothing law   An action potential occurs only if the stimulus is above a certain threshold value. When an action potential is produced it is always the same size.

Antagonistic muscles   Muscles working in pairs to produce a movement.

Antidiuretic hormone (ADH)   A hormone produced by the pituitary gland which makes the walls of the distal convoluted tubule and collecting ducts of the kidney nephron more permeable to water.

Aqueous humour   The watery fluid filling the front of the eye between the lens and the cornea.

Arthropod   An invertebrate animal with a segmented body, jointed limbs and an external skeleton, e.g. an insect, spider or beetle.

Association areas   The parts of the cerebral cortex that receive information from sensory areas and interpret it using previous experiences and memory.

Atmosphere   The gases surrounding Earth.

ATPase   An enzyme used in the synthesis of ATP from ADP and inorganic phosphate.

Autecology   The study of the ecology of a single species.

Autonomic nervous system   Part of the nervous system controlling involuntary effectors.

Autosome   A chromosome not involved in sex determination. The diploid human genome consists of 46 chromosomes: 22 pairs of autosomes, and 1 pair of sex chromosomes (the X and Y chromosomes).

Autotroph   An organism that is able to form complex organic molecules from simple inorganic molecules, usually carbon dioxide.

Axon   The fibre of a neurone which conducts nerve impulses away from the cell body.

β-cells   Cells in the islets of Langerhans that secrete insulin.

Base sequence   The order of nucleotide bases in a DNA molecule.

Basement membrane   A membrane that supports a layer of cells.

Belt transect   A method of sampling in which a strip (usually 0.5 m in width) across a study area is sampled using a quadrat.

Binocular vision   The overlapping of the visual fields of both eyes so that both eyes focus on the same object.

Binomial system   An international convention used to name living organisms. The genus name is written first, starting with an upper case letter, followed by the species name, starting with a lower case letter, both in italic.

Bioaccumulation   The accumulation of pesticides and other fat-soluble chemicals in an organism's fatty tissue.

Biochemical oxygen demand (BOD)   The amount of dissolved oxygen needed by aerobic decomposers to break down organic materials.

Biodegradable   Describes a material that can be broken down into simpler substances by bacteria or other decomposers.

Biological control   A method of pest control that involves the use of naturally occurring disease organisms, parasites or predators to control pests.

Biomagnification   An increase in the concentration of a pesticide in organisms at successively higher trophic levels of a food chain or web.

Biomass   The total quantity or mass of organisms in a given area or volume.

Biome   A large, relatively distinct ecosystem characterised by similar climate, soil, plants and animals, regardless of where it occurs on Earth.

Biosphere   The part of Earth that supports life.

Biotic   The living component of the environment.

Biotic potential   The maximum rate at which a population can increase.

Bipolar neurone   A cell in the retina that links one or more photoreceptor cells to a ganglion cell.

Bivalent The association of a homologous pair, each with two chromatids, that occurs during prophase I of meiosis.

Bladder (urinary) A muscular, extensible organ in which urine is stored before expulsion.

Bleaching The splitting of a light-sensitive pigment when it absorbs light.

Blind spot The point where the optic nerve leaves the retina. There are no light-sensitive cells at this point.

Carbon cycle The recycling of carbon.

Cardiac muscle Heart muscle.

Carnivore A plant or animal that feeds on animal flesh; also known as a secondary consumer.

Carrier molecules Coenzymes used to transfer molecules from one reaction to another.

Carrying capacity The highest population that can be maintained for an indefinite period of time by a particular environment.

Cell body Part of a neurone that contains the nucleus and other organelles.

Cellular respiration The process involving the release of energy and carbon dioxide from the breakdown of carbohydrates.

Central nervous system The brain and spinal cord.

Central thermoreceptors Sensory cells in the hypothalamus that detect changes in blood temperature.

Centromere A specialised region of a chromosome to which spindle fibres attach during cell division.

Cerebellum Part of the hindbrain that receives information from sense receptors and uses this to co-ordinate movements, such as posture.

Cerebral cortex The outer layer (about 3 mm thick) of the cerebrum. It is responsible for all higher functions and for initiating voluntary movement.

Cerebral hemisphere One of the two halves of the cerebrum.

Cerebrum The main part of the forebrain which controls conscious feelings and voluntary movements.

Chiasma (plural chiasmata) Points at which crossing over occurs between maternal and paternal chromosomes during meiosis, visible under a light microscope during late prophase I and metaphase I of meiosis.

Chi-squared (χ^2) test A statistics test that is used to compare observed frequencies with expected frequencies.

Chlorophyll A green pigment used to trap light during photosynthesis.

Chloroplast An organelle in plants containing light-trapping pigments and the enzymes, coenzymes and carriers used in photosynthesis.

Cholinergic nerves Nerves that release acetylcholine as a neurotransmitter.

Chordates A subgroup of the animal kingdom that includes animals with an internal skeleton.

Choroid The part of the eye containing blood vessels.

Chromosomes The self-replicating genetic structures of cells containing the cell DNA that carries genes in a linear sequence.

Ciliary muscle (of eye) A ring of smooth muscle in the eye that controls the shape of the lens.

Class A subset of a kingdom and phylum.

Classification The grouping and assigning of different organisms into groups.

Climax community The stable community that develops through succession.

Codominant alleles Alleles whose effects both show in the phenotype of a heterozygote.

Coenzyme A A coenzyme used to carry a two-carbon acetyl group into the Krebs cycle.

Coenzymes Organic molecules used by some enzymes to donate or accept molecules involved in an enzyme-controlled reaction.

Collecting duct A duct in the kidney that carries the urine from several nephrons to the ureters.

Commensalism A type of symbiosis in which one organism benefits and the other one is neither harmed nor helped.

Community All the populations of different species that live and interact together in the same area at the same time.

Competition The striving of different organisms to obtain resources from the environment.

Competitive exclusion The exclusion of one organism from a niche as a result of competition between two species.

Compost The final product of composting.

Composting The breakdown of dead organic matter by decomposers.

Cone cell (of retina) A light-sensitive cell in the eye, mainly responsible for vision in bright light and for detection of colour.

Consumer An organism which obtains energy by eating other living things.

Continuous variation Variation in which differences in phenotype do not show clear categories into which an individual can be placed. The phenotypes are often quantitative features, such as height, mass or shade of colour.

Convergence The connection of more than one rod cell with a single bipolar neurone thus increasing the ability of the brain to detect a small amount of light.

Co-ordinator The part of the brain or spinal cord that receives impulses from receptors and sends impulses to the appropriate effectors. Endocrine glands can also act as co-ordinators by responding to hormones from receptors and releasing hormones to appropriate effectors.

Core body temperature The temperature of blood flowing through the hypothalamus.

Corpus callosum A band of neurones that connects the cerebral hemispheres.

Cortex The outer part of the kidney.

Countercurrent flow mechanism Two liquids flowing past each other in opposite directions to maximise the rate of exchange between them.

Crop   Plant grown for food.

Crop rotation   The planting of different crops in the same field over a period of time.

Crossing over   The breaking during meiosis of one maternal and one paternal chromosome, the exchange of corresponding sections of DNA, and the rejoining of the chromosomes. This process can result in an exchange of alleles between chromosomes.

Cyclic GMP   A component of the membrane in receptor cells.

Cytochromes   Complex organic molecules used to transfer electrons during respiration and photosynthesis.

Dark adaptation   The condition of the eye after exposure to darkness, in which the breakdown of rhodopsin in the rod cells is slowed.

Deamination   The removal of an amino group and a hydrogen atom from an amino acid; these combine to form ammonia.

Death phase   The phase following the stable phase in which the growth rate of a population falls.

Decarboxylation   A chemical reaction during which carbon dioxide is removed from a molecule.

Decomposer   An organism that breaks down complex organic molecules into simple inorganic molecules that can be recycled. Also known as a saprophyte.

Dehydrogenation   A chemical reaction during which hydrogen is removed from a molecule.

Dendrite   The fibre of a neurone that conducts nerve impulses towards the cell body.

Denitrification   The conversion of nitrate to nitrogen.

Denitrifying bacteria   Bacteria that convert nitrate to nitrogen in the process of denitrification.

Depolarisation   The movement of sodium ions into a nerve cell, which reduces the potential difference across the membrane.

Detritivore   An organism that feeds on dead organic matter.

Detritus   Dead or decaying matter.

Detritus food chain   A food chain in which a primary consumer feeds on dead or decaying matter.

Diabetes insipidus   A condition in which excess urine is produced. This is usually the result of a faulty pituitary gland which does not produce enough ADH.

Diabetes mellitus   A condition in which the blood glucose levels are not properly controlled. This can be caused by a lack of insulin or by the body being unable to respond to insulin.

Dicotyledon   A plant that has two seed leaves.

Differential mortality   The death of organisms with features that are unable to resist damage from environmental factors, such as low pH or extremes of temperature. These organisms eventually die out.

Differential survival   The survival of organisms with features that enable them to resist damage from environmental factors, such as low pH or extremes of temperature. These organisms eventually become more frequent.

Diploid (2n)   Describes a nucleus that has the full number of chromosomes in homologous pairs.

Directional selection   Natural selection that favours a particular phenotype at one end of the phenotype range. It results in a change in phenotype of the whole population towards the favoured phenotype.

Discontinuous variation   Variation in which differences in phenotype show distinct categories into which individuals can be placed. The phenotypes are often qualitative features, such as blood group.

Disruptive selection   Natural selection that favours phenotypes at each end of the phenotype range. It results in two different populations with phenotypes at the two extremes of the phenotype range.

Distal convoluted tubule   Part of the kidney nephron where the exact balance of salts and water in the blood is carefully regulated.

Dominant allele   An allele whose effects always show in the phenotype, even in a heterozygous individual.

Ecological niche   The position an organism fills in its environment, comprising its habitat, the resources it uses and the time at which it occurs there.

Ecology   The study of the relationships between organisms and their surroundings.

Ecosystem   An area in which organisms interact with each other and with their physical environment.

Effector   Part of the organism that responds to a stimulus. Effectors are usually muscles or glands.

Efferent arteriole   An arteriole that carries blood away from a structure.

Electron carrier   A complex organic molecule used to transfer electrons.

Electron transfer   The movement of electrons from one molecule to another. It is often linked to ATP synthesis.

Electrons (e⁻)   Negatively charged particles that surround the nucleus of an atom. During oxidation electrons may be removed from an atom.

Emigration   The movement of organisms from one area to another which results in the loss of individuals from a population.

Emotional tears   Tears produced in response to an emotional change.

Endocrine gland   A gland that secretes hormones into the bloodstream.

Endothelium cells   Cells that line an internal tissue, e.g. capillary endothelium.

Energy   The capacity or ability to do work.

Energy flow   The flow of energy through an ecosystem.

Environment   The influences that act upon an organism.

Environmental resistance   Conditions that reduce the growth rate of a population.

Epiphyte   A small plant that lives attached to the bark of a tree's branches.

Epistasis   (= to stand upon) The expression of one gene hides that of another. It occurs in metabolic processes controlled by enzymes coded by different genes.

Eutrophication   The enrichment of a lake or pond by nutrients, such as nitrates and phosphates.

Evolution   The gradual change in living organisms over long periods of time, leading to the development of new species. It occurs as a result of mutation and natural selection in different environments.

Excitatory postsynaptic potential (EPSP)   The depolarisation caused in a postsynaptic neurone. If the EPSP is above the threshold value, an action potential is set up in the postsynaptic neurone.

Excreta   Waste discharged from the bodies of animals, in particular faeces and urine.

Exploitation   The process leading to competition because there has been a reduction in the supply of an essential resource.

Exponential phase   The phase following the lag phase in which there is a sharp rise in the population growth rate.

Factor VIII   A blood-clotting protein.

FAD (flavine adenine dinucleotide)   A carrier used to transfer hydrogen during respiration.

Family   A subset of an order.

Fever   An abnormally high temperature.

Fixation   The conversion of a simple inorganic molecule to a complex organic molecule.

Food chain   A very simple diagram showing how energy flows through an ecosystem.

Food web   A diagram showing all the feeding relationships in a single ecosystem/community.

Forebrain   The part of the brain made up of the cerebrum, thalamus and hypothalamus.

Fovea   The point on the retina where most cones are present. This makes it the area of greatest visual acuity.

Frame quadrat   A wooden frame that can be split into equal parts.

Frontal lobe   The part of the brain that controls conscious motor movements, speech and thought processes.

Fructose bisphosphate   A hexose sugar with two phosphate groups formed during glycolysis.

Fundamental niche   The potential ecological niche of an organism.

Fungi   A kingdom of eukaryotic organisms with chitin cell walls. They are heterotrophic, either saprophytic or parasitic.

Fungicide   A chemical that kills fungi.

Gamete   A mature male or female reproductive cell with a haploid set of chromosomes (23 for humans).

Ganglion   A collection of cell bodies of neurones in the peripheral nervous system.

Ganglion cell   A cell that passes nerve impulses to the optic nerve.

Gastrodpod   A class of invertebrates that move by means of a large muscular foot, e.g. snails or slugs.

Gated channels   Protein channels in the cell surface membrane that can open and close in response to a stimulus.

Gene   The fundamental physical and functional unit of heredity. A gene is an ordered sequence of nucleotides located in a particular position on a particular chromosome that codes for a specific functional product.

Gene expression   The process by which a gene's coded information is converted into the molecules present and operating in the cell. Expressed genes include those that are transcribed into mRNA and then translated into protein and those that are transcribed into RNA but not translated into protein (e.g. transfer and ribosomal RNA).

Gene pool   All the alleles of all the genes in a population of an organism, which result in variation.

Gene product   The RNA or protein resulting from gene expression. The amount of gene product is used to measure how active a gene is; abnormal amounts can be correlated with disease-causing alleles.

Generator potential   A depolarisation of the membrane of a receptor cell.

Genetic resistance   Any inherited characteristic that decreases the effect of a pesticide.

Genetics   The study of the patterns of inheritance of specific traits.

Genotype   The alleles of a gene (genetic constitution) that an individual inherits.

Genus (plural genera)   A subset of a family. Species with similar features are grouped into a genus.

Glial cells   Cells found in the nervous system that do not conduct nerve impulses but provide support to neurone networks.

Glomerulus   A ball of capillaries in the renal capsule where ultrafiltration takes place.

Glucagon   A hormone secreted from the α-cells in the islets of Langerhans. It has the effect of raising blood glucose levels.

Gluconeogenesis   A process in which lipids and proteins from body tissues are broken down to make glucose.

Glycerate-3-phosphate   A three-carbon compound formed in the Calvin cycle.

Glycogenesis   The formation of glycogen from glucose. This takes place in the liver.

Glycogenolysis   The breakdown of glycogen to form glucose.

Glycolysis   A series of chemical reactions in cellular respiration during which glucose molecules are oxidised and split to form pyruvate.

Granum (plural grana)   A series of stacked membranes found in chloroplasts, containing chlorophyll and other pigments.

Grazing food chain   A food chain in which a primary consumer feeds on living matter.

Gross primary productivity (GPP)   The rate at which chemical energy is stored by plants.

Growth rate   The rate of growth of a population.

Habitat   The place in which an organism is found.

Haploid (n)   Describes a nucleus that has only a single set of chromosomes, one from each homologous pair.

Hatch and Slack pathway   An alternative pathway to the Calvin cycle used by some plants to 'fix' carbon dioxide.

Heat conservation responses   Activities that help the body to retain heat, vasoconstriction, piloerection, reduced sweating. Behavioural changes, including huddling and reduction of surface area, may also occur.

Heat generation responses   Activities that help the body to generate heat to replace heat losses, including shivering and increasing metabolic rate.

Heat loss responses   Activities that help the body to lose heat, including increased sweating and vasodilation.

Hepatic portal vein   A blood vessel carrying blood from the small intestine to the liver.

Herbaceous plants (herbs)   Plants with soft green stems.

Herbicide   A chemical that kills plants.

Herbivore   An organism that eats plants, also known as a primary consumer.

Heritability   The proportion of total variation due to genetic effects.

Heterogametic sex   The sex that produces gametes containing sex chromosomes of two types. In humans, males produce gametes containing either an X or a Y chromosome.

Heterosomes   Chromosomes involved in sex determination which are different in appearance. In humans the Y chromosome, which determines male sexual development, is much shorter than the X chromosome.

Heterotroph   An organism that obtains energy from complex organic molecules.

Heterotrophic   Obtaining food from organic substances.

Heterozygous   Possessing different alleles of genes at one or more loci on homologous chromosomes.

Hierarchy   A large group that is subdivided into subgroups which in turn are subdivided into even smaller groups.

Hindbrain   The part of the brain that contains the medulla oblongata and which controls vital functions such as heart rate.

Homeostasis   The way in which the body regulates its physiological processes so that it keeps its internal environment as stable as possible.

Homeotherm   (may also be spelt **homoiotherm**) An animal that can regulate its body temperature.

Homogametic sex   The sex that produces gametes containing sex chromosomes of the same type. In humans, females produce gametes that all contain an X chromosome.

Homologous chromosomes   A pair of chromosomes containing the same gene sequences, each derived from one parent.

Homozygous   Possessing the same alleles of genes at one or more loci on homologous chromosomes.

Homunculus   An abstract represention of a human in which the body parts are drawn in proportion to their sensitivity or mobility.

Hormones   Chemicals secreted by endocrine glands into the bloodstream, which modify the function of distant target tissues and organs.

Horner's syndrome   A condition of the eye in which sympathetic nerves are interrupted.

Host   An organism that has a parasite.

Huddling   A behavioural response in mammals to low temperature. Groups of animals move closer together to retain more heat within the centre of the group. Individuals change places between the inside and outside of the group.

Hybridisation   Fertilisation of one species by a different species producing organisms with chromosomes from two different species.

Hydrosphere   Earth's water supply.

Hyperglycaemia   A condition in which the blood glucose level is too high.

Hypermetropia   Long sightedness, in which objects close to the eye form a blurred image on the retina.

Hyperpolarisation   An increase of the potential differences across a membrane.

Hyperthermia   The state of the body resulting from an increase in body temperature above the normal range of values.

Hypha (plural hyphae)   The hollow tube of a fungal cell body.

Hypoglycaemia   A condition in which the blood glucose level is too low.

Hypothalamus   A region at the base of the brain, important in controlling many homeostatic processes.

Hypothermia   The state of the body resulting from a fall in body temperature below the normal range of values.

Immigration   The movement of new individuals into an existing population.

Independent assortment of non-homologous pairs   The separation of non-homologous pairs during anaphase I of meiosis such that either member of a pair can end up at a pole along with either of the members of the other homologous pair.

Inhibitory postsynaptic potential   The hyperpolarisation of a postsynaptic membrane which inhibits the development of an action potential.

Insecticide   A chemical that kills insects.

Insulin   A hormone secreted from the β-cells in the islets of Langerhans. It has the effect of reducing blood glucose levels.

Integrated pest management   A combination of pest control methods such as biological, chemical and cultivation.

Interference   The process leading to competition because an individual has physically prevented a second organism from living in the same habitat.

Interphase   The period in the cell cycle when DNA is replicated in the nucleus.

Interspecific   Between members of different species.

Intraspecific   Between members of the same species.

Invertebrate   Any animal that does not have an internal skeleton.

Involuntary muscle   Smooth muscle.

Iodopsin   The light-sensitive pigment in cone cells.

Iris (of the eye)   Part of the choroid which contains radial and circular muscles. This controls the amount of light entering the eye.

Irritant tears   Tears produced when the eyes are irritated.

Islets of Langerhans   Part of the pancreas which acts as an endocrine organ, secreting insulin from the β-cells and glucagon from the α-cells.

Isolation   The separation of a population into different groups, each ending up in a different environment.

Kinetic energy   Movement energy.

Kingdom   The largest taxonomic group used in the classification of living organisms. Five kingdoms are recognised: prokaryotes, protoctists, fungi, plants and animals.

Kite diagram   A special type of bar graph used to display transect data.

Krebs cycle   A series of reactions in respiration during which pyruvate is oxidised by removing hydrogen. Carbon dioxide is a waste product.

Lag phase   The phase in which the initial growth rate of a population is slow.

Leaching   The process in which various chemicals in the upper layers of soil are dissolved and carried to lower layers and groundwater.

Lens   The part of the eye which focuses light on the retina.

Light adaptation   The condition of the eye after exposure to light, in which rhodopsin in the rod cells is broken down faster than it can be reformed.

Light-dependent reactions   A series of reactions in photosynthesis during which light energy is trapped and used to split water molecules and synthesise ATP.

Light-independent reactions   A series of reactions in photosynthesis during which sugars are synthesised from carbon dioxide and hydrogen using energy from ATP.

Limiting factor   A factor that reduces the growth rate of a population.

Line transect   A method of sampling in which a tape or rope is stretched across a habitat and sampling occurs at regular intervals with a quadrat.

Link reaction   A reaction that feeds pyruvate into the Krebs cycle.

Lithosphere   The soil and rock of the Earth's crust.

Locus (plural loci)   The position on a chromosome of a gene or other chromosome marker. Also, the DNA at that position.

Loop of Henle   Part of a kidney nephron which is important in building up a high salt concentration in the kidney medulla, increasing water reabsorption.

Mean   The mid-point between the first and last numbers in a sequence of data. It is calculated by adding together all the values of the data and dividing by the total number of data points.

Medulla   Inner part of the kidney.

Medulla oblongata   Part of the hindbrain which controls important reflexes such as breathing, blood pressure and heart rate.

Meiosis   The process of two consecutive cell divisions in the diploid cells which give rise to gametes. Meiosis results in four rather than two daughter cells, each with a haploid set of chromosomes.

Melanin   A dark pigment present in skin, hair and iris.

Metaphase   A stage in mitosis or meiosis during which the chromosomes are attached at the equator of the spindle.

Microhabitat   An area within a habitat which has specific conditions.

Micrometre (μm)   A unit of measurement: $1\,\mu m = 10^{-6}$ metre.

Micturition   The release of urine from the bladder, or urination.

Midbrain   The part of the brain that contains nerve fibres which connect the forebrain and hindbrain.

Migration   The movement of an organism from one area to another.

Mitochondrion (plural mitochondria)   An organelle containing the enzymes and carriers used during respiration.

Mitosis   The process of nuclear division in cells that produces daughter cells which are genetically identical to each other and to the parent cell.

Monocotyledon   A plant that has one seed leaf.

Monoculture   Cultivation of a single crop, usually on a large area of land.

Motor areas   Regions of the cerebral cortex that send impulses to effectors.

Motor end plate   The end of an axon where it synapses with a muscle fibre.

Motor neurones   Neurones that carry information from the central nervous system to effectors.

Multiple alleles   Genes that have more than two different alleles.

Multiple sclerosis   A chronic, often debilitating disease of the central nervous system.

Mutation   Any heritable change in DNA sequence.

Mutualism   An association between pairs of species in which both species benefit.

Myasthenia gravis   An autoimmune disorder in which sufferers have fewer acetylcholine receptors than usual. This reduces their ability to use their muscles.

Mycelium   The mass formed by the hyphae of fungi.

Myelin sheath   A fatty insulating layer around nerve axons, formed by Schwann cells.

Myofibril   A subunit of a muscle fibre.

Myosin   A protein forming thick filaments in muscle fibres, used in muscle contraction.

NAD (nicotine adenine dinucleotide)   A coenzyme used to transfer hydrogen during respiration.

NADP (nicotine adenine dinucleotide phosphate)   A coenzyme used as an acceptor of hydrogen ions and electrons in the light-dependent reaction of photosynthesis.

Nanometre (nm)   A unit of measurement: $1\,nm = 10^{-9}$ metre.

Natural selection   A process that acts on phenotypes so those organisms with the best features survive to breed.

Negative feedback   A system in which the outputs tend to reduce the inputs. This tends to stabilise the system.

Nephron   One of more than a million tube-like structures that form the functional component of the kidney.

Net primary productivity (NPP)   The energy that remains after the energy 'used' in respiration has been subtracted from the gross primary productivity.

Neuromuscular junction   The point where a nerve cell communicates with a muscle fibre.

Neurones   Cells in the nervous system which are able to conduct impulses.

Neurotransmitter   A chemical released at a synapse which fits into specific receptors in the postsynaptic membrane, resulting in a change in polarity.

Nitrification   The process whereby ammonia is converted via nitrite to nitrate.

Nitrifying bacteria   Bacteria that chemically alter most of the ammonia via nitrite to nitrate in the process of nitrification.

Nitrogen cycle   The recycling of nitrogen.

Nitrogen fixation   The conversion of nitrogen to ammonia by soil bacteria.

Nitrogen-fixing bacteria   Bacteria that convert nitrogen to ammonia in the process of nitrogen fixation.

Node of Ranvier   A space between Schwann cells where ion exchange can take place.

Non-biodegradable   Material that is not broken down by decomposers.

Non-persistent   Describes certain chemicals that are not stable and may be broken down easily into simpler forms.

Non-shivering thermogenesis   A heat gain mechanism used by babies.

Null hypothesis   A hypothesis that states that there will be no significant difference between the observed and the expected frequencies.

Nutrient cycle   A food chain with decomposers added.

Occipital lobe   The part of the brain that receives and processes information from the eyes.

Oligotrophic   Relatively poor in plant nutrients, such as a lake.

Omnivore   An organism that eats plants and animals.

Opsin   A component of rhodopsin, the light-sensitive pigment in rod cells.

Optic chiasma   The point where the right and left optic nerves meet.

Optic nerve   Nerve carrying impulses from the rods and cones in the retina to the brain.

Order   A subset of a class.

Ornithine cycle   A metabolic pathway occurring in the liver, in which highly toxic ammonia is converted to urea, which is less toxic.

Osmoreceptor   A cell that detects changes in water potential.

Oxidation   A chemical reaction during which hydrogen or electrons are removed from a molecule, or oxygen is added to a molecule. Most biological reactions involve removing hydrogen or electrons.

Oxidative phosphorylation   A series of reactions in respiration during which ATP is synthesised using energy from the movement of electrons caused by the energy released from the oxidation of glucose.

Panting   Quick, shallow breaths of air which evaporate water from the mouth and tongue, producing a cooling effect in some animals.

Parasite   An organism living on or in another and benefiting at the expense of the other.

Parasitism   A symbiotic relationship in which one member benefits and the other is harmed.

Parasympathetic nervous system   A subdivision of the autonomic nervous system concerned with the body's normal functions.

Parietal lobe   The part of the brain associated with the sensory cortex that interprets sensory information about touch, taste, pressure, pain, heat and cold.

Partial permeability   The property of a membrane that allows some molecules to pass through but not others.

Pathogen   A disease-causing organism.

Pedigree   A record of the inheritance of particular phenotypes through many generations. Breeders of animals and plants keep breeding records of the parents used to produce a particular offspring.

Pelvis   An area in the kidney that carries urine from the pyramids into the ureters.

Percentage cover   The proportion of the ground area, viewed from directly above, covered by the above-ground parts of a species.

Peripheral nervous system   All the nerves and sense organs that send information to the central nervous system, or take information from the central nervous system to effectors.

Peripheral thermoreceptors   Temperature receptors in the skin.

Peristalsis   Muscular contractions in the gut wall or ureters that move substances along.

Persistence   A characteristic of certain chemicals that are extremely stable and may take many years to be broken down into simpler forms.

Pest   Any organism that interferes in some way with human welfare or activities.

Pesticide   Any toxic chemical used to kill pests.

Phenotype   The features of an individual that result from the expression of genes and their interaction with environmental factors. Differences in phenotype can be measured or described.

Photoautotrophs   Organisms that trap light energy and convert it into chemical energy in ATP molecules during the process of photosynthesis.

Photolysis   The splitting of water molecules during the light-dependent stage of photosynthesis.

Photon   Packet of energy that makes up light.

Photophosphorylation   A series of reactions in the light-dependent stage of photosynthesis during which ATP is synthesised using energy from the movement of electrons caused by light energy.

Photopsin   A component of iodopsin, the light-sensitive pigment in cone cells.

Photoreceptor cell   A receptor cell that detects light.

Photosynthesis   The process carried out by green plants that converts carbon dioxide and water to carbohydrate and oxygen, using solar energy.

Phylum   A subset of a kingdom.

Phytoplankton   Microscopic plants in an aquatic environment.

Pigments   Coloured molecules able to absorb light of specific wavelengths.

Piloerection   Contraction of the erector pili muscles in the skin, pulling hairs in the skin upright. In hairy and furry mammals, this has the effect of trapping a layer of insulating air which helps to keep them warm.

Ploidy   Refers to the number of sets of chromosomes in a cell.

Podocytes   Cells that form the wall of the renal capsule. They have large gaps between them.

Point quadrat   A quadrat consisting of vertical legs across which is fixed a horizontal bar with ten small holes along it.

Polarised   Describes the inside of an axon that is negatively charged with respect to the outside of the axon.

Pons   Part of the hindbrain that connects the medulla oblongata and spinal cord to the higher centres of the brain.

Population   A group of organisms of the same species that live together in the same area at the same time.

Postsynaptic neurone   The neurone that the neurotransmitter binds to at a synapse.

Potential difference   A difference in charge between one point and another.

Potential energy   Stored chemical-bond energy.

Predation   An interspecific interaction in which individuals of one animal species (the prey) are killed and eaten by individuals of another species (the predator).

Predator   An animal that kills and eats individuals of another animal species.

Presynaptic neurone   The neurone at a synapse which releases a neurotransmitter.

Prey   An animal that is killed and eaten by individuals of another animal species.

Primary consumer   An organism that eat plants.

Primary succession   The change in species composition over time that occurs in a habitat which has not previously been inhabited.

Producer   An organism that uses solar energy in photosynthesis to produce carbohydrates.

Prokaryotes   A kingdom containing prokaryotic organisms, bacteria and cyanobacteria.

Protoctists   A kingdom containing simple eukaryotic organisms not belonging to any other kingdom.

Proton (H⁺)   A positively charged particle found in the nucleus of an atom. The nucleus of a hydrogen atom consists of a single proton.

Protozoan (plural protozoa)   A unicellular organism.

Proximal convoluted tubule   Part of the kidney nephron where many of the useful substances from the filtrate (e.g. water, glucose and amino acids) are reabsorbed into the blood.

Pupil   The hole that allows light into the eye. The size of the pupil is controlled by the iris.

Pyramid   A structure in the kidney where the urine from several collecting ducts is carried to the pelvis.

Pyramid of biomass   A diagram that shows the total biomass at each trophic level in an ecosystem or food chain.

Pyramid of energy   A diagram that shows the flow of energy through each trophic level of an ecosystem or food chain.

Pyramid of numbers   A diagram that shows the number of organisms at each trophic level in an ecosystem or food chain.

Pyrogen   A substance released from cells of the immune system which causes fever.

Pyruvate   A three-carbon compound formed at the end of glycolysis.

Quadrat   A frame that outlines a known area for the purpose of sampling.

Random sampling   A sampling method in which sampling points are chosen using random numbers.

Randomising   The use of random numbers in sampling populations.

Realised niche   The actual ecological niche of an organism.

Receptor protein   A protein molecule within a membrane to which a specific molecule such as a hormone can bind.

Receptor cells   Cells that detect stimuli.

Recessive allele   An allele whose effects only show when there are no dominant alleles present. A recessive phenotype is always homozygous.

Recombination   The process by which offspring derive a combination of genes that is different from that of either parent. In higher organisms this can occur by crossing over.

Red-green colour blindness   A defect of colour vision in which people have difficulty in distinguishing red and green.

Redox reaction   A reaction during which one molecule is reduced by reacting with another molecule, which becomes oxidised as a result of the reaction.

Reduction   A chemical reaction during which hydrogen or electrons are added to a molecule, or oxygen is removed from a molecule. Most biological reactions involve adding hydrogen or electrons.

Reflex   An automatic response to a sensory stimulus.

Reflex arc   The pathway of neurones involved in a reflex action.

Reflex tears   Tears produced when the eyes are irritated.

Refractory period   The brief period after the sodium gated channels close, during which a neurone cannot respond to a stimulus.

Renal artery   A blood vessel bringing oxygenated blood to the kidneys.

Renal capsule   The part of the nephron in which blood is filtered under pressure.

Renal threshold   The size of molecule that is unable to pass through the filtering system in the renal capsule.

Renal vein   A blood vessel taking deoxygenated blood from the kidneys back to the heart.

Respiration   A series of reactions during which energy in the chemical bonds of glucose is transferred into ATP molecules.

Response   A change caused by a stimulus.

Resting potential   The potential difference across a nerve cell membrane when it is not conducting an impulse.

Retina   Part of the eye that contains light-sensitive cells.

Retinal   A component of iodopsin and rhodopsin, the light-sensitive pigments in cone and rod cells.

Rhodopsin   The light-sensitive pigment found in rod cells.

Ribulose bisphosphate (RuBp)   A five-carbon compound that accepts carbon dioxide to start the Calvin cycle.

Rod cell (of retina)   A light-sensitive cell in the eye, mainly responsible for vision in dim light.

Saltatory conduction   The method by which nerve impulses are propagated along a myelinated axon. Ion exchange occurs only at the nodes of Ranvier.

Sampling   A method in which samples are taken to represent the whole population of a species.

Saprophytic nutrition   The type of nutrition in which an organism secretes digestive enzymes onto dead and decaying matter and then absorbs the products of digestion.

Sarcolemma   A membrane surrounding a muscle fibre.

Sarcomere   A unit of muscle fibre containing actin and myosin filaments.

Sarcoplasm   The cytoplasm inside a muscle fibre.

Sarcoplasmic reticulum   Infoldings of the sarcolemma which spread lengthways across the muscle fibre. In a resting muscle, the sarcoplasmic reticulum accumulates calcium ions.

Schwann cell   A type of glial cell that grows spirally around axons, providing an insulating layer of myelin around the axon.

Sclera   The tough outer layer of the eye, containing many collagen fibres.

Secondary consumer   An organism that eats a primary consumer.

Secondary succession   The change in species composition over time that occurs in a habitat which has previously been inhabited.

Selective forces   Environmental factors that determine survival of living organisms.

Sensitivity   The ability of a cell or body part to respond to a stimulus.

Sensory areas   Parts of the cerebral cortex that receive information from sense receptors.

Sensory neurones   Neurones that carry impulses from receptors to the central nervous system.

Sere   Stage through which a community develops.

Sex chromosomes   The X and Y chromosomes in human beings, which determine the sex of an individual. Females have two X chromosomes in diploid cells; males have an X and a Y chromosome.

Sex linkage   Genes, other than those that determine sexual features, which occupy a locus on one sex chromosome but not the other.

Shivering   Rapid contraction and relaxation of muscles to generate heat.

Sigmoid growth   The population growth curve found in most natural populations in which the population number reaches a maximum and stabilises.

Significance   A measure of whether a difference has occurred by chance.

Single-gene disorder   Hereditary disorder (e.g. cystic fibrosis, haemophilia, sickle cell disease) caused by a mutant allele of a single gene.

Skeletal muscle   Striped or voluntary muscle, which is under conscious control.

Sliding filament hypothesis   A hypothesis used to describe muscle contraction.

Slurry   A semi-liquid mixture of fine particles and water.

Smooth muscle   Involuntary muscle.

Sodium–potassium pump   A protein in cell membranes which actively transports sodium ions out of the cell and potassium ions in.

Solar energy   Energy from the Sun.

Somatosensory area   The area of the brain that receives impulses from receptors originating from feet, legs, trunk, arms, face, i.e. most parts of the body.

Species   A group of organisms with similar features that share a common gene pool, so they are able to interbreed and produce fertile offspring.

Sphincter muscle   A circular muscle.

Sponges   A group of living organisms with a unique cellular organisation. They are not included in the five-kingdom classification system.

Stabilising selection   Natural selection that results in no change in the phenotype of a population.

Stable phase   The phase following the exponential phase in which the growth rate of a population has levelled off.

Standard deviation   A statistics test that is used to show how spread out a number of observations are around the mean.

Stimulus (plural stimuli)   A change in the environment that causes an organism to respond.

Stretch receptor   A receptor that sends nerve impulses along sensory nerves to the central nervous system.

Stroma   The part of a chloroplast where the light-independent reaction takes place.

Substrate   The substance that an enzyme helps to react, in order to form a product.

Subthreshold stimulus   A stimulus that is too weak to cause an action potential.

Succession   The process by which a community develops over time.

Suspensory ligaments   In the eye, these connect the lens to the ciliary muscle.

Sweat   A secretion from the skin consisting of water, with some salts and urea. When sweat evaporates, it has a cooling effect on the body.

Symbionts   The partners of a symbiotic relationship.

Symbiosis   An intimate relationship or association between members of two or more species.

Sympathetic nervous system   A subdivision of the autonomic nervous system concerned with the body's responses to stress.

Synapse   The junction between two neurones.

Synaptic cleft   A gap about 20 nm wide between two neurones at a synapse.

Synaptic knob   The swollen end of an axon at a synapse with a postsynaptic neurone.

Synaptic vesicle   One of many membrane sacs found in synaptic knobs, which contain a neurotransmitter substance.

Synecology   The study of organisms and their environment.

Systematic sampling   A sampling method in which sampling points occur at regular intervals.

Systematics   The study of the diversity of living organisms.

Taxon (plural taxa)   A recognised group of organisms at any level.

Taxonomy   The study of methods of how to group organisms in terms of similarities and differences.

Tear duct   The ducts by which tears flow from the tear glands to the eye.

Temporal lobe   The part of the brain that receives and interprets information from the ears, processing language and the hearing of words.

Tertiary consumer   An organism that eats a secondary consumer.

Test cross   Cross-fertilisation carried out between an individual of unknown genotype showing the dominant phenotype with an individual showing the recessive phenotype.

Thalamus   The part of the brain that relays information from the sense organs to the cerebrum.

Thallus   Undifferentiated plant tissue.

Thermoreceptor   A sensory cell that detects temperature changes.

Thermoregulation   The maintenance of body temperature within a narrow range.

Threshold value   The intensity a stimulus must reach if an action potential is to be produced.

Transect   A type of systematic sampling.

Transverse system (T-system)   Infoldings of the sarcolemma which spread across the muscle fibre and carry impulses into the muscle fibre.

Trichromatic theory of colour vision   A theory to explain colour vision which proposes that there are three types of cone cell, each detecting either red, blue or green light.

Trophic level   A feeding level in a food chain.

Tropomyosin   A protein that prevents actin and myosin from contracting.

Troponin   A protein that prevents actin and myosin from contracting.

Ultrafiltration   Filtration in the kidney brought about by blood pressure.

Urea   A nitrogenous waste product made in the liver from ammonia. Ammonia is produced when excess amino acids are deaminated.

Ureter   A muscular tube carrying urine from the kidney to the bladder.

Urethra   The opening of the bladder through which urine is released from the body.

Urine   An excretory product produced by the kidney containing salts, water and urea.

Variation   Small differences in phenotype that exist between members of the same species.

Vasoconstriction   Contraction of smooth muscle in the arterioles, leading to narrowing of capillaries, restricting blood flow. In the skin, this helps to conserve heat because less heat is lost by radiation.

Vasodilation   Relaxation of smooth muscle in the arterioles, leading to dilation of the capillaries, increasing blood flow. In the skin, this allows more heat to be lost by radiation.

Virus   An organism that has only a protein coat surrounding nucleic acid. A virus can only reproduce inside other cells, and is not considered to be living in the usual sense. Viruses are not included in the five-kingdom classification system.

Visible spectrum   The wavelengths of light that can be detected by the human eye.

Visual acuity   The ability of the eye to see detail, which results from only one cone cell connecting with each bipolar neurone.

Visual cortex   The part of the brain that receives nerve impulses from the optic nerve and analyses visual information.

Visual field   The region of the environment from which each eye collects light.

Visual processing   The analysis of visual information by the visual cortex.

Vitreous humour   A transparent gel-like fluid in the eye which supports the retina and keeps the eyeball spherical.

Woody plants   Plants with additional supporting tissue forming a central mass. A bark is present on the outside of the stem.

Zooplankton   Microscopic animals in an aquatic environment.

Zygote   The single cell with the diploid number of chromosomes formed as a result of fertilisation.

Index

Definitions in the Glossary are indicated by the suffix g.